The Heavens Above

A RATIONALE OF ASTRONOMY

BY J. B. SIDGWICK, F.R.A.S.

*Member of the British Astronomical Association
and of the Société Astronomique de France*

AMERICAN EDITION PREPARED BY
WARREN K. GREEN

*Professor of Astronomy at Amherst College
and Director of the Amherst College Observatory*

NEW YORK

OXFORD UNIVERSITY PRESS

1950

TO K. M. S.

Singulariter sum ego donec transeam

Preface to the English Edition

One of the less dramatic developments of the period between the wars was the appearance of Astronomy in the best-seller market—that most restricted if not most select of worlds. Whereas at one time the astronomer was not encouraged by the reading public to issue from his observatory in an official capacity, one now finds (or, at any rate, found at the height of the boom) hardly a station bookstall without its volume of celestial revelations.

During the war itself, two factors conspired to continue this trend. The blackout made the night sky visible to the townsman for the first time since the introduction of street lighting; and a variety of national duties gave both town and country dwellers plenty of opportunity for seeing it.

Thus it has come about that a wide public is in somewhat precarious possession of the more spectacular results of modern astronomical research without quite knowing how these have been established. For fine superstructures must of necessity stand upon firm foundations, and many of these astronomical dilettanti must have wondered just how such sensational results were obtained; they may, too, have speculated vaguely upon the basic principles, the trains of reasoning, and the observations without which this elegant and mysterious edifice could never have been built.

Even the simplest of everyday assumptions appears, on close inspection, to be riddled with pitfalls. Indeed, the 'simpler' it is, the more difficult its substantiation frequently is: it is easier to play a first-class game of chess than to make a rational and convincing defense of the popular notions concerning time, causation, or the existence of a material world—a defense which a professional philosopher could not tear to shreds in half a minute. Ask anyone without warning why he believes that the earth rotates on its axis, or that it revolves about the sun rather than the sun about it, and he will in all likelihood be unable to provide a sufficient reason without several false starts—if then. The answer that that is what he has always been taught, or, ultimately, that that is the considered view of individuals who have studied the facts, is no real answer. It may well be his reason for holding the belief, but it is certainly not a sufficient reason.

In the pages that follow, an attempt has been made to give a systematic demonstration of the more complex facts of Astronomy, starting from simple assumptions at which not even the most skeptical reader could cavil. So far as is convenient, the various artificial aids of the natural senses, such as the telescope and the spectroscope, are drawn into the discussion in their historical sequence. Thus, in Part I the evidence of the naked eyesight is examined, and the fullest possible use made of it by the reasoning faculty; only then is the evidence of the telescope invoked. Data provided by the spectroscope are confined to Part II, the initial chapter of which introduces the subject of spectroscopy and sketches in the background of atomic physics.

Much play has in the past been made of astronomical distances by 'popular' writers on the subject. The size of the known universe is certainly one of its more awe-inspiring features, and sizes and distances on the astronomical scale are clearly a gift to any journalist endeavoring to make a write-up exciting. The determination of all astronomical distances from the smallest to the greatest constitutes a single logical process, a fact which is often not made clear in introductions to the subject intended for the general reader. Not all astronomical amateurs would go so far as George Bernard Shaw, who once roundly accused all astronomers of being liars; but owing to the basic importance of the distance determinations, combined with the somewhat sketchy manner in which they are often treated, the average man may be forgiven a certain degree of puzzlement, if not skepticism.

For these reasons, the means whereby man has put a scale to the visible universe are in Part I presented as a continuously unfolding story, and the interrelated character of all stages in the extrapolation emphasized. The aim of the first five chapters, in other words, is to describe the size, shape, and structure of the astronomical region and its contents, together with the methods by which the results have been obtained. In Part II a different approach is adopted, and the various bodies whose distances have been their primary interest in the preceding section are considered as things in themselves, rather than as anonymous points in a spatial pattern.

From time to time during the development of the argument, reference is made to evidence provided by an instrument not yet described. When this happens, however, it is never to forge a link in the main chain of the argument, but to provide subsidiary interest or contributory evidence of an already established conclusion. Brief descriptions of certain unproved hypotheses—such as the solar origin of the planets, the origin of the lunar craters, the subatomic sources of stellar energy— are inserted for the same reason.

Finally, a word of reassurance to the mathematically timid. Figures have purposely been kept to a minimum, but certain facts and trains of reasoning are of their nature more cogently and conclusively expressed in mathematical than in verbal terms. A few figures do accordingly appear from time to time, but in no case would they present any difficulty to a schoolboy at matriculation standard. Moreover, should the reader on encountering them still prefer to skip to the next piece of firm ground, he may do so without losing the thread of the argument. For in every case the point is summarized verbally.

I should like to acknowledge here my extreme indebtedness to Professor H. H. Plaskett, whose assistance, encouragement, and constructive criticism are in large measure responsible for whatever value this book may possess; also to Dr. W. H. Steavenson for reading the book in proof and making many helpful suggestions, as well as correcting a number of factual errors; and to Mrs. Doreen Marston for giving me the initial idea.

J. B. S.

London
January 1947

Preface to the American Edition

The galley proofs for *The Heavens Above* came to my attention approximately two years ago. At that time I was impressed by the novelty of Mr. Sidgwick's approach to a clear understanding of the fundamental problems of both classical and modern astronomy. I felt that the book would have an appeal to American readers.

In the preparation of the American edition the sequence of topics in the English text has been followed. In a few places extensive rewriting has seemed desirable to adapt the book for the American public. In this rewriting the editor has attempted to adopt Mr. Sidgwick's pleasing style. No attempt has been made to indicate those sections which have been rewritten and it is my hope that no American reader will be able to detect them.

During the time that has elapsed since the appearance of the completed volume in England there have been a number of advances toward the understanding of some of the more controversial or speculative issues raised by Mr. Sidgwick. However, none of these controversies or speculations can be considered as settled at the present time and it has seemed better to leave them at the point where they were left by the author. In the cases where new discoveries have been made (for example, the fifth satellite of Uranus) the new material has been included in the American edition.

W. K. G.

Amherst, Massachusetts
February 1950

Contents

List of Plates

PLATE I. The Milky Way in Perseus. (*Courtesy of the Yerkes Observatory*)

PLATE II. Galactic Clusters: The Double Cluster in Perseus. (*Courtesy of the Harvard College Observatory*)

PLATE III. The Globular Cluster M.13 Hercules, exposure 11 hours, 60-inch reflector. (*Courtesy of the Mt. Wilson Observatory*)

PLATE IV. A portion of the irregular Galactic Nebula in Cygnus, exposure 6½ hours, 60-inch reflector. (*Courtesy of the Mt. Wilson Observatory*)

PLATE V.   Diffuse Nebulosity around Merope (Pleiades), exposure 5 hours, 60-inch reflector. (*Courtesy of the Mt. Wilson Observatory*)

PLATE VI. Large Magellanic Cloud. (*Courtesy of the Harvard College Observatory*)

PLATE VII. Central portion of the Great Spiral Nebula Andromeda, exposure 2 hours, 60-inch reflector. (*Courtesy of the Mt. Wilson Observatory*)

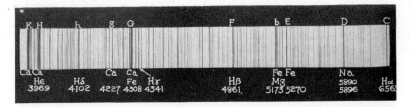

PLATE VIIIa. The visual solar spectrum with some of the principal Fraunhofer lines indicated.

PLATE VIIIb. Spectrum of the star Ursa Majoris showing the strong absorption lines of the Balmer series of hydrogen. (*Courtesy of the Harvard College Observatory*)

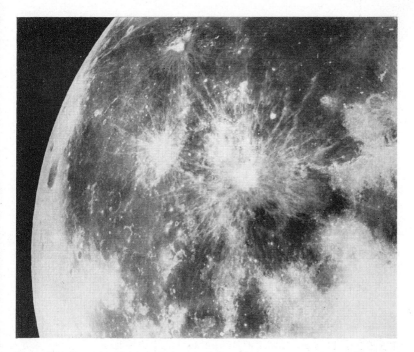

PLATE IX.   East central portion of Moon, age 15 days, 100-inch reflector. (*Courtesy of the Mt. Wilson Observatory*)

PLATE Xa. Photograph of the planet Saturn and the rings. (*Courtesy of the Yerkes Observatory*)

PLATE Xb. Drawing of the planet Saturn and the rings made at a time when the earth was in the plane of the rings. (*Courtesy of the Yerkes Observatory*)

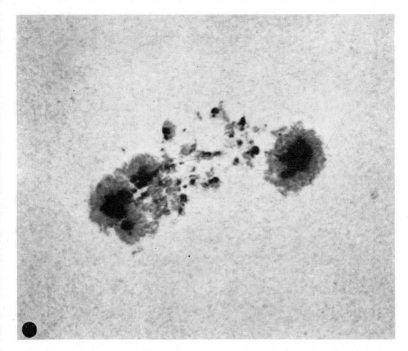

PLATE XI. The Great Sunspot Group of February 1917. (*Courtesy of the Mt. Wilson Observatory*) The black circle in the lower left-hand corner represents the size of the earth on the scale of the photograph.

PLATE XII. The Solar Corona, photographed at Wallal, Australia, 22 September 1922. (*Courtesy of the Lick Observatory*)

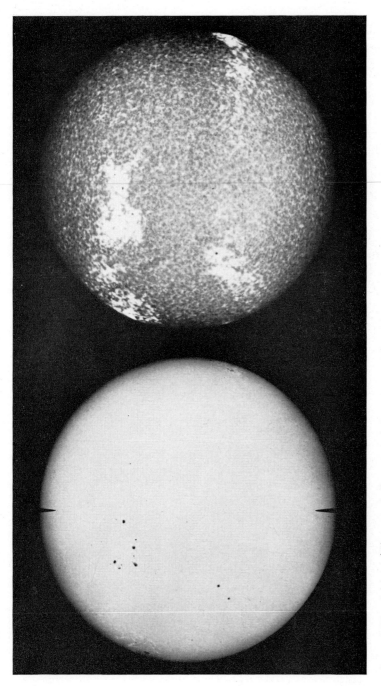

PLATE XIII.   Calcium (K) spectroheliogram and direct image of the Sun, 11 January 1926. (*Courtesy of the Mt. Wilson Observatory*)

PLATE XIV. Hydrogen (H) spectroheliogram and direct image of the Sun, 16 June 1926. (*Courtesy of the Mt. Wilson Observatory*)

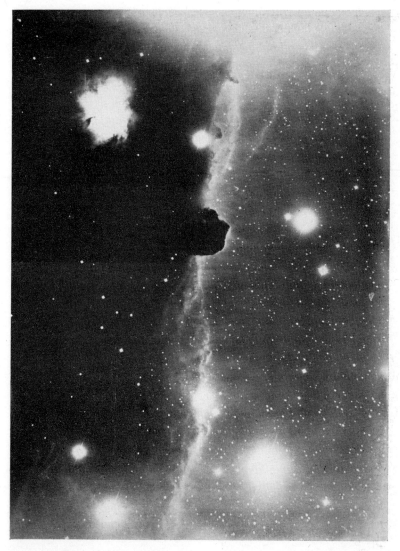

PLATE XV. Bright and dark (Horsehead) Nebulosity in Orion, exposure 3 hours, 100-inch reflector. (*Courtesy of the Mt. Wilson Observatory*)

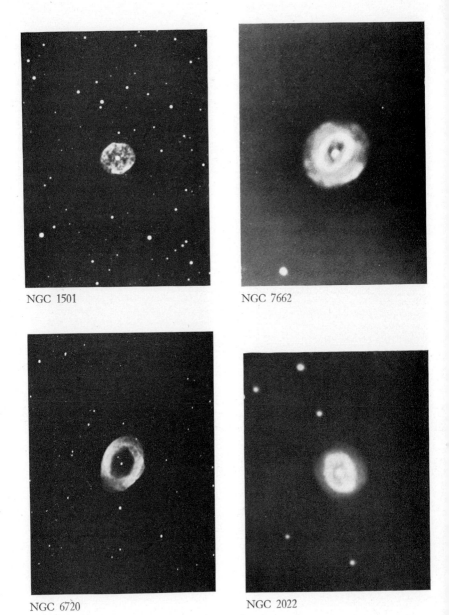

NGC 1501

NGC 7662

NGC 6720

NGC 2022

PLATE XVI. Planetary Nebulae. (*Courtesy of the Mt. Wilson Observatory*)

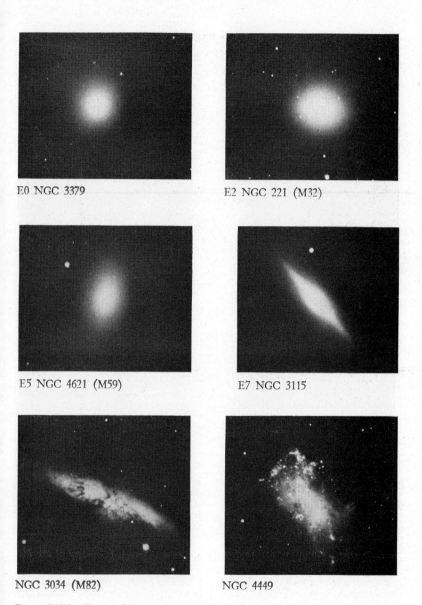

E0 NGC 3379   E2 NGC 221 (M32)

E5 NGC 4621 (M59)   E7 NGC 3115

NGC 3034 (M82)   NGC 4449

PLATE XVII. Types of Extragalactic Nebulae. (*Courtesy of the Mt. Wilson Observatory*)

PLATE XVIII. Spiral Nebula, N.G.C. 5194, Canes Venatici. (*Courtesy of the Mt. Wilson Observatory*)

PLATE XIX. Spiral Nebula viewed from a point near the projection of its central plane, N.G.C. 4565, Coma Berenices. (*Courtesy of the Mt. Wilson Observatory*)

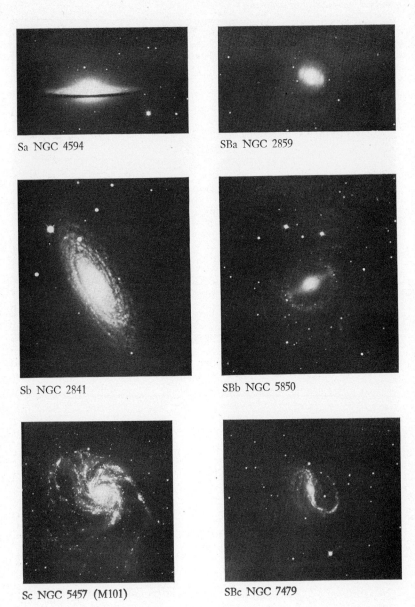

Sa NGC 4594

SBa NGC 2859

Sb NGC 2841

SBb NGC 5850

Sc NGC 5457 (M101)

SBc NGC 7479

PLATE XX. Types of normal and barred Spirals. (*Courtesy of the Mt. Wilson Observatory*)

I. The Problem Stated: Apparent Motions

The history of man's growing knowledge of the heavens, and of the movements, sizes, distances, and chemical and physical constitution of the various heavenly bodies, is largely the story of his invention and progressive refinement of numerous instruments whose function is to increase the scope of his natural senses and powers of reasoning. Of these instruments, the more important are:

i. Telescopes of a variety of types.

ii. Micrometers (instruments for the accurate measurement of minute angular distances and differences of position).

iii. Cameras.

iv. The spectroscope.

v. The spectroheliograph.

vi. Mathematics, particularly trigonometry and the calculus.

With the aid of this battery of instruments, the astronomer is able to project his inquiring mind into the furthermost corners of the visible universe.

NAKED-EYE ASTRONOMY

But the first of these instruments to be discovered (excluding from consideration mathematics, a mental rather than a physical instrument) did not appear until the early seventeenth century,* and by that time a great deal had already been learned of the relative positions and movements of the sun, moon, earth, and the other planets. This knowledge was erected upon a foundation of naked-eyed observations, refined to a certain extent by the use of primitive measuring instruments of the yardstick and sextant type. Thus the mind of man is capable of building a considerable edifice of astronomical knowledge with no materials

*A passage in one of Leonardo da Vinci's *Notebooks* suggests that he may have constructed a primitive telescope and used it for astronomical purposes.

other than the evidences of his unaided senses. The history of the science has taught us, however, that this may only be achieved on the fulfilment of two conditions:

i. The mind must be free at the outset from preconceived ideas of what *ought* to be, and prepared to reason from the evidence of the senses *alone*.

ii. The eye must be trained to make accurate observations of the motions and positions of the celestial objects that it perceives. This is the more easily fulfilled condition of the two.

THE FORM OF THE EARTH

There is a preliminary point to be settled before we go out of doors to study the day and night skies and to note carefully the behavior of the celestial bodies, in an endeavor to re-create the history of astronomy up to the time of Galileo. What is the true shape of the earth, that station from which all our observations must necessarily be made? It may be objected that the earth is spherical and that any fool is perfectly well aware of the fact. This objection, however, overlooks the professed aim of this book—to demonstrate the more complex conclusions of astronomical research by working upwards from simple assumptions that cannot rationally be denied, demonstrating each step where it can be demonstrated and at other times indicating the possible alternatives and the reason for believing one in particular to be the more probable. In short, to take the bare minimum for granted. Now, it is far from self-evident that the earth is not flat. In fact, every reader of these words has at some period during his early life received a profound shock on being told quite seriously that (i) the earth is the same shape as an orange, and that (ii) the inhabitants of Australia not only hang upside down like flies, but solemnly affirm that not they but the inhabitants of the United States live in this inconvenient attitude. It is undeniably true that the 'flat earthists' have the fact of immediate obviousness in their favor. Yet they are considered cranks. The following are some of the more important reasons why the evidence of their senses is denied by the vast majority of civilized adults:

i. However far, and in whatever direction, one travels over the surface of the earth, one never comes to an edge.

ii. Moreover, as the sixteenth-century explorers discovered, it is possible to arrive at the point from which one starts merely by following one's nose for a sufficiently great distance.

iii. The telescope reveals the true shape of a number of bodies in space whose nature cannot be discovered by the naked eye. Though many of these, including those which (for reasons not yet stated) are believed most closely to resemble the earth, are spherical, not one has yet been discovered which is flat—i.e. a plane body of negligible thickness.

iv. When ships approach the horizon, their hulls disappear first, then their funnels, and lastly their masts. This can only occur in a world whose seas, and therefore that world itself, are convex.

v. The curvature of the earth's surface can actually be seen. Since this curvature is very slight, a smooth sheet of horizontal surface of considerable extent is needed for the experiment. A large pond protected

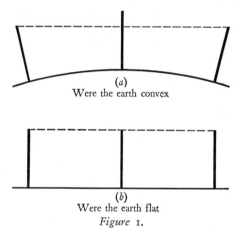

(a)
Were the earth convex

(b)
Were the earth flat

Figure 1.

from high winds will serve admirably. Suppose the reader were to drive three stakes into the bottom of the pond, two at the edges and another midway between them. He would have to be careful to see that each stake projected above the surface of the water by the same amount, say 1 foot. If then he placed a telescope upon the first stake and tried to sight on the top of the stake on the opposite side of the pond he would find that he could not do so. His view would be obstructed by the middle stake. The significance of this fact is made clear by Fig. 1.

If the distance between the stakes at the edges of the pond were exactly 1 mile and the midway stake were exactly halfway between the extremes, then the line of sight from the top of the first to the top of the third would hit the middle stake about 2 inches below the top.

vi. Points (i), (iv), and (v) prove that the earth's surface is convex, while point (iii) suggests that it is spherical. This conclusion is confirmed by eclipses of the moon. Under certain circumstances, to be described later, the earth passes directly between the sun and the moon. When this happens its shadow falls upon the surface of the moon. It is found that the edge of this shadow is always an arc of a circle; this is the shape of the shadow cast by a spherical body. We may, then, assume as our starting-point that the earth is not a flat but a spherical body, and that it is suspended in space by some means still to be determined.

THE SIZE OF THE EARTH

It is of importance that we should know at the outset of our investigations not only the shape of the earth but also its size. It might be supposed, since we can never get far enough away from the earth to be able to see it as a whole, and since it is not practicable to walk round it with a tape measure, that its measurement must present a very difficult, if not an insoluble, problem. This is not the case, however, the theory of the process being extremely simple. Such difficulties as are encountered are practical ones.

Let us go out of doors on a clear and preferably moonless night. At once it will be seen that the sky is dotted with innumerable points of light, the stars. These stars have several interesting properties which are perceptible to the unaided eyesight, but for the moment we shall confine our attention to one only. Quite a short period of observation of the southern sky will reveal the fact that the stars are moving *en bloc*—that is, without altering their relative positions, one to another—from east to west. This absence of relative motion makes it possible for us to imagine that they are fixed to the inner side of a gigantic vault with the earth at its center, and that this vault is in rotation, carrying the stars with it.

Imagine, for a moment, a large bowl on the inner surface of which are marked a number of dots; the bowl is pivoted at the center of its base and may be rotated about this pivot (Fig. 2). If the bowl is made to rotate through one quarter of a turn, the dots which were at *a,b,c,d,e,* and *f* will now be in positions *a',b'* . . . *f'*, and the paths that they have traced out will be the dotted lines in the diagram. A study of this diagram will reveal two obvious, but important facts.

i. The nearer a dot is to the center of rotation, the shorter will be its path for a given movement of the bowl.

ii. The dots on the opposite sides of the pivot move in opposite directions. In the figure the rotation is clockwise, with the result that those dots above the pivot move from left to right and those below it from right to left.

We shall return now to the night sky; careful observation shows that stars about halfway up the southern sky move farther—i.e. describe a longer arc—in a given period of time than those at a greater distance above the horizon; and those, in turn, move farther than the ones directly overhead. And so on until we reach a point in the sky about midway between the northern horizon and the zenith (the point directly

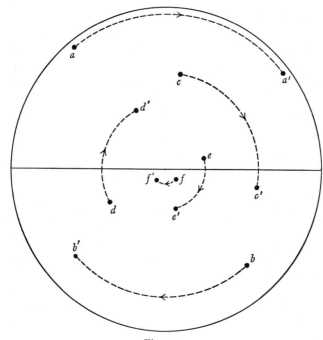

Figure 2.

above the observer's head). At this point in the northern sky there happens to be a star which, during the course of an hour's observation, apparently does not move at all. Even longer periods of observation fail to detect any motion in it, and we may therefore conclude that it must lie very near the point on the star sphere about which the whole vault revolves (see *ff'* in Fig. 2). This star is called Polaris, or the Pole Star, and the point on the star sphere close to it (about which the whole sphere revolves) the north celestial pole. The point diametrically opposed to it is the other pivot, the south celestial pole; this obviously cannot be seen from places in the northern hemisphere of the earth, any more than inhabitants of the antipodes can see Polaris. We may therefore define the celestial poles as those points upon the star sphere which have no diurnal (or twenty-four hourly) motion.

In accordance with the second result derived from our experiment with the bowl, those stars above the north celestial pole—i.e. those between it and the zenith, *plus* those between the zenith and the southern horizon—revolve in an east-west direction; while those below or to the north of it revolve in the opposite direction, from west to east. These elementary facts of the diurnal rotation of the star vault will be obvious to anyone who has spent an hour or two in intelligent observation of the night sky.

All this is preliminary to the determination of the earth's size. It has been discovered that the angular elevation of the Pole Star (which, it will be remembered, is very near the north celestial pole) above the northern horizon, depends upon the position of the observer on the earth's surface—more accurately, upon his latitude. In our latitudes, approximately midway between the equator and the north pole, Polaris is seen to lie approximately midway between the zenith and the northern horizon. As we travel north, the Pole Star rises higher and higher in the sky until, when we arrive at the north pole itself, it is directly overhead. Similarly, as we move south towards the equator it sinks lower and lower toward the northern horizon. When we reach the equator itself we find that it lies on the northern horizon; further southward movement will render it invisible, since it lies below this horizon. Put in another way, we may say that when the north celestial pole has an altitude of 90° (is overhead) our latitude is 90° (the north pole); when its altitude is 45° our latitude is 45° (we are midway between the equator and the north pole—at Minneapolis, perhaps); and when its altitude is 0° (actually on the horizon) our latitude is 0° (the latitude of the equator). Incidentally it is to be noted that this fact provides us with another reason for believing that the earth is spherical—or at any rate not flat—for if it were, the elevation of the celestial pole above the horizon would be the same for all points of observation.

In fact, the latitude of a place is nothing more than the angular elevation of the north celestial pole (or the south celestial pole in the southern terrestrial hemisphere) above the northern (or southern) point on the horizon as observed from that place. The reader who has a sextant available can quite easily determine his latitude. If he lives in New York he will find that the angle between the Pole Star and the horizon averages about 41°; if he looks in his atlas he will find that New York is close to the 41st parallel of latitude. Since the Pole Star is actually about 1° from the celestial pole of rotation he will find that his measurements will differ if taken at the same time in the evening throughout the year. However, the average of a long series of observations will give him a good value of his latitude.

The ground is now cleared for the determination of the earth's size. First, two points on the earth's surface, exactly north and south of each other, are chosen, and the distance between them determined. Then the latitude of each point is found by observations of the stars. From the difference of latitude and the linear distance between the two points the size of the earth may be determined. Suppose, to make the explanation concrete, that the two stations are 69.5 miles apart and that their difference of latitude is 1°. Then, since the circumference of a circle contains 360°, the circumference of the earth should be 360×69.5 or 25,000 miles (approximately). Then by using geometry—with which high-school students should be familiar—the diameter, radius, and volume of the earth may be deduced. The figures have been kept approximate and simple intentionally; in practice the distances between stations is determined by geodetic survey and the latitudes obtained by precise astronomical methods.

Having prepared the way for our inquiry by discovering what sort of a body it is that we inhabit, and from which we must perforce make all our astronomical observations, we can proceed to the investigation of the motions and, so far as they can be deduced without the aid of instruments, the positions and distances of those other celestial bodies that are visible in the day and night skies. It is assumed that the reader undertakes to spend a short time in the open each evening, there to study the appearance of the night sky.

DIURNAL ROTATION OF THE STAR SPHERE

The stars are sizeless points of light, varying in brightness and also in color. The differences in color shown to the naked eye by individual stars are not striking. Nevertheless, they can be noticed quite clearly in the case of a number of the brighter stars.

We have already discovered that the star sphere rotates steadily from east to west (if we are looking at that part of it that lies south of the north celestial pole—as we usually are, since it is by far the larger part) about a pivot in the northern sky which is nearly marked by the star

Polaris. Since we are now engaged in practical observation, it will be as well to find this star at once. One obviously important function of Polaris is to give the direction of the true north to any sailor or other observer situated north of the equator; another, as we have seen, to give the latitude of all places from which it is visible. Most people who know no other astronomy are familiar with that group of northern stars known variously as the Big Dipper, the Great Bear, and Ursa Major; it is represented in Fig. 3. If the observer carries his eye along the line joining the stars marked β and α for a distance equal to about five

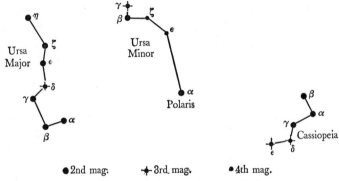

Figure 3.   Three circumpolar constellations.

times that separating them, he will find a star which, though of only medium brightness, is nevertheless rendered unmistakable by its isolation. This is Polaris.

One feature following from the rotation of the heavens about the north celestial pole will soon be noticed. The elevation of Polaris above the horizon, is, as we have seen, equal to the latitude of the observer. But this angular elevation is the shortest distance from Polaris to the horizon. Hence a star which is distant from Polaris by a number of degrees equal to the observer's latitude (41° in the case of New York) will never dip below the horizon in the course of its rotation about the pole. It will indeed just touch the horizon once in every diurnal period, and may therefore set if the northern horizon is not clear of obstructions. But all stars nearer to Polaris than this will never set at all—the whole of their circuit about the pole must be described above the horizon. Such stars are called circumpolar, and in our latitudes the stars of the Big Dipper are an example of this class. All stars farther from the Pole Star than the latitude of the observer will, of course carry out part of their circuit below the horizon, rising above it in the east and setting below it in the west. This distinction will be made clear by a glance at Fig. 4.

The reader will perhaps have been impressed by the fact that the star sphere has many points of resemblance to a model globe of the

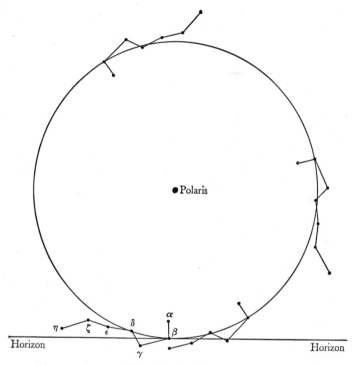

Figure 4. Circumpolar stars. The altitude of Polaris in the diagram (the radius of the circle) is 33°. The appearance represented is, therefore, that of the northern sky as seen from any place whose latitude is 33°, e.g. the Sea of Galilee or Charleston, S.C.

earth* such as is to be found in most schoolrooms. In the first place the globe rotates between two pivots which correspond with the north and south celestial poles. Furthermore, if we imagine a plane to lie horizontally through the center of the globe it will be appreciated that

*This statement does not beg the question of the earth's rotation; the demonstration of this fact will come later. A comparison is simply being made between the star sphere and the type of model mechanism of which a child's globe is an example.

the pivot which we call the north celestial pole lies not immediately above it (i.e. at the zenith) but at a point intermediate between the zenith and the horizon. In the model we must call this section of the horizontal plane the north horizon. By rotating the globe and watching the parallels of latitude (which may be regarded as the paths of certain stars in their diurnal rotation about the earth) the difference between circumpolar stars and stars that rise and set will immediately be made plain.

Midway between the pivots of the globe is drawn a great circle—i.e. a circle whose plane passes through the center of the globe—

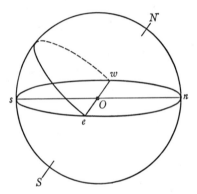

Figure 5. The circle *sSnN* represents the observer's meridian on the star sphere, bisecting which is the observer's horizon *nesw*. The observer is situated at *O*, and *N* and *S* are the north and south celestial poles. It will be seen that the celestial equator, of which only the visible half is shown, cuts the horizon at points due east and due west of the observer, and reaches its maximum altitude due south of him.

known as the equator. Similarly, in the celestial sphere there is an imaginary circle drawn about the whole heavens, the visible section of which lies between the American observer's zenith and his southern horizon. A moment's thought will reveal the fact that this circle, the celestial equator, will cut his horizon at points due east and due west of him, and will attain its maximum height above the horizon where it is due south (Fig. 5). By definition, the shortest distance of any point on the celestial equator from the north celestial pole (or the south celestial pole, which is below our horizon, for that matter) is 90°. In the same way all points on the terrestrial equator have a latitude of 0°, that of each pole being 90°. This is, of course, only another way of saying that the celestial equator bisects the star sphere into two hemispheres, in each of which one of the poles is centrally placed.

THE SIDEREAL DAY

Having noted the fact of the rotation of the star sphere about the earth, and having discovered the positions of the pole of this rotation and of the celestial equator, we must now discover the time required for one complete rotation of the sphere. The obvious way of doing this is to note the time at which some conspicuous star is due south—or, to express it in technical language, the time that it transits or culminates on the meridian, the meridian being that great circle that connects the pole, the zenith, and the north and south points of the horizon—then to note the time of the next culmination, and to measure the time interval separating the two observations.

We shall suppose that the observer produces a compass during the day preceding his first observation, and discovers that the point on his horizon that is due south of him is marked by a church spire. On the succeeding night he goes out at 8 p.m. and notes that there is a bright star slightly to the east of the vertical line passing through the steeple— that is to say, east of the meridian. He therefore waits, and at 8:30 precisely he decides that the star is directly over the steeple. He makes a note of the time and perhaps constructs a rough star map of the southern sky so that he will be sure of recognizing his star on the next occasion.

The following night he again begins observation at 8 p.m. and notes that the appearance of the southern sky is, so far as he can tell with the naked eye, exactly the same as on the preceding night. Not only are the stars in their same relative positions—that, as we have seen, is to be expected—but their positions in the sky, their compass bearings, appear to be the same. He therefore jumps to the conclusion that the star sphere rotates in a period of twenty-four hours. However, being of a scientific disposition, he decides to wait and see if his star really will culminate at 8:30, thus substantiating his guess. He waits less patiently this time, and when at last the star appears to be directly over the steeple he glances at his watch. He finds that the time is not, as he had expected, exactly 8:30, but about 8:26. Unfortunately, his disposition is not truly and sufficiently scientific. He comes therefore to one of two conclusions, perhaps to both. Since this observation is not in accordance with his preconceived notion that the star sphere rotates in exactly twenty-four hours (a guess based on comparatively inaccurate data, be

it noted), then one or other of his observations was inaccurate and that
the star was not *exactly* over the spire; or else his watch needs regulating.

But when he comes out on the third evening he is disturbed to find
that the discrepancy between the expected and the observed is even
greater. The star culminates at, according to his watch, 8:22 and at
8:30 it is quite obviously to the west of the spire. Clearly something
has gone wrong, and as the result of a little thought he decides that
his guess at twenty-four hours as being the exact period was slightly
in error; further, that this error has now been doubled by the second
rotation of the star sphere, thus becoming more easily detectable. He
therefore begins all over again, and a week's observations carefully
made and recorded show him where his mistake lay. The star sphere
does not rotate in precisely twenty-four hours, but in a period about
4 minutes shorter, known as the sidereal day. Thus, if our observer
began his observations on Sunday night and the star was then due
south at 8:30, on Monday it would culminate at 8:26, and at 8:30 would
be a short distance past (i.e. to the west of) the meridian; on Tuesday
it would culminate at 8:22; on Wednesday at 8:18; on Thursday at
8:14. Since the star makes a complete circuit of the heavens in about
twenty-four hours, it will travel an appreciable distance in a quarter
of an hour and will therefore be very noticeably to the west of the
meridian at 8:30 on Thursday night. It will, in fact, be to the west of
the meridian by a distance equal to one ninety-sixth of its entire circuit
of the star sphere.

ANNUAL ROTATION OF THE STAR SPHERE

This discrepancy of four minutes *per diem* between the sidereal and
the solar day has an important effect upon the appearance of the night-
sky. At 8:30 p.m. on Monday all the stars in the southern sky will be
slightly farther west than they were at the same time on Sunday: stars
that were on the meridian will now be slightly to the west of it; stars
that were on the east horizon, now slightly above it; stars that were
exactly on the west horizon will now have sunk below it and will be
invisible. The difference in the aspect of the heavens occasioned by the
passing of one day is of course small, since the diurnal shift accomplished in four minutes is only slight. But consider what happens as
the result of a lapse of three months. The stars which were originally
on the meridian at 8:30 p.m. are now on the west horizon at that hour;
stars that were on the east horizon are now on the meridian; and a
number of new stars which were invisible below the eastern horizon are
now rising above it.

In fact, the star sphere makes one complete revolution in one year in addition to its diurnal motion. One year after his first observation, our observer will again notice that his star is on the meridian at 8:30 p.m. In the meanwhile every star that crossed his meridian between 8:30 on that original Sunday and 8:26 on the following Monday (only about half of which he could have seen, the others being above the horizon during the daytime) will have been on the meridian, or at any rate very near it, at 8:30 p.m. on one of the 364 intervening nights. In other words, the summer stars, those that occupy the southern sky on summer midnights, let us say, are not the same as the winter stars. (Note in passing that the circumpolar stars will have been visible throughout every one of the intervening nights.) Hence anyone familiar with the constellations and the motions of the star sphere who had fallen asleep like Rip Van Winkle and awakened during a clear night could determine at once what the season was. If he heard a clock strike he would be able to make an accurate guess at the month. If in addition he were armed with a set of astronomical tables, he would be able to deduce the date—though not, of course, the year.

THE MOTION OF THE MOON

The next celestial body to be studied is the moon, and a single month's observation, for a few minutes each night, reveals the main characteristics of its motion and varying appearance. Further observations, made during subsequent months, will show that these features are recurrent or cyclic: the moon does the same things in the same order month after month.

The first thing that the observer will notice, and a few hours' or even minutes' observation are all that are required, is that the moon shares the stars' diurnal east-west motion. It rises in the east, though this may be cloaked by the fact of its rising in the daytime, and sets in the west, rising again in the east *about* twenty-four hours later. It will be remembered that the star sphere is, so to speak, rotating more rapidly than the passing of our terrestrial days (which are measured by solar, not sidereal, time); that every star arrives at the meridian, or any other selected point on the star sphere, a little ahead of solar time. Now the moon does somewhat the same thing, though in the opposite direction. In short, it is, as has been said, carried round the star sphere from east to west with the stars, but its motion appears to be slower. Thus the stars in its neighborhood are always passing it, with the result that it has a residual west-east motion in respect of them.

Suppose, for example, that on Sunday at midnight the moon is due south of the observer. He memorizes its position with reference to a bright star which is also on the meridian, but further south, i.e. directly below the moon. As he watches, he notices that the moon and the star (together with all the other stars) are moving across the sky towards the western horizon. But since, in this motion, the moon is proceeding more slowly than the star, he will on the next night observe that when the star is again on the meridian the moon has been left a certain distance behind. It is now considerably to the east of the star and he would say that besides its diurnal east-west motion the moon has a motion of its own from west to east, relative to the starry background. As a result of this motion the moon is displaced to the east at a given time on succeeding nights. Whether the observer regards the moon as traveling eastward of its own accord while at the same time being carried westward by the diurnal motion of the star sphere, or regards the moon as having no true eastward motion but only as traveling westward with the star sphere though more slowly than it, is immaterial. What is important to realize is that the moon takes more than twenty-four hours to make a diurnal circuit of the heavens, while the stars take slightly less.

THE MOON AND THE ZODIAC

A careful observer will also notice that the moon is not only moving slowly eastward relative to the star sphere, but that it is also slowly moving north or south relative to the stars. This motion is restricted to a comparatively narrow path on the star sphere known as the zodiac. This parallel-sided belt, 18° in width, was recognized at least 4000 years ago. For all residents of Europe, and for those of the United States north of the latitude of Atlanta or Los Angeles, the zodiac crosses the meridian between the zenith and the south point of the horizon. Along this celestial highway the moon (with, as we shall see, certain other objects) always moves; sometimes nearer one side of the road than the other, but never jumping the curb.

THE LUNAR PHASES

The most interesting point to be noticed with the naked eye is the cycle of the moon's phases and the time it requires to complete one eastward circuit of the star sphere. It will be remembered that owing to the fact of the stars revolving *en bloc* in slightly less than twenty-four hours, it requires a lapse of a year for a given star once more to be in the same position in the sky at the same time of night. Owing to the moon's considerable lag among the stars, it returns to the same position with reference to the stars after an interval of about twenty-seven and a third days. This is known as the sidereal period of the moon.

For the layman, the lunar month starts when for the first time he sees the moon as a fine crescent low down in the west, soon after sunset. Two things are to be noticed: the moon is close to the sun in the sky, and the illuminated sickle lies on that side of the moon that faces the sun. Disregard of the latter fact has led artists to perpetrate absurdities times without number. As the month proceeds, the moon moves eastward along the zodiac. With its daily recession from the sun the proportion of its whole face that is illuminated increases. In a week it is on the meridian at about the hour that the sun sets; it is now half illuminated, or dichotomized, the illuminated hemisphere being that on the right-hand side, the side facing the sun. During the second week the moon continues its course away from the sun, and the terminator (i.e. the boundary between the illuminated and the unilluminated portions of its disk) moves further across its face from west to east (right to left). At the end of the second week, midway through the lunar month, it is fully illuminated, and rises in the east at about sunset. Halfway through the night, when the sun, below the horizon, has traversed half its course from the west horizon to the east, the moon will be on the meridian. As it sets in the west, the sun rises.

The moon is now as far from the sun, measuring angularly around the star sphere, as it ever can be: the two bodies are 180° apart, i.e. at diametrically opposite points on the sphere. In continuing its eastward motion, therefore, the moon begins to approach the sun again, but from the opposite side. During the first half of the month (new-full) it has been moving away from the *east* side of the solar disk. Henceforth (full-old) it is approaching its *west* side. As it does so, the terminator, which has vanished at full, reappears as before at its west limb and moves eastward across its disk; but now the opposite hemisphere is illuminated —darkness on the west, light on the east—since the moon's other limb is now nearer the sun. After three weeks the moon is about 90° to the west of the sun: it is on the meridian at sunrise, setting towards midday. It is again dichotomized; the illuminated hemisphere, being that facing the sun, is on the left-hand or east side of the disk. During the final week of the month it approaches nearer and nearer to the sun, becoming an increasingly narrow sickle as it does so, rising above the eastern horizon later each night, and setting in the west later and later in the afternoon. Toward the end of the fourth week it is a very fine sickle, rising shortly before the sun. Finally, as its eastward motion continues, it becomes invisible in the sun's glare. Thus invisible, it passes the sun and a few days later is again visible as the new moon low down in the west shortly after sunset. Another lunar month has begun.

THE MOTION OF THE SUN

The investigation of the sun's motions and positions is complicated by the fact that when we can observe the sun we cannot observe the stars. Since the sky is itself a featureless waste it is a great convenience to have the stars, whose motions we have studied and can allow for, as reference points. It is easy, for instance, to determine the exact position of the moon throughout the lunation, for we only have to make a direct observation of it and then plot the observed position upon a star map. In dealing with the sun, indirect methods of study must be used.

But no special observations are required to establish our first point; common experience and what we have already discovered of the motions of the stars provide the necessary data. We know that, whatever the season, the sun is always due south at midday.* We also know that the same star is not always south at midnight. Each twenty-four hours it has moved a little more than once round the star sphere and the sum of these daily increments amounts to one complete circuit in a year. Combining this knowledge of the movement of the stars with the observed fact that the sun is always due south at midday, we see that the sun must have a motion relative to the stars, and, moreover, that it must complete one west-to-east revolution of the star sphere in a year. It also makes a diurnal apparent circuit of the earth, rising in the east and setting in the west. During this interval it will have moved across the (invisible) starry background approximately one three hundred and sixty-fifth of its complete circuit. Thus, like the moon, the

*The term midday is used here to indicate the middle of the interval between sunrise and sunset and not, necessarily, 12 o'clock as indicated by a mechanical clock. It would be 12 o'clock as indicated by a properly adjusted sundial. Owing to two factors, of which we shall learn more later (the obliquity of the ecliptic and the eccentricity of the earth's orbit), the apparent motion of the real sun is not uniform. On some days it moves slightly faster than average and on others slightly slower. For convenience in building mechanical clocks, a fictitious object, known as the mean sun, is defined. The mean sun moves with uniform motion along the celestial equator. Time measured by the real sun is known as local apparent time (LAT) while that measured by the mean sun is called local civil time (LCT). The difference between the two, in the sense local apparent time minus local civil time; is called the equation of time (LAT–LCT=equation of time). Still more complication is introduced by the use of Zone, or Standard, time.

sun has an individual motion among the stars, though a slower one, since it accomplishes in a year what the moon does in a month.

THE ECLIPTIC

The general fact of the sun's motion among the stars is thus not very difficult to establish. But a question will have been suggested to the observer which the practical difficulty already referred to makes less easy to answer immediately. He has discovered that the moon's possibilities of position upon the star sphere are strictly limited; as we have seen, it never moves off a track 18° wide—an angular distance about equal to that covered by a stick 9 inches long when held at arm's length against the sky. Since the star sphere appears to be curved—it looks like the inner side of a hollow sphere, not like a flat surface—the lines traced out by all celestial objects in the course of their motions are likewise curved. In watching the moon pursue its curved and circumscribed path across the heavens, the observer will have been struck by the fact that this is just about, as far as he can judge with the naked eye, the same path as that pursued by the sun during the daytime. It is in endeavoring to find out more about this interesting and as yet inexplicable correspondence that he will encounter the difficulty already referred to. He is therefore forced to deduce the position of the sun in relation to the stars, from its observed position in the day sky, by an indirect method. There are several such methods to choose from. That employed by the ancient Egyptian astronomers, though not particularly accurate, is easily understood. Since, the Egyptians reasoned, we cannot observe the sun and the stars simultaneously, and yet want to know the position of the former relative to the latter, we must do the next best thing, which is to observe them in the quickest possible succession. Consequently they systematically noted the last bright star visible near the east horizon before sunrise, and by its aid deduced the approximate position of the sun in relation to the star's invisible neighbors.

Thus the path of the sun across the star sphere can be mapped and our observer's suspicions are confirmed: the sun's path does in fact lie very close to that of the moon. This path is known as the ecliptic (which is, strictly, the path traced out by the center of the sun's disk in the course of a year) and so nearly does it coincide with that of the moon that it is possible to trace out a zone 18° wide in which the ecliptic is centrally placed and out of which the moon never moves. This is the zodiac, which is, in fact, that strip of star sphere that extends 9° on each side of the ecliptic. The zodiac is divided into twelve sections of equal size, known as the signs of the zodiac. Since the sun completes one circuit of the zodiac in a year, it passes one month in each sign.

THE SUN AND THE SEASONS

There is still one further characteristic of the sun's yearly motion that must be mentioned. It is a fact of common experience that the sun is higher in summer than in winter; also that the days are longer in the former season than in the latter. The first fact can be used to determine the length of the year, and in primitive times was so used. Let the reader mark on the ground a north-south line and at its southern end fix a vertical stick. Now when the stick's sun-cast shadow lies along the line the time must be midday and the sun at its maximum height above the horizon. Between sunrise and this time it will have been rising progressively higher in the sky from the eastern horizon; from then until sunset it will sink lower and lower towards the western.

The passage of the seasons provides us with a rough and ready method of determining the length of the year, but the result obtained can never be more than very approximate, except by a fluke. A study of the stick's shadow, on the other hand, allows the determination to be made with some accuracy. Suppose that every day the reader makes a scratch on the ground to mark the apex of the noon shadow. If he begins his experiment at about Christmas-time he will find that the shadow is slightly shorter each day until it reaches a minimum value on 21 June. Thenceforward until about 21 December it will grow progressively longer again. Since the seasons are regulated by the noon-day height of the sun, and the length of the shadow gauges this with fair accuracy, we are now in a position to say that the interval from 21 December to 21 June is half a year and that the total number of days in a complete year is equivalent to double the number in this interval.

THE GNOMON

It is interesting to note in passing that this most primitive of astronomical instruments, the gnomon, is possessed of considerable versatility in the hands of ingenious users. We have already seen that it can be used as a calendar, to measure the length of the year. The varying directions of the shadow on either side of the marked line record the passing of the hours, i.e. the time of day. It can be used to measure the obliquity of the ecliptic—a point to which we shall return. And, finally, it presents an alternative and approximate way of determining the observer's latitude. Suppose that W (Fig. 6(i)) is the apex of the sun's longest shadow (on the shortest day), and S the apex at midsummer, when the shadow is shortest and the day longest. Both these distances can be measured, as can the height of the gnomon, AB. Since WAB

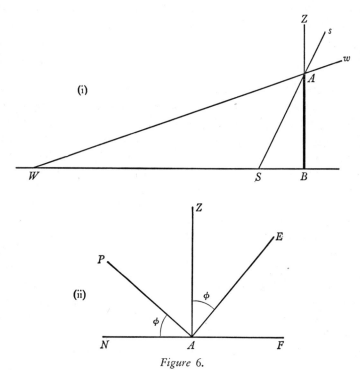

Figure 6.

ınd SAB are right-angled triangles, a simple trigonometrical operation will give the angles WAB and SAB.* But these angles=angles ZAw and ZAs respectively. These are clearly the sun's maximum and minimum zenith distances, and their mean equals the angular distance from the zenith to the celestial equator, since the sun is on the equator when midway between its maximum and minimum altitudes. (This

*Suppose, for instance, that $WB=14$ ft., $SB=2$ ft., and $AB=4$ ft. Then

$$\tan \angle WAB = \frac{14}{4}, \text{ and } \tan \angle SAB = \frac{2}{4}$$

Hence $\angle WAB \simeq 74°$, and $\angle SAB \simeq 27°$.

fact will be made clear in the next paragraph.) We have thus succeeded in discovering the angle subtended between the celestial equator and the zenith. Refering for a moment to Fig. 6 (ii), *A* is the position of the observer, *NAF* his horizon, *AP* the direction of the celestial pole, and the angle *NAP* his latitude. *AE* is the direction of the celestial equator, the angle *PAE* being a right angle by definition. The angle *ZAE* is the zenith distance of the equator, which we have already discovered, and this is clearly equal to the angle *NAP*. Hence the angle *ZAE* is the observer's latitude, φ.

OBLIQUITY OF THE ECLIPTIC

It will immediately be asked how this annual bobbing up and down of the sun in the sky is connected with its west-east path among the stars. Having plotted the daily position of the sun on a star map throughout a complete year, we find that the ecliptic (its path) is neither coincident with the celestial equator, nor is it parallel to it. They are, in fact, related to one another in the same way as two hoops jammed together, one within the other (Fig. 7). Now since the latitude of any given point on earth is invariable, the altitude of the north celestial pole is also invariable. Thus the altitude of the point of inter-section of the meridian and the celestial equator is the same on every day of the year. Since the sun, in its course about the ecliptic, is some-times north of the celestial equator and sometimes south of it, its mid-day elevation above the horizon will vary from season to season. When it is at one or other of the points of intersection of the equator and the ecliptic—when, in fact, it lies on the equator—the days and nights will be of equal duration, the sun will rise due east and set due west (since we have seen that the celestial equator always cuts the observer's horizon at points due east and west of him), and its altitude at noon will be midway between its maximum (summer solstice) and its minimum (winter solstice). These points are called the equinoxes, and the sun arrives at them on or about 21 March (vernal equinox) and 23 September (autumnal equinox).

The angle between the ecliptic and the celestial equator is about $23\frac{1}{2}°$ and is known as the obliquity of the ecliptic. It follows that when the sun is at its farthest from the celestial equator (at the solstices) the distance is $23\frac{1}{2}°$. Hence the midday sun in midsummer is $47°$ higher above the horizon, for observers outside of the tropics, than is the midday sun in midwinter.

It is quite simple for the reader to determine the value of the obliquity of the ecliptic for himself by means of the gnomon. As before (p. 21 and Fig. 6) we shall assume that *AB*, the height of the gnomon, is 4 feet, that *WB*, the length of the noon shadow at the winter solstice, is 14 feet, and that *SB*, the length of the noon shadow at the time of the summer solstice, is 2 feet. Now since the difference

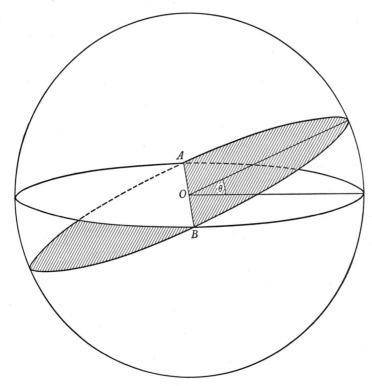

Figure 7. The circle represents the star sphere, seen from without. The intersecting great circles may represent the celestial equator and the ecliptic, in which case *A* and *B* are the equinoxes and θ = 23½°; or they may represent the moon's orbit and the ecliptic, in which θ = 5° and *A* and *B* are the nodes. In either case the earth is at *O*, the center of the sphere.

in the angular height of the sun above the horizon at the two solstices is double the angle between the ecliptic and the celestial equator the angle *sAw* is twice the obliquity of the ecliptic. But *sAw*=*WAS*, and this angle=*WAB*—*SAB*, both of which we have determined to be 74° and 27°, respectively (p. 21, n.). Hence *WAS*=47° and the obliquity of the ecliptic is half this value or 23½°.

THE PLANETS

We now come to the last class of celestial object that repays study with the naked eye. When we made our observations of the stars we found that one of their most obvious characteristics was their immobility relative to one another. Thus, if we were to make a map of some conspicuous star group (the Great Bear, say) we should find that year after year it would be as accurate as on the day it was made. Yet if the reader observes regularly he will sooner or later discover that there are exceptions to this rule: there are stars (or so they seem) which not only change their positions relative to the vast mass of their neighbors but also relative to one another. These objects are called planets, and five are visible to the naked eye.* The word 'planet' is connected philologically with the idea of a wanderer. In appearance the planets are indistinguishable from stars; only their motion, which requires serial observation for its detection, can infallibly betray their different nature to the naked eye. It is widely supposed that whereas on some nights the stars twinkle, the planets never do. But this is an unsure guide, and it is extremely doubtful if anyone unfamiliar with the appearance of the night sky could distinguish stars from planets by this means alone.

MOTIONS OF THE OUTER PLANETS

Careful observation of the successive positions of the planets reveals the fact that they may be divided into two groups, the members of which behave in quite different ways. We shall consider the planets belonging to the larger group first. They are three in number and to them the names Mars, Jupiter, and Saturn have been given. Like the sun and moon they travel eastward among the stars, but their motions differ from those of the brighter bodies in two important respects:

        i. they are very much slower;
       ii. they are not smooth, but erratic.

Taking the second point first, the motion of a planet belonging to this group may be described as follows (Fig. 8). When first observed we shall suppose that it is moving eastward with increasing velocity. After an interval, the length of which varies from planet to planet, it begins to slow down, finally becoming stationary among the stars.

*A sixth, Uranus, is just visible to the naked eye when its position is known beforehand. It was not known to the ancients, however, and was discovered telescopically by Herschel in the eighteenth century.

Then it begins to move in the reverse direction (westward), accelerating at first, then slowing again, until once more it is stationary. Lastly it resumes its eastward motion. Thus the planets Mars, Jupiter, and Saturn move eastward in a series of loops; since more ground is always covered by the direct motion than by the retrograde there is a residual eastward motion. Observations over a number of years permit the determination of the period required by each planet for one circum-ambulation of the star sphere. It is found that for Mars this is about one and three-quarter years, for Jupiter about twelve years, and for Saturn about twenty-nine years.

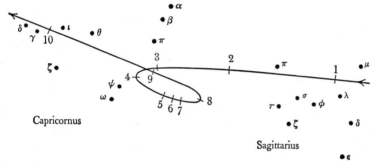

Figure 8. Successive positions of Mars in the constellations Sagittarius and Capricornus during 1939:

1. 1 April	6. 27 July
2. 1 May	7. 1 August
3. 1 June	8. 1 September
4. 1 July	9. 1 October
5. 23 July	10. 1 November

During July and August the planet was retrograding.

MOTIONS OF THE INNER PLANETS

The second planetary group has two members, Venus and Mercury. As with all the other bodies we have so far considered, the motions of these planets are recurrent. To illustrate them we shall describe a single cycle in the motion of Venus. Let us suppose that when first observed, Venus is situated in the southwest sky in the evening; it is visible for several hours after sunset before following the sun below the horizon. Nightly observations will show that at a given time each evening Venus is a little nearer the horizon. Thus the period of its visibility is steadily diminishing, since the sun's glare does not permit it to be seen till some time after sunset. Eventually the planet has moved so near the sun in the sky that it is not visible until on the point of setting. Last of all, it becomes entirely invisible, for by the time that the sky is dark enough for its visibility, it has already set.

The observer need not feel stultified by this disappearance, for the situation is not without precedent in his experience. In his observations of the moon he encountered an analogous case: once in each lunar month the moon approaches so near that part of the sky occupied by the sun that it becomes invisible (new moon), appearing on the other side of the sun after a suitable lapse of time. It will obviously be worth scrutinizing the eastern horizon before dawn in the hope that Venus too will pass through the sun's glare and reappear on its western side. The observer's foresight and patience will eventually be rewarded. Low down in the east he will notice, shortly before dawn, a shining point of light which in a few minutes is rendered invisible by the rising sun. As the days pass he will notice that Venus is slightly farther from the sun when first seen and is consequently visible for a longer period of time. Day by day its angular distance from the sun increases.

Unlike the moon, however, Venus does not recede continuously from the sun, eventually to approach it again from the opposite (eastern) side. When it has receded about 48° from the sun it stops in its westward progress and begins to retrace its steps towards the sun's west side. Eventually it is lost in the morning glare just as formerly, when an 'evening star,' it was lost in the glare of the setting sun.

Thus Venus swings back and forth from the east of the sun (when it is visible as an 'evening star') to the west ('morning star') and back to the east once more. This cycle is repeated endlessly. Mercury's motion is of exactly the same type. It differs from Venus in two respects: it never recedes as far from the sun as its brighter neighbor (the maximum distance between Mercury and the sun is only 28°), and it completes its cycle of changes in a shorter period of time. Because of the first point of difference, it is in practice very much more difficult to observe than Venus. Most people are familiar with the appearance of Venus as the 'evening star,' but few who have not deliberately set out to do so have ever caught a glimpse of the fugitive Mercury.

Thus we see that neither Venus nor Mercury can ever be in opposition to the sun, as can the planets Mars, Jupiter, and Saturn.

THE PLANETS AND THE ZODIAC

Lastly, let an important point be noted. All the five planets are confined to the zodiac. Like that of the moon, their paths are neither coincident with nor parallel to the ecliptic, but are inclined to it at small angles (all less than 9° since they never move out of the 18°-wide zodiac) in the same way that the ecliptic is inclined to the equator.

RECAPITULATION

In the present chapter we have reviewed the main characteristics of the motions of the sun, moon, stars, and planets as they may be discerned by elementary naked-eye observations. A number of facts have been omitted. The sun and moon do not, for instance, move absolutely uniformly in their courses, though the irregularities in these motions are neither so noticeable nor so important as those affecting the planets. Again, Polaris has not always marked, and will not always mark, even the approximate position of the north celestial pole. But to explain the growth of our astronomical knowledge step by step and yet to keep the account within manageable proportions one must inevitably omit less important points. All those facts that are stepping stones to the demonstration of further astronomical essentials have been included.

These leading facts may be summarized as follows:

1. The earth is approximately spherical and its size can be determined with great accuracy.

2. Every object in the sky makes one complete east-west circuit of the star sphere in *about* twenty-four hours. This circuit is known as the diurnal revolution of the body in question.

3. The star sphere rotates as a coherent body between two poles—the north and the south celestial poles.

4. The stars are mere points of light and do not change their positions relative to one another—at any rate not noticeably within the period that can be covered by the observations of a single man.

5. The period of the diurnal rotation of the star sphere being slightly shorter than twenty-four hours of solar time, the stars appear to be moving steadily westward, one complete circuit being accomplished in a year.

6. Besides its diurnal east-west motion, the moon has a monthly west-east motion. During the month it passes through a cycle of phases which has been described.

7. All the planets and the moon are confined, in their motion across the star sphere, to a zone 18° wide. It is known as the zodiac, and placed centrally within it lies the ecliptic, i.e. the yearly path traced out by the center of the sun's disk.

8. The ecliptic is inclined to the celestial equator at an angle of $23\frac{1}{2}°$. The fact that the sun is therefore carried to either side of the celestial equator originates the terrestrial seasons, the sun being higher in summer than in winter.

9. The sun makes its west-east circuit of the star sphere in one year. (This is the same as five, looked at from the reverse point of view.)

10. Besides partaking of the east-west diurnal motion of the star sphere, the planets have proper motions of their own among the stars. In this respect they may be clearly divided into two groups:

i. Mars, Jupiter, and Saturn. Their paths are looped, i.e. at times they are traveling not eastward, but westward. Nevertheless, their eastward motions always more than counterbalance their periodic retrograde motions.

ii. Venus and Mercury. They oscillate from one side of the sun to the other, but do not exhibit the looping that characterizes group i.

11. i. Jupiter requires a longer period for its circumambulation of the star sphere than Mars, and Saturn a longer period than either of them.

ii. Mercury never recedes from the sun to so great a distance as Venus, and completes one oscillation in a shorter period of time.

The problem is to find a single hypothesis that explains this variety of observed appearances and/or facts.

II. The Problem Solved: Real Motions

The most obvious explanation of these phenomena is that the heavens as a whole revolve about a stationary earth in slightly under twenty-four hours, and that the sun, moon, and planets, while partaking of this motion, have in addition motions of their own, for the most part in the reverse direction. This possible explanation being the first to hand, it will be convenient to develop it in ways suggested by a more detailed consideration of the visible behavior of the sun, moon, planets, and stars, and to see whether it can be made to render a coherent and reasonable account of these.

THE PTOLEMAIC UNIVERSE

Such an investigation was made by Ptolemy (*fl. c.* A.D. 130), working along lines suggested by Hipparchus some three hundred years earlier. Ptolemy made three basic assumptions, the first two being dependent upon the obvious evidence of the senses and the third upon fallacious *a priori* reasoning:

i. Since the celestial bodies appear to revolve about the earth, they do so revolve.

ii. Since the earth appears to be motionless, it is motionless.

iii. The circle is the most perfect figure, and therefore the celestial bodies must move in orbits that are either circles or else are compounded of circles. Furthermore, not to detract from this mystical perfection, their motions in their orbits must be uniform—they must neither accelerate nor decelerate.

Centrally placed in the universe lies the motionless earth. On the confines of the universe are the stars. These are regarded as being equidistant from the earth and embedded in a giant sphere centered upon the earth, the star sphere. It is the rotation of this sphere that

29

causes the diurnal motion of the stars. Within the space between the earth and the star sphere are situated seven other spheres,* each of which bears an orbit†—either of the sun, or the moon, or of a planet. That the more distant bodies may not be obscured by the spheres carrying the nearer, these spheres are regarded as composed of perfectly transparent crystal. We have already seen that the sun and moon pursue direct, unfaltering courses across the heavens. Hence these bodies may be regarded as moving with a uniform velocity about circular, circumterrestrial orbits.

To explain the periodic retrograding of Mars, Jupiter, and Saturn in terms of uniform circular motion, Ptolemy was forced to introduce epicycles. The planet does not itself move in a circular circumsolar orbit but about a second orbit, smaller but also circular; the center of this epicycle lies on the main orbit, or deferent, and travels uniformly around it (Fig. 9). Furthermore, the radius of the epicycle which connects each of the planets with its fictitious planet (i.e. the center of the epicycle—the point that travels around the deferent) must be parallel to the line joining the earth and the sun.

A moment's thought, and the study of Fig. 9, will show that such an arrangement will in fact impart to the planet an apparently looped motion, despite the fact that it is moving with uniform velocity in an orbit composed entirely of circles—the 'perfect' figure. In copying in this way the *particular* motion of each individual planet, Ptolemy and subsequent astronomers experienced a good deal of difficulty, but it is easy to see that in general the plan will work. The planet's motion in that part of the epicycle marked by the letters a—b will be observed as acceleratingly direct; from b—c deceleratingly direct; at c it will appear to pause momentarily, and then from c—d to move with increasing velocity in a retrograde direction; from d—a its velocity will be on the decrease again, and at a itself the planet will be momentarily stationary. Then once more it begins its direct eastward motion.

To see how Ptolemy accounted for the observed motions of Venus and Mercury, we must first comment upon his estimation of the relative distances of the various celestial bodies from the earth. Of two bodies traveling with the same velocity, that which is nearer the observer will appear to be the faster moving. Thus, to an observer sitting

*The crystal spheres were, strictly speaking, a feature of the Aristotelian system (which Ptolemy was seeking to reconcile with the observational facts), though he never explicitly disclaims them.

†Actually, in most cases, a deferent: *vide infra.*

on an esplanade seat, the people strolling past at perhaps 2 m.p.h. move
farther across the field of vision during a given interval than a ship on
the horizon traveling at 2 m.p.h.—or even 20 m.p.h.

We have seen that, of all the celestial bodies, that which makes a
complete circuit of the heavens to its original position in the shortest
time is the moon: it circuits the star sphere in one month. Of those

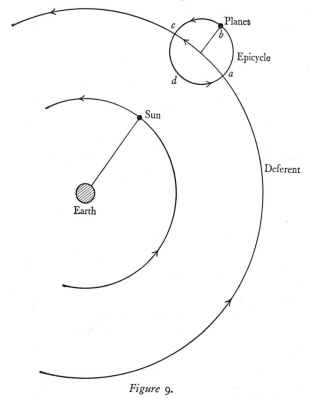

Figure 9.

bodies that appear to swing back and forth on either side of the sun,
Mercury moves more quickly than Venus and has the apparently
smaller orbit; both of them complete one cycle from elongation to
elongation in less than a year. Next comes the sun, which requires a
full year to circuit the heavens; then Mars, Jupiter, and Saturn in
that order. Ptolemy therefore concluded that the moon was the nearest
body to the earth; then Mercury, then Venus, then the sun. Now since
Mercury and Venus are limited in the distance that they may retreat
from the sun, Ptolemy decided that the motion of their epicycles must

be such that it is always possible to join their centers, the earth, and the sun by a single straight line. Their oscillations on either side of the sun would then result simply from their epicyclic revolution, one complete revolution being accomplished in the observed period. Figure 10 will show that if this condition is fulfilled, their epicyclic motions will in fact cause their observed motions. It will also demonstrate the interesting fact that Venus and Mercury, if they shine only by reflected light,

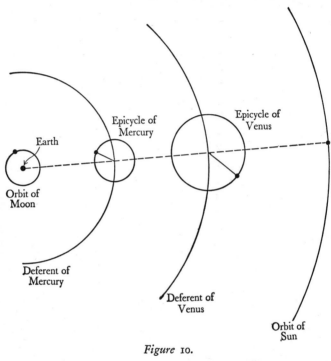

Figure 10.

can, under the Ptolemaic dispensation, never appear more than half illuminated to an observer on earth.

A further device that Ptolemy was forced to introduce—tied as he was by the twin considerations of explaining the observational facts while invoking none but 'perfect' circular motions—was that known as movable eccentrics. This highly artificial arrangement consists of a planetary orbit whose center does not coincide with that of the earth, but lies always on the line joining the earth and the planet in question. Thus the earth was not, after all, at the center of the universe though it was admittedly nearer to it than any other body.

PTOLEMAIC DIFFICULTIES

This, in general outline, is Ptolemy's geocentric theory of the structure of the solar system. Up to a point it works admirably. But as it became possible to make more and more accurate measurements of the positions of the sun, moon, and planets it was found that the model, as it stood, did not exactly represent the observed phenomena. In fact, the sun, moon, and planets do not move exactly as they should were Ptolemy's account of their relative positions and orbits correct. Consequently, the theory had to be patched up, and the more accurate astronomical observation became, the more drastic had the patching to be.

First, it was found sufficient to elaborate and proliferate the movable eccentrics, applying them also to the epicycles. But the tale of woe did not end there. Still the observed positions of the planets did not agree with the theoretical positions (derived from the application of Ptolemy's hypothesis), and it became necessary to add further epicycles. Instead of a planet's moving around an epicycle moving around a deferent— which many people will think a sufficiently complicated and unnatural arrangement—the planet was supposed to move around an epicycle which itself moved around an epicycle which in turn moved around an epicycle . . . which moved around a deferent. Soon the number of epicycles in the system, if it were to work, had mounted to eighty, and the geocentric hypothesis had become one of literally inconceivable complexity.

More fatal to its chances of being true than its superficial complexity was the fact that its complexity was not of the type that rests upon a fundamental simplicity or unity—it was impossible to formulate any general laws regulating the behavior of the bodies concerned. Each individual body had to be given individual attention, and it was not possible to relate the mass of particular variations and idiosyncrasies to a single elementary hypothesis. To account for the observations of each planetary motion it became necessary to employ a separate and highly complicated piece of juggling with the relative lengths of the radii of the epicycles (with additional new epicycles if required), with the velocity of the planet about its epicycle and of the epicycles around one another and around the deferent, and also with the degree of eccentricity of the epicycles and deferent. And then the publication of a newer and more accurate set of observations would necessitate still more juggling, still more 'saving of the phenomena.' That the mechanics of the heliocentric cosmology—to be described presently—are based upon a single, simple hypothesis (as Newton showed), the apparent complexity of which is owing to the manifestation under the varying conditions of this single hypothesis, is perhaps the most impressive argument in support of the heliocentric theory.

THE GEOCENTRIC HYPOTHESIS REFUTED

Since this is not a strictly historical survey, it is unnecessary to follow step by step the overthrow of the geocentric hypothesis. It will be enough to consider certain of its essential implications and then to show that these are not substantiated by observational data. For this the following points will be sufficient:

i. The solar system consists of a number of nearly concentric crystal spheres which contain the sun, moon, and planets or their deferents.

ii. Neither Venus nor Mercury, supposing they were large enough to have sensible disks (the telescope was, of course, not invented till long after Ptolemy's day), could ever show more than a single hemisphere illuminated by the sun.*

iii. The earth is motionless upon its axis.

iv. The earth has no orbital motion; on the contrary, it is the sun, together with the rest of the solar system, which revolves about it.

THE CRYSTAL SPHERES

Points (ii), (iii), and (iv) are essential to the hypothesis. If it can be demonstrated that they are false, the hypothesis falls to the ground. Point (i) is not essential since there is no evidence to show that the deferents are not unsupported in space. Nevertheless, it was this point that was first called into question, and its failure to stand up to examination marked the beginning of the overthrow of the entire hypothesis. In the sixteenth century the Danish astronomer Tycho Brahe was able, from his observations of comets, to demonstrate conclusively that these objects pass freely to and fro through the space supposed to be occupied by the crystal spheres. The spheres, as material objects, clearly did not exist.

THE PHASES OF VENUS

More accurate observations—this time made by Galileo, armed with the recently invented telescope—then showed that Venus passes through

*That is to say they would never show an apparent phase greater than 'half moon.'

a complete series of phases exactly similar to those of the moon; the same was later shown of Mercury. It is clear, again, that Ptolemy was in error, at least as regards the relative positions of the earth, the sun, Venus, and Mercury.

ROTATION OF THE EARTH

But the foundation of the geocentric system (disregarding the irrational assumption that the circle is the 'perfect' figure and that therefore the planetary orbits must be circles or composed of circles) is that the earth is motionless. It is this conception that makes the whole complicated system of epicycles and circumterrestrial motions necessary. Once it is shown that the earth moves—that it rotates on its axis, or revolves about the sun, for instance—the basic assumption of the hypothesis is demonstrated to be false. Thenceforward we may legitimately look for a hypothesis that gives a more natural and universal explanation of the facts.

In 1851 Foucault devised an experiment that established once and for all the fact that the earth rotates on its axis. If a heavy weight is suspended by a considerable length of wire, no rotation of the support to which the wire is attached will alter the plane in which the weight is set swinging. Suppose that the wire is fixed to a movable beam in the roof of a lofty hall and that the weight is set swinging accurately north and south. Suppose, too, that at the outset of the experiment the beam also lies along a north-south line. Then if it is rotated slowly through 90°, so that it is now lying east-west, it will be found that the pendulum is still swinging north-south. Further rotation of the beam has no more effect: however the support is rotated, the pendulum always swings in the plane in which it is started. The reason for this is that it is easier for the wire to twist* than for the heavy weight to alter its direction of swing.

Here, then, in the immovable plane of the swing of a freely suspended pendulum, we have something not provided by the stars—a reference system which we know to have no motion of its own. When we see the stars apparently moving around the earth there is no *a priori* means of knowing whether the stars are really moving from east to west or whether the earth is rotating from west to east: the two motions would result in the same appearance. But the pendulum always swings in the same plane in space, and therefore if we find that the earth

*If the bearing is frictionless, or practically so, even the torsion of the wire is eliminated.

appears to move relative to it (or vice versa, it is the same thing) we know that it really is the earth, and not the plane of swing, that is changing its position.

Foucault used a heavy iron bob and suspended it from the 200 feet high roof of the Pantheon. To the lower side of the bob he attached a pointer of just the right length to scratch a groove in a tray of sand on the floor as it swung; in this way the direction of each swing could be recorded. After the pendulum had been swinging a few minutes, the startling discovery (it would at any rate have startled Ptolemy) was made that the direction of the swing was slowly changing relative to the walls of the room: its plane was rotating. But we know that this cannot be so. Hence it must be the earth that is rotating and carrying the Pantheon and the tray of sand with it. If the pendulum were suspended at the north pole it would be found that its plane of swing would require twenty-four hours to make one complete rotation. The earth rotates on its axis once in twenty-four hours.

This provides satisfactory evidence that the apparent diurnal rotation of the star sphere may be due to the earth's rotation in the reverse direction, i.e. from west to east. There are several other experiments that add support to this hypothesis. One of them was suggested by Newton in 1679: If the earth is at rest and a weight is dropped from a height—down a long elevator shaft, let us say—it will land at a point vertically below the point of release. But suppose that the earth is rotating from west to east; in that case the top of the shaft will have a slightly greater speed toward the east than the bottom since its distance from the axis of rotation is the greater. Hence the weight, since it will retain its eastward speed, will land at a point slightly to the east of the point vertically below the point of release. The effects of air resistance complicate the actual observational results, but the results obtained from a number of experiments are in accord with the result predicted on the assumption that the earth is rotating.

It is clear, therefore, that we are not compelled to hypothesize a stellar universe rotating daily about a central and stationary earth. A spinning earth will give exactly the same appearance of rotation to the star sphere, though, necessarily in the reverse direction. Most people have, at some time in their lives, been seated at the window of a railroad train that is standing in a station with another train standing close beside it. They observe that the near-by train appears to move and are unable to determine, merely from visual observation of the side of the other train, which of the two is actually in motion. Not only is the conclusion that the earth is rotating on its axis a great advance upon Ptolemy's hypothesis from the point of view of simplicity and economy of means, but it is categorically forced upon us by experimental evidence, such as that mentioned above.

EFFECTS OF THE TERRESTRIAL ROTATION

There is a further aspect of terrestrial motion that we have not yet considered: the earth, we have learned, rotates on its axis in a period of twenty-four hours; does evidence exist of motion in any direction other than this? Since the earth undeniably feels and appears to be at rest, yet equally undeniably is in motion about its axis, we need feel neither outraged nor surprised should we discover any such evidence.

The ancients, refusing to believe that the apparently solid, unmoved, and immovable earth could be in rotation, were forced to read the effects of this rotation into the external universe. Let us reverse this process, deducting the effects of the earth's rotation from the apparent motions of the heavenly bodies, and see what is left. Let us, in fact, suppose that the earth's axial movement is arrested, and that (for simplicity) this occurs on either 21 March or 23 September, the vernal or the autumnal equinox.

Thenceforward the sun will be alternately above and below the horizon for six-monthly periods. It will proceed steadily and slowly eastward across the sky, spending, as we have seen, one month in each of the signs of the zodiac. Only its diurnal east-west motion will have been eliminated. In the same way, the moon and planets will perform their west-east motions, the moon passing through its phases and the planets pursuing their looped or back-and-forth motions, undisturbed by daily risings in the east and settings in the west.

It will be seen that we have only eliminated the appearance of the *daily* rotation of the heavenly bodies about the earth, not their slower rotation—yearly in the case of the sun, longer for Mars, Jupiter, and Saturn. The question we must now try to answer is, is *this* motion really inherent in the bodies concerned or is it the effect of another and as yet undiscovered terrestrial motion? Are these bodies really revolving about the earth in their different periods?

THE ABERRATION OF STARLIGHT

The final and ineluctable answer to these questions was provided by Bradley, the then Astronomer Royal, in 1727. It is a commonplace that although a heavy downfall of rain, falling vertically on a windless day, strikes a man on the top of his head as long as he stands still, yet it strikes his face once he starts to walk or run forward. Everyone who has tilted his umbrella forward as he hurries for shelter is well aware of this fact. Again, the vertically falling rain seen from inside a stationary railroad car does indeed appear to be falling vertically;

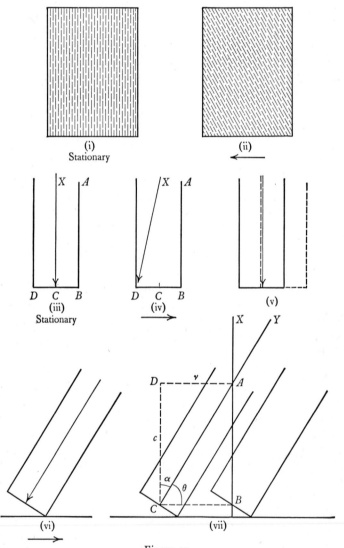

Figure 11.

but when the train is in motion the falling drops are seen to cross the window from the upper forward corner toward the lower rear (Fig. 11 (i) and (ii). The faster the train is moving, the farther from the vertical does the direction of the downpour appear to be displaced.

A different example will help to show why it is that the apparent direction from which the rain is coming is deflected toward the direction of the observer's motion. Figure 11 (iii) illustrates a rigid tube standing upright in our vertically falling rain storm. A drop entering the center of its mouth will fall axially down the tube and strike the base centrally. Now let us suppose that during the time that the drop is falling from X to the bottom of the tube, the tube itself has moved horizontally through a distance equal to half its diameter. While the drop is falling from X toward C, C has moved away to its right and its place has been taken by D. Consequently the drop will have fallen slantwise down the tube from X to D (Fig. 11 (iv), (v)). If we wish to prevent this slantwise motion of the drop within the tube, while retaining the tube's horizontal motion, we must tilt the tube over until its sides are parallel to XD, as in Fig. 11 (vi); in other words we must draw back the bottom of the tube by an amount equal to the tube's horizontal motion during the interval required by the drop to pass down it. This is of course what the pedestrian does when he tilts his umbrella forward to protect his face against the rain which is falling vertically relative to the ground, but slantwise relative to him.

It can now be seen that the more rapidly the tube is moved across the direction of the rainfall, the farther back must the lower end of the tube be drawn in order to keep the drops traveling within it parallel to its axis. In other words, the apparent displacement of the direction from which the rain is coming depends upon the relative speeds of the tube in the horizontal plane and the rain in the vertical plane. In Fig. 11 (vii) the drops fall from A to B in the same time that the tube moves from C to B, the drop thus being kept in the axis of the tube. Clearly then, the distances AB and CB are proportionate respectively to the velocity of the rain and of the tube. If we write c for the former and v for the latter, we have

$$AB = CD = c,$$
$$CB = AD = v,$$

and α, the tilt of the tube, is given by

$$\tan \alpha = \frac{v}{c}$$

showing clearly that the apparent displacement of the direction from which the rain is falling depends on the relative velocities of the tube and the rain. When c is very large compared with v, the displacement will be small, and vice versa.

THE EARTH'S ORBITAL MOTION

The reader may well be wondering what all this has to do with the astronomical status of the earth. The connection is this: if for our tube we substitute a telescope, and for the rain drops a ray of light, we encounter a similar phenomenon. Just as the motion of the tube, or of the walker in the rain, makes rain coming from X appear to come from Y, so motion of the telescope toward B makes the light from, say, a star whose true direction is BX appear to come from the direction CY; in other words, the star appears to be displaced in the same direction as the observer's motion.

Such an effect can only result from the combined motions of what for the moment we shall call the light rays, and of the telescope. The Danish astronomer Römer had demonstrated as early as 1675 that light travels with a finite, though very great, velocity.* But what of the required motion of the telescope? Since it is at rest relative to the earth, the earth itself must necessarily be moving. Let us suppose for the sake of argument that the earth is traveling in a circular orbit about the sun; then deduce from our previous experience of the tube and the umbrella what the nature of the resultant stellar displacements would be; and, finally, compare these with the observed displacements. If the two tally, we have a convincing proof of a terrestrial motion in an orbit about the sun.

Figures 12 (i) and (ii) represent this hypothetical orbit, at the center of which (not shown) lies the sun; the four positions, A, B, C, and D are those which the earth would occupy at three-monthly intervals. To be quite sure of our ground, let us once again refer to the results of our experiments: (i) if the motion of the telescope is inclined to the light rays, the source of the latter will appear to be displaced in the direction of the telescope's motion; (ii) if the telescope moves in the direction of the light waves, the source will suffer no displacement; if, in Fig. 11 (iii), the tube were moved vertically upward or downward, the drops would still fall parallel with its axis.

Returning to Fig. 12 (i), we shall suppose that there is a star in the direction AS at right angles to the plane of the orbit; to make the

*See p. 214.

diagram clearer, the plane is drawn in, though it, of course, has no material existence. Owing to the phenomenon of aberration, the earth moving toward *B*, the star will appear to lie in the direction *AS'*; at *B* it will appear to be displaced outward from the page since the earth at this point is moving toward the reader; from *C* it will appear to lie in the direction *CS'*, displaced toward the right; and at *D* it will be displaced 'into the page,' since the earth is here moving directly away from

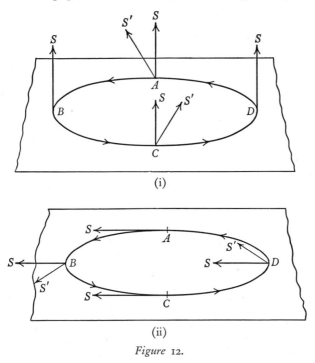

(i)

(ii)

Figure 12.

the reader. The star, in fact, will in one year appear to describe a small circle on the star sphere, a minute replica of the earth's orbit.

But consider (Fig. 12 (ii)), a second star lying not at the pole of the orbit, but in its plane. From *A* it lies in the direction *AS*, and since the earth is moving toward *S*, it will also appear to lie in this direction, that is, it will not be displaced. At *B*, the earth is approaching us 'out of the page' and the star will appear to be similarly displaced toward *S'*. At *C*, the earth is moving directly away from the star, which will again be undisplaced. Finally, at *D*, the star will appear to be displaced 'into the page' in the direction *DS'*. It has thus in the course of one year moved back and forth over a straight line from a central undisplaced position (earth at A) to maximum displacement 'out of the page' (earth at B), back to the undisplaced position (earth at C), and on to maximum displacement 'into the page' (earth at D), ending up again with no displacement (earth at A, whence it started). A moment's thought will show: (i) the nearer a star is to the pole of the orbit, the more closely will its aberrational displacement approximate to a true circle, while the nearer it is to the plane of the orbit, the more elliptical will it become, until in the plane itself it will have been flattened completely

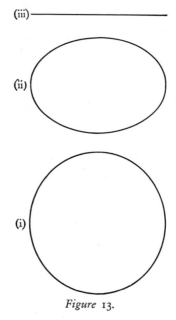

Figure 13.

to a straight line (Fig. 13); (ii) in every case the major axis of the ellipse must be parallel to the plane of the orbit.

Now if, as we are supposing, $ABCD$ is the earth's circumsolar orbit, the intersection of the plane of this orbit produced to meet the star sphere will be the ecliptic, for in looking at the sun (i.e. in looking at a point on the ecliptic) the terrestrial observer must necessarily employ a line of sight that lies in the plane of the earth's heliocentric orbit. Thus,

from A the sun's position on the star sphere will be beyond C,
from B the sun's position on the star sphere will be beyond D,
from C the sun's position on the star sphere will be beyond A,
from D the sun's position on the star sphere will be beyond B,

and one revolution of the earth about the sun will result in the sun's making a complete apparent circuit of the star sphere.

Therefore Fig. 13 (i) should represent the annual aberrational displacement of a star at the pole of the ecliptic, (ii) of a star midway between the pole and the ecliptic, and (iii) of a star lying on the ecliptic.

Bradley, with the aid of telescopic equipment denied to Kepler, showed that the stars do actually exhibit annual displacements of this character, and thus clinched for all time the heliocentric argument. The earth revolves about the sun.*

EFFECTS OF THE EARTH'S ORBITAL MOTION

Here, then, is an entirely new (and, so far, much more promising) foundation for our speculations and deductions concerning the observational facts outlined in the last chapter. We do not have to go right back to the beginning, to the Ptolemaic hypothesis in its entirety, for the basis of our reconstruction, since we have already discovered that the earth possesses a motion of axial rotation and have reasoned how this rotation must affect the apparent motions of the heavenly bodies. Subtracting the effect of the earth's rotation from the observed solar motion, we were left with the sun moving steadily eastward round the ecliptic, completing one circuit in a year. Now exactly this effect will be produced if the earth revolves about the sun in a period of one year. In Fig. 14 the inner circle represents the earth's orbit, the sun being centrally placed within it, and the outer circle the star sphere (or, more accurately, a section of it, which is the ecliptic) against which the sun is projected. When the earth is in position e_1 the sun appears to be at a point on the star sphere marked by the symbol S_1; when the earth has moved to e_2 the sun appears to be at S_2; when at e_3, at S_3. By the time the earth has completed a quarter-revolution the sun will be at S_4, having also completed one quarter of its entire yearly circuit of the ecliptic.

THE HELIOCENTRIC HYPOTHESIS AND THE FOUR-MINUTE DISCREPANCY

One further point connected with the apparent motion of the sun must be cleared up. It will be remembered that every star culminates four minutes earlier each night. We may express this fact in a dif-

*Two further phenomena which are only explicable in terms of the heliocentric hypothesis—the parallactic motions of the stars, and certain periodic shifts in stellar spectra—will be described later. At this juncture, the aberration of starlight is sufficient to establish the earth's heliocentric motion.

ferent way by saying that the sidereal day (the period required for one complete revolution of the star sphere) is slightly shorter than the solar day (the time required by the sun for one complete diurnal circuit of the heavens). This discrepancy is simply accounted for on the assumption that the earth is moving round the sun, with the result that the sun appears to be slowly advancing from west to east. In fact this is just what we should expect to find were the earth truly revolving

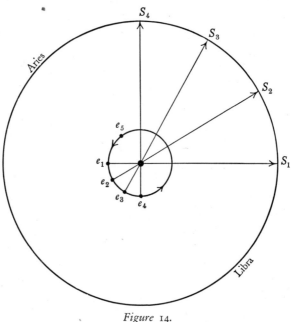

Figure 14.

about the sun. Figure 15 (which, to make the demonstration clearer, is not drawn to scale) represents the sun, the earth's orbit, and the earth in two positions in that orbit. These two positions are those that would be assumed at each end of a time interval of twenty-four sidereal hours—the period of one complete axial rotation. In the first position an observer at *a* sees the sun on his meridian at the same time that an observer at *b*, in the antipodes, sees a certain star on his. But when the earth has completed one rotation its orbital motion has changed its spatial position and therefore the direction of the sun, but not that of the incomparably more distant star. The result is that when the night-side observer, now at *b'*, sees his star on the meridian (the figure shows the earth and the two observers at this moment) the day-side observer, now at a', observes the sun still to the east of his meridian. The sun will not culminate until the earth has rotated a little further—through the angle θ, in fact. Hence the interval between successive culminations of the sun is a little longer than that between successive culminations of the star. Actually, the time required for the earth to rotate through the angle θ is about four minutes. Hence the solar day is some four minutes longer than the sidereal day, the discrepancy being caused by the earth's orbital motion.

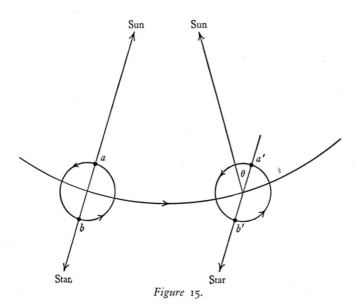

Figure 15.

THE LUNAR MOTION

The moon appears to circle around the earth in a period of one month. Can it be that the earth is really revolving round the moon? The answer must be negative, because if the moon is revolving steadily around the sun, and the earth around the moon, then the sun would appear to move across the sky in a series of loops, just as the epicyclic motion of the planets in Ptolemy's model gave them a looping motion. If, however, we suppose that the moon revolves about the earth, and the earth about the sun in a simple circular orbit, this difficulty vanishes. The moon, then, retains its Ptolemaic status; it is a satellite of the earth, and revolves about its primary.

EXPLANATION OF THE LUNAR PHASES

In this way, too, the lunar phases are simply accounted for.* When the moon (Fig. 16) is in position *a* in its orbit, it is invisible; for not only is it so near to the sun in the sky that it is swamped in the latter's

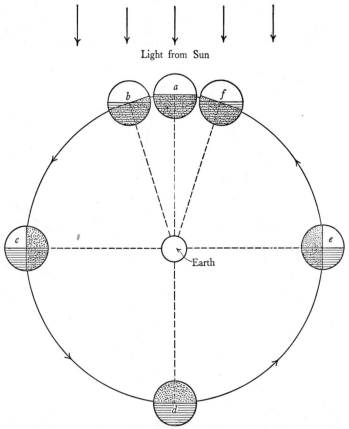

Figure 16. The hemisphere of the moon facing the earth is stippled. The hemisphere on which the sun is not shining is shaded.

glare, but its illuminated hemisphere is turned directly away from the earth. A few days later it has moved to *b* and is then far enough (angularly) from the sun for a narrow crescent of the illuminated hemisphere to be seen from the earth. At *c* it has moved round one

*Though this in itself is no advance, since they were also accounted for in the Ptolemaic system.

quarter of its orbit and, as can be seen from the diagram, is dichotomized as observed from the earth. A week later it has reached d when it will be full, its illuminated hemisphere being turned directly toward the earth: as seen from the moon, the earth and sun are both in the same direction. Three weeks after new it will be at e and will once more be dichotomized. But now the left-hand, or eastern, half of its disk is illuminated, whereas at the end of the first week it was the right-hand, or west, side. This, as will be remembered from our account of the monthly apparent behavior of the moon, exactly fits the facts. Finally, toward the end of the fourth week, it is once more a narrow sickle; the east (left-hand) side being illuminated, whereas at b it was the west.

THE HELIOCENTRIC HYPOTHESIS AND THE OUTER PLANETS

We saw in the last chapter that the planets Mars, Jupiter, and Saturn make complete circuits of the star sphere. And since the periods in which they do so are all longer than that in which the sun appears to make one circuit (i.e. one year) it follows that it is possible for any of these planets to be in that part of the zodiac that is diametrically opposite to that containing the sun. That is, they may culminate at midnight. Thus it is possible for any of them to be in Aries, for instance, when the sun is in Libra (Fig. 14). But when the sun is in Libra the earth is in position e_5 approximately. It is obvious that if one of these planets is to be between the earth and that part of the star sphere opposed to the sun, then it cannot be between the earth and the sun. The orbits of Mars, Jupiter, and Saturn, in fact, must lie *outside* the orbit of the earth. And since their apparent velocities across the star sphere, and hence their periods of revolution, can be used to gauge their relative distances, we may conclude that the relative positions of their orbits to that of the earth are as shown in Fig. 17.

Regarding the planets Mars, Jupiter, and Saturn, therefore, our hypothesis requires that

    i. These planets (and the earth) all revolve about the sun.

    ii. They revolve about the sun in orbits situated outside that of the earth.

    iii. It takes longer for them to traverse these longer orbits than it does for the earth to traverse its smaller one.

Assuming that this is so, can we account for their apparent looping motions as projected against the star sphere? The answer is that we can, quite simply and inevitably, and without having recourse to any complicated system of epicycles.

Figure 18 shows the orbits of the earth and of some outer planet (Mars, for example), with both orbits assumed to be circular and with the two bodies in corresponding positions in their respective orbits. When the earth is at e_1, Mars is at m_1; when at e_2, Mars is at m_2, and so on. These positions are marked on the diagram according to our maxim that the earth revolves about the sun in a shorter time than any of the outer planets. The apparent motion of Mars upon the star sphere

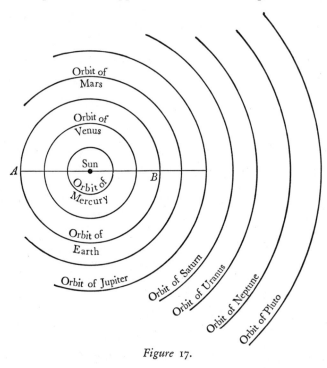

Figure 17.

is clearly the resultant of its own orbital motion and that of the observer's motion on the terrestrial orbit. This apparent motion is shown on the outermost circle, which represents the distant starry background against which Mars is, to a terrestrial observer, projected. It will be seen that at first Mars appears to be moving in a direct west-east direction, but with decreasing speed; the interval M_1-M_2 being longer than M_2-M_3, which in turn is longer than M_3-M_4. At position 5 it appears to pause, and then doubles back in its tracks to position 6; this retrograde (east-west) motion continues as far as position 7, when the planet again appears to pause, being for a short time stationary on the star

sphere. Then it resumes its direct motion, passing eastward through
8, 9, 10, and 11 with increasing speed. This accounts for the direct and
retrograde motions which are observed for the outer planets. By a
further assumption that the planes containing the orbit of the earth
and the orbit of the planet are slightly inclined to each other, the looped
motion shown in Fig. 8 can be explained. Thus the observed effect of
the earth's circumsolar motion upon that of an outer planet is to make
it move eastward across the star sphere in a series of loops. These loops

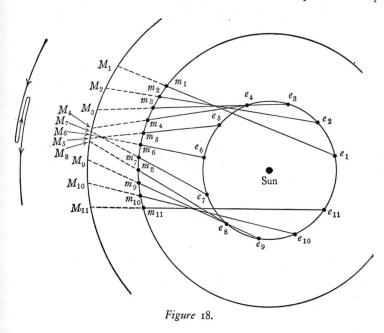

Figure 18.

occur when the planet is in opposition to the sun (that is in that portion
of the zodiac opposite to the one occupied by the sun) and in this
position the outer planet is closest to the earth. The explanation of the
looped motion in terms of a heliocentric system is more satisfactory
than that of Ptolemy. It is more satisfactory because it is simpler,
eliminating the necessity for complex and quite arbitrary epicyclic
gearing.

THE HELIOCENTRIC HYPOTHESIS AND THE INNER PLANETS

Early in our observations we found that the planets had to be divided
into two groups, the dissimilarity between the members of which is

manifested in their completely dissimilar apparent motions. Since one group consists of those planets (Mars, Jupiter, and Saturn) that we now know to lie farther from the sun than the earth, we might make a guess at the nature of the other group and say that Venus and Mercury are nearer to the sun than is the earth. We can establish this result by better methods than hit-or-miss guessing. Three bits of observational evidence point to this conclusion:

i. We have seen that if a planet revolves about the sun in an orbit more distant from the sun than that of the earth then it must at times culminate at midnight—that is to say be in opposition to the sun. In this position the angle measured at the earth between the planet and the sun (defined as the angle of elongation) will be 180°. Venus and Mercury can never occupy these positions at midnight since their maximum elongations are limited to 48° in the case of Venus and 28° in the case of Mercury. Hence they cannot be farther from the sun than is the earth.

ii. From time to time both Venus and Mercury transit the sun; that is, they are observed to cross the sun's disk. When in transit Venus is visible to the naked eye (if the eye is shielded with a dark glass) as a small black dot moving across the face of the sun. Now a glance at Fig. 17 will show that under no circumstances could an outer planet ever be in a position between the earth and the sun. Hence Venus and Mercury must move in orbits situated between that of the earth and the sun itself.

iii. Figure 19 is drawn to represent the orbits of the earth and an inner planet, with both orbits assumed to be circular. The points e_1, e_2, e_3, et cetera indicate positions of the earth corresponding in time to positions of the inner planet represented by p_1, p_2, p_3, et cetera. The position of the sun is indicated by S. The positions e_1 and p_1 show the inner planet at maximum eastern elongation with the angle $Sp_1 e_1$ equal to 90°. Since the illuminated face of a planet must always be directed toward the sun, the apparent phase of the inner planet at maximum elongation will be that of 'half-moon' or, in other words, the planet is dichotomized. As the earth and the planet move along in their orbits, the apparent phase of the planet will become crescent. The crescent will diminish as the earth and the planet move along until the planet disappears in the glare of the sun. At a point between e_2 and e_3 the planet will be in inferior conjunction with the sun and would appear to be in 'new phase' if it could be seen at all. At inferior conjunction a transit of the sun by an inner planet may occur. The planet will next make its appearance west of the sun and will be in a narrow crescent phase. This crescent will increase in size until maximum western elongation is reached, at a point between e_3 and e_4, and the planet will again be dichotomized. From this point the western elongation will decrease, but the phase of the planet will increase until the planet is again lost in the glare of the sun. Superior conjunction will occur at a point between e_5 and e_6, and

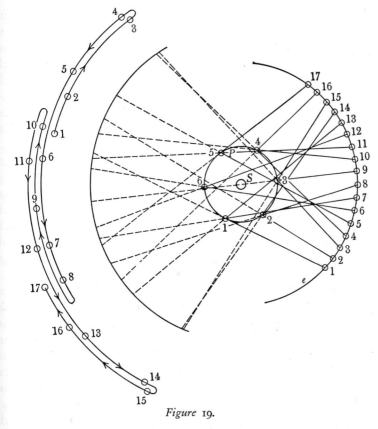

Figure 19.

at this time the planet will appear in full phase. The planet next appears east of the sun and the gibbous phase steadily decreases until greatest eastern elongation is reached, at a point between e_7 and e_8, where the planet is again dichotomized. To the naked eye neither Venus nor Mercury exhibits the complete phase cycle described above, although the apparent brightness of either planet does vary with change of elongation. The fact that these phases were not visible without tele-

scopic aid prevented Ptolemy and his immediate successors from detecting an important error of his system, in which an inner planet could
never exhibit any phase greater than 'half-moon.' It was not until the
seventeenth century that Galileo first observed the phases of Venus
through a telescope and thus provided strong evidence for the validity
of the heliocentric hypothesis.

In regard to the relative positions of Mercury and Venus, we may
now confidently assert that Mercury is closer to the sun than Venus.
The maximum elongation of Mercury is only 28° whereas Venus may
recede to 48° from the sun, or nearly twice as far.

Projection of the lines connecting the simultaneous positions of the
earth and the inner planet to the star sphere will indicate that an inner
planet has both direct and retrograde motion. In Fig. 19 this motion is
indicated on the outer edge. By making the further assumption that
the plane containing the orbit of the inner planet is inclined to the plane
containing the orbit of the earth we can show that the inner planets, as
well as the outer, move across the star sphere with a looped motion as
shown in Fig. 8. Furthermore the retrograde motion of the inner planet
occurs when the planet is close to inferior conjunction, or, in other
words, when it is closest to the earth.

DIURNAL MOTIONS OF THE PLANETS EXPLAINED

So far, we have only considered the annual motions of the planets, but
there is the discrepancy between the diurnal period of each of the
planets and that of the stars, which we discovered when making the
observations recorded in the last chapter. It will be clear by now that
this discrepancy between the time interval separating successive culminations of a star and of any of the planets is due to two factors—the
earth's orbital motion and that of the planet. When its orbital motion
is carrying an outer planet eastward among the stars, with an apparent
velocity that is partly determined by the earth's motion, it will require
longer than the stars to complete one diurnal revolution. But, when
retrograding (and the apparent retrogressions of the outer planets are
due entirely to the earth's orbital motion) the outer planet will accomplish two successive culminations in a period slightly *shorter* than the
23h. 56m. required by the star sphere. In the same way the apparent
motions of the inner planets among the stars cause a small difference
between their diurnal periods and that of the stars, and the apparent
motions are due both to the orbital motions of the inner planets themselves and also to the orbital motion of the earth.

THE COPERNICAN COSMOLOGY

The concept of a heliocentric system goes back for something more than 3000 years, for we find Pythagoras and other philosophers of ancient Greece, as well as philosophers of the countries east of the Mediterranean, speculating about the possibilities of a heliocentric system of planets and a rotating earth. However, the philosophy of Aristotle, with its geocentric universe and its perfect curves (circles), carried far too much weight. This formed the basis for the so-called Ptolemaic system and later became the authority and dogma of the Church.

Copernicus*, after a careful study of all available observational material, became convinced that the sun and not the earth was the body about which the rest of the solar system revolved. He also realized that the apparent diurnal revolutions of the stars and planets could be explained on the basis of a rotation of the earth on an axis just as easily as by a rotation of the star sphere itself. This transfer of the center of the system from the earth to the sun was as far as he, a devout church-man, felt that he could go. He retained the 'perfect curves' of the Aristotelian philosophy and assumed that the earth and all of the other planets must move in circles. Try as he would he could not satisfy all of the available observational material on the simple assumption that all planetary motions were in circles centered on the sun. He was forced to introduce a few epicycles and to assume that the circular planetary orbits themselves were not exactly centered on the sun.

TYCHO AND KEPLER

The years immediately following the publication of the Copernican hypothesis were exciting ones to all persons who had any interest in the universe in which they lived. A few were willing to accept the break with Aristotelian philosophy that the hypothesis required, but the great majority sought earnestly for a return to the older doctrines. Among these was Tycho Brahe (1546-1601), the eldest son of a wealthy Danish nobleman. Tycho was sent to the University of Copenhagen to study law but he became interested in astronomy. He could not accept the new hypothesis and set to work to prove that it was wrong, not by philosophical reasoning, but by means of accurate observations of

---

*Copernicus (Nikolaus Kopernicki 1473-1543), a Polish churchman, completed the publication of the first complete account of the heliocentric hypothesis in *De revolutionibus caelestium* during the last years of his life.

the planets. Tycho was never successful in the development of astronomical theories, but as an instrument designer and as a careful observer he was without an equal. His first instruments yielded data of an accuracy never before attained and his zeal attracted the attention of the Danish king. Under royal grants Tycho built Europe's first real astronomical observatory at Uraniburg in 1576. He spent the next fifteen years tirelessly collecting observational data regarding the planets, but was never able to publish any truly satisfactory theory regarding planetary motions. Eventually he incurred the wrath of the King of Denmark and was banished from his native land. He wandered all over Europe, carrying with him his previously collected data and setting up portable instruments to make further observations whenever opportunity presented itself. At this time Emperor Rudolph wanted an accurate set of tables of planetary motions for use by astrologers, and in 1599 he invited Tycho to come to Prague. There Tycho met Kepler and this meeting was of far-reaching importance for science in general and astronomy in particular.

Johannes Kepler (1571-1630) was born of humble parentage in Württemberg. By hard work and frugality he was able to obtain the funds needed for his matriculation at the University of Tübingen. There he displayed a remarkable aptitude for mathematics and theoretical astronomy. Being a devout churchman he could not accept the Copernican hypothesis and he was destined to spend the rest of his life in the vain search for some theory that would bring back into cosmology that simplicity and perfection that is required by Aristotelian philosophy. His first attempt was a complex geometrical hypothesis, published in 1597, which satisfied Kepler only in that it employed the regular solids approved by Aristotle as perfect. The hypothesis has but little astronomical value, but its publication had an indirect effect of great importance. Emperor Rudolph heard of it and immediately invited Kepler to Prague to work on the Rudolphine Tables. Tycho was also at Prague, with his mass of accurate planetary observations that extended back for a period of about thirty years. Kepler set to work to unravel the mysteries contained in Tycho's data, but he was unable to reconcile the observations either with the Ptolemaic or the Copernican hypotheses. He then abandoned all attempts to fit the data with any previously published theories and in 1609 published the volume that contains the first two of his now famous laws of planetary motion.

Kepler was not at all pleased with these laws for, as we shall see below, they violated the Aristotelian perfection. Nevertheless, in the spirit of the true scientist, he published the relations that would best satisfy the data at hand. Nine years later he was able to publish a second volume on planetary theory, which contained the third, or the harmonic, law. This was the relationship that Kepler regarded as his greatest triumph, for it at least approximated the Aristotelian doctrine of harmony and perfection. The Rudolphine Tables of planetary motions, embodying Kepler's theories and Tycho's observations in support of the theory, were finally published in 1627 and were used for many years by astrologers, astronomers, and by navigators.

KEPLER'S LAWS OF PLANETARY MOTION

i. The orbit of each planet is an ellipse, having the sun at one of its foci. The non-mathematical reader may not have a very clear idea of what an ellipse is (many people suppose that an egg is elliptical), and the simplest way of elucidating the matter is to draw one. Rule a line across a sheet of paper and fix the sheet to a drawing board or table-top with drawing pins. Then stick two ordinary pins firmly into the sheet, piercing the line and lying about 3 inches apart. Make a loop of thick cotton or fine string and place it over the pins. Pulling the loop tight, and keeping it so with the point of a pencil, draw a free curve from that part of the transverse line on the left of the left pin to that on the right of the right pin. Then place the loop on the opposite side of the line and draw the other half of the curve. It will then be seen that an ellipse is nothing more than a foreshortened circle; it is a circle looked at not from directly above, but aslant. Alternatively it may be regarded as a circle with two centers—the points marked by the pins—instead of one; these points are known as the foci, and if the ellipse we have drawn represents the orbit of a planet the sun will be situated at one of them. It should be noted, by experimenting with different positions of the pins but using the same sized loop, that the eccentricity of an ellipse depends upon their distance apart: the greater this distance the flatter the ellipse, the nearer together the closer the approximation to a circle. When they are as close together as they can be—that is, in the same position—the figure described is a circle. This is what is meant when it is said that the ellipse may be regarded as a circle with two centers.

ii. Kepler discovered that even if the planets move in elliptical orbits, the sun occupying one of the foci, they will not behave in the observed fashion so long as their motion is uniform; i.e. so long as they travel around their orbits with unvarying velocities. The second part of his problem was to formulate the law that states the orbital velocity of a planet at any point in its orbit. After following up a number of false trails, he eventually arrived at the solution: the motion of each planet is such that the radius vector describes equal areas in equal times. (The radius vector is the line joining the planet and the sun.) Figure 20 represents a planetary orbit with the sun at the focus *S*. Within this orbit are described four sectors, all of whose areas are equal. Now, according to Kepler's second law, the radius vector will sweep out these sectors in equal times. Hence the planet will require the same interval to travel from *A* to *B* as from *C* to *D*, *E* to *F*, and *G* to *H*. A general and less precise way of expressing this law is to say that the orbital

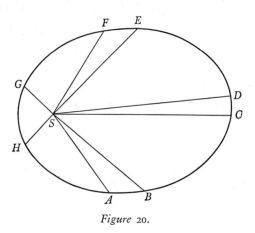

Figure 20.

velocity of a planet depends upon its distance from the sun: the nearer to the sun it is, the more rapidly it moves.

iii. But Kepler still had one further point to clear up. As we have seen, the more distant planets require a longer period in which to complete one circuit of the star sphere than those nearer the sun. Kepler was convinced that this fact could be expressed in an exact form. As before, the solution persistently evaded him, but finally he discovered that there was, as he had suspected, a strict relation holding between the distance of a planet from the sun and the period in which it revolves about it. This relation may be expressed in several forms, of which this is one: if the squares of the periods in which the planets describe their respective orbits are divided by the cubes of their mean solar distances, the quotient will be the same for every planet; in other words, the squares of their periods are proportional to the cubes of their mean solar distances. Thus, if P and p are the periods of two planets, D and d their mean distances from the sun, then

$$\frac{P^2}{D^3} = \frac{p^2}{d^3}$$

and this is true for any two planets that happen to be chosen. Hence, if the periods of two planets are known, their mean solar distances in terms of each other may be calculated. To take an example, suppose that the periods of the two planets are 0.24085 years and 248.43 years respectively (Mercury and Pluto). Then

$$\frac{0.058010}{D^3} = \frac{61717}{d^3}$$

therefore $0.058010 \, d^3 = 61717 \, D^3$

or $d^3 = \dfrac{61717}{0.058010} D^3$

and $d = \sqrt[3]{\dfrac{61717}{0.058010}} \, D = 102.09 \, D$

That is, the mean distance of Pluto from the sun is about 102 times the mean distance of Mercury from the sun. If we could determine the mean linear distance of any one planet from the sun, we could, by applying the harmonic law, calculate the mean solar distances of all of the other planets in the same linear units. For instance if we knew that Mercury were 36 million miles from the sun, from the relation demonstrated above we should know that the mean distance of Pluto from the sun must be more than 3675 million miles. In the same way the linear mean solar distances of all other planets could be calculated from their known sidereal periods.

KEPLER'S ACHIEVEMENT ANALYZED

It is worth while summarizing the methods by which we may assume that Kepler reached these results, for otherwise his immense achievement must appear as mysterious as that of a conjuror who produces rabbits from an empty hat. His first task was to determine the true motions and orbits of the planets from their apparent motions, i.e. from the observed motions described in the previous chapter and as they were recorded in Tycho's observations. This in itself could not have been accomplished until after Kepler was willing to accept the hypothesis of the heliocentric system and the moving earth. To solve the problem Kepler had to find a way of allowing for the effects of the earth's motion and then subtracting this effect from the observed motions of the planets. Before his solution of the problem can be understood, the reader must be introduced to the relation between synodic and sidereal periods.

SIDEREAL AND SYNODIC PERIODS

Figure 21 shows the circumsolar orbits of two planets, A and B, drawn on the assumption that both orbits are circular. The assumption is also

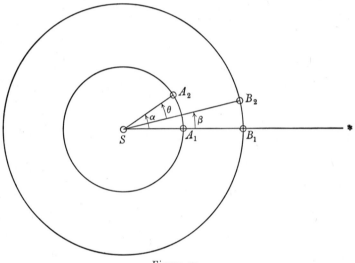

Figure 21.

made that the planet closer to the sun (A in Fig. 21) moves with greater angular speed than the outer one. At a certain time both of the planets are on the line SA_1B_1 drawn from the sun to a star. The sidereal period of either planet is defined as the time required for the planet to make one journey around the sun and return to this star again. In any given unit of time, say T, A will move from A_1 to A_2 (i.e. through the angular distance α as measured from the line between the sun and the star) and B will move from B_1 to B_2 (i.e. through the angle β). Because of the fact that A is moving more rapidly than B, the two objects will no longer be on a line from the sun and a hypothetical observer on the sun would notice that A had gained on B by the angular distance θ in the time interval T. The time required for A to gain one complete lap on B and return to a line drawn from the sun to B is defined as the synodic period of A relative to B (synodic coming from a Greek word signifying a meeting).

Returning to Fig. 21 we see that $\alpha = \beta + \theta$. Now let P_a represent the sidereal period of A, P_b represent the sidereal period of B, and S represent the synodic period of A relative to B. Since there are $360°$ in a circumference and we have said that α, β, and θ represent angular motions in the time interval T, we have

$$\alpha = \frac{T}{P_a}360°, \quad \beta = \frac{T}{P_b}360° \quad \text{and} \quad \theta = \frac{T}{S}360°.$$

Substituting these fractions in $\alpha = \beta + \theta$ and canceling out the common factors we have

$$\frac{1}{P_a} = \frac{1}{P_b} + \frac{1}{S} \qquad \frac{1}{P_b} = \frac{1}{P_a} - \frac{1}{S}.$$

For a consideration of the earth and the planets we will now let A represent the earth when B is an outer planet, or B represent the earth when A is an inner planet. If we let E represent the sidereal period of the earth, P the sidereal period of a planet, and S represent the synodic period of the planet relative to the earth we have

$$\text{for an inner planet} \quad \frac{1}{P} = \frac{1}{E} + \frac{1}{S} \qquad \text{(i)}$$

$$\text{for an outer planet} \quad \frac{1}{P} = \frac{1}{E} - \frac{1}{S} \qquad \text{(ii)}$$

The great value of these expressions lies in the fact that the sidereal period of a planet may be determined from the motions of the planet on the star sphere relative to the sun. For the inner planets we need only to determine the time from maximum elongation, either east or west of the sun, back to the same maximum elongation, and then compute the sidereal period of the planet in terms of that of the earth. For the outer planets the time from opposition (i.e. culmination twelve hours after the culmination of the sun) back to opposition again can be determined and the sidereal period determined. For the ancient astronomers, without telescopic aid, this was of great advantage.

DETERMINATION OF THE MARTIAN ORBIT AND THE DISCOVERY OF THE FIRST TWO LAWS

The planet Mars is a very important planet from the astrologer's point of view, and Kepler was working on the Rudolphine Tables for the use of astrologers. Hence Kepler concentrated his attention first on the orbit of Mars. Tycho, perhaps because Mars was of importance to astrologers, had a large number of observations of this planet and they were just what Kepler needed.

Figure 22 shows the orbits of the earth and of Mars. We shall suppose that Mars is first observed from position E_1; after one sidereal period

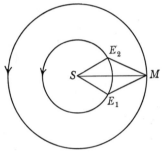

Figure 22.

Mars will again be back at M, but the earth, with its more rapid motion, will have carried out more than one revolution and have arrived at some point E_2. Mars is now reobserved from E_2. Knowledge of the earth's motion gives the values of SE_1, SE_2, and the angle E_1SE_2, the latter depending upon the interval between the two observations. The observations themselves (E_1M and E_2M) give the values of the angles SE_1M and SE_2M. These five quantities are sufficient for the solution of the quadrilateral SE_1ME_2, whence SM and the angle E_2SM can be calculated: SM is the distance of Mars from the sun when at point M in its orbit, and E_2SM its direction as seen from the sun.

Thus by means of a series of paired observations, the members of each pair being separated by 687 days (the sidereal period of Mars), spread over two sidereal periods, a large number of points on the Martian orbit may be plotted and the complete orbit reconstructed, showing both its size and its form.

Once the orbit had been determined in this way, simple inspection led to the discovery of the first law; and since the times of the various observations were known, together with the solar distance of the planet at each, trial and error would eventually lead to the formulation of the second law.

DISCOVERY OF THE THIRD LAW

Having reached this stage, it only remained to discover the nature of the relationship which Kepler was convinced held between the planets' periods and their distances from the sun. The sidereal periods of the planets were easily deduced from Tycho's observations by means of the equations (i) and (ii), given on p. 59. Kepler still had to discover their relative distances. We have seen how easily these may

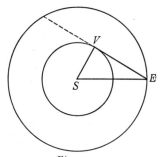

Figure 23.

be deduced from their periods by means of the harmonic law, but Kepler obviously could not avail himself of this device as he was still in the process of discovering it. An independent geometrical method is illustrated in Fig. 23, which shows the orbits of the earth and of an inner planet. As the figure stands, the planet is at greatest elongation: the line of sight from the earth to the planet, *EV*, is therefore a tangent to the orbit, and the angle *EVS* a right angle. *VES*, the angular separation of the planet and the sun, is measured, whence $VSE = 180° - (90° + VES)$. These data permit the calculation of the relative lengths of *SV*, the solar distance of the planet, and *SE*, the solar distance of the earth. The method is essentially similar, though rather more involved, in the case of an outer planet.

Kepler was now in a position to tabulate his information as follows:

PLANET		SIDEREAL PERIOD (P)		MEAN SOLAR DISTANCE (D)
Mercury	..	0.241 years	..	0.3871
Venus	..	0.615	..	0.7233
Earth	..	1.000	..	1.0000
Mars	..	1.881	..	1.5237
Jupiter	..	11.862	..	5.2028
Saturn	..	29.458	..	9.5388
Uranus	..	84.015	..	19.1910
Neptune	..	164.788	..	30.0707
Pluto	..	247.7	..	39.5

The final stage in the solution of the problem of planetary motion consisted of the identification of a single relationship which held between each of the first six pairs of figures in the table. (Uranus, Neptune, and Pluto were not known in Kepler's day.) A laborious process of trial and error eventually revealed the relationship expressed in the third law: the square of the ratio of a planet's period to that of the earth equals the cube of the ratio of the planet's mean solar distance to that of the earth. This, then, was the climax of Kepler's life work, and of it he wrote exultantly, 'The die is cast, the book is written, to be read either now or by posterity, I care not which; it can await its reader; has not God waited six thousand years for an observer?'

NEWTON'S LAW OF UNIVERSAL GRAVITATION

Some fifty years after Kepler had enunciated the three empirical laws of planetary motion Sir Isaac Newton (1642-1727) formulated his law of universal gravitation. This law states that every particle of matter in the universe attracts every other with a force that is proportional to the product of the masses of the two particles and inversely proportional to the square of the distance between them. This may be expressed symbolically as

$$F = G\frac{m_1 m_2}{d^2}$$

in which G is a numerical factor of proportionality whose value depends upon the units in which mass and distance are expressed. The idea that a gravitational force might exist between physical objects dates back several millenniums. From the first announcement of a heliocentric universe scientists had been speculating that it might be this mysterious gravitational force that held the planets in their orbits. It remained for

Newton to prove that this could be the case. The importance of the Newtonian law lies not so much in its accuracy, although this was never seriously questioned until the announcement of the theory of relativity during the early years of the twentieth century, but rather in its ability to synthesize so many apparently diverse physical phenomena. The motions of the planets about the sun, the motions of two stars about their common center of gravity, the motions of the stars in general about the common center of gravity of all stars can all be explained, within observational limits, on the basis of the Newtonian law. By this law the weight of all objects on the earth can be determined, and the ability of a planet to hold an atmosphere be established. Even the tides in the ocean can be calculated, principally, by the gravitational pulls of the moon and the sun on the water of the ocean.

Those readers who do not shy away from a little elementary algebra may be interested to see how the inverse-square character of the Newtonian law may be established on the basis of the information that was available to Newton. In the first place, he was familiar with Kepler's harmonic law, which is expressed analytically as

$$K = \frac{d^3}{P^2} .$$

Newton also was familiar with the character of that force required to hold a rock that is being whirled about in a circle at the end of a string. If P is the period of revolution of the rock, d is the radius of the circle, and m is the mass of the rock, the tension in the string (which is equal to the so-called centrifugal force) may be expressed as

$$F_c = k\frac{4\pi^2 md}{P^2}$$

in which k is a factor of proportionality whose value depends upon the units used for mass, distance, and time. This expression had been developed and published before Newton used it in his gravitational research, but there is some question about whether he had actually seen it or whether he developed it independently. Let us now assume, with Newton, that the gravitational attraction between two masses varies as the product of the masses and that it is some inverse function of the distance between the masses, i.e. that the force diminishes as the distance increases. Then we should have an analytic expression for the gravitation attraction between the sun of mass M and a planet of mass m distant d units from the sun as

$$F_g = G\frac{Mm}{d^x},$$

in which the exponent of d (i.e. x) is unknown. If the planet is going around the sun in a circular orbit, then there will be a centrifugal force that must be counterbalanced by the gravitational attraction. Hence

$$k\frac{4\pi^2 md}{P^2} = G\frac{Mm}{d^x},$$

which may be transposed by ordinary algebra to

$$\frac{dd^x}{P^2} = \frac{GM}{k4\pi^2}.$$

All of the terms in the right hand side of this expression are numerical constants and the equation may now be written as

$$\frac{d^{(1+x)}}{P^2} = K \qquad \text{(a constant)}.$$

We have seen above the Kepler's harmonic law may be written as

$$\frac{d^3}{P^2} = C \qquad \text{(a constant)}$$

and we see that $1 + x = 3$ or $x = 2$ and the force of gravitational attraction must vary directly as the product of the masses and inversely as the square of the distance between the sun and the planet. This is one of the simplest of the many problems that Newton had to solve. In some of them he had to develop new methods of mathematical analysis. Nevertheless, with the inverse square law established in Newton's mind, perhaps on the basis of the harmonic law as discussed above, Newton set to work and was able to prove that all three of the Keplerian laws are direct consequences of the fundamental law of universal gravitation.

NEWTON'S MODIFICATION OF KEPLER III

Mention must be made here of a slight modification which Newton made in the harmonic law as enunciated by Kepler. The planets move in the manner described by Kepler since they are acting under the central gravitational influence of the sun, which attracts each planet with a force inversely dependent upon the square of the distance separating the two bodies. But another factor that enters into this attraction is the respective masses of the sun and the planet concerned:

the attraction is in fact reciprocal, the planet tending to make the sun revolve around it at the same time that the sun makes it revolve about it. That the law as stated by Kepler appears to give a satisfactory account of appearances means that the mass of any planet is so small compared with that of the sun as to be, for practical purposes, negligible: this conclusion will be shown accurate when we come to determine the masses of the sun and planets. But when the masses of the two bodies are less disparate than those of the sun and a planet—for example, in the case of a double star—the mass of each body has to be taken into account, and this is what Newton's modification of Kepler III does. Where Kepler's third law states that

$$\frac{P^2}{D^3} = \frac{p^2}{d^3}$$

Newton's modified form of the equation states that

$$\frac{P^2\,(M + m_1)}{D^3} = \frac{p^2\,(M + m_2)}{d^3}$$

where M=mass of the sun, and m_1, m_2 the masses of the two planets. It can be seen that where m_1 and m_2 are negligible, as in the case of the planets, we are simply multiplying both sides of the equation by M, thus not materially affecting Kepler's equation.

THE MASS OF THE EARTH

In the description of the physical properties of the earth in the previous chapter, one in particular was not mentioned: its mass. Now that something has been learned of the law of universal gravitation it will be well to return to this point, for not only does it illustrate very clearly the power and application of Newton's law, but the value for the earth's mass so derived is a stepping stone to further astronomical quantities, as described in Chapter VII. First, a possible source of confusion must be cleared up. The distinction between mass and weight is usually a little difficult to grasp when encountered for the first time, but to put the matter simply we may say that the mass of a body is the quantity of matter in it, and that the spring balance measures weight while the scales measure mass. If a body just turns the scales at one pound it will always do so, no matter how strong or weak the gravitational field in which the scales are set up: the mass of the body does not vary with the forces to which it may be subjected. On the other hand, the stretch of a spring balance depends both upon the mass of body being weighed and on the gravitational field attracting it: the weight of a body, unlike its mass, does vary with the strength of the gravitational field within which it is situated.

Expressed in mathematical terms, Newton's law states that

$$F = G\frac{m_1 m_2}{d^2}$$

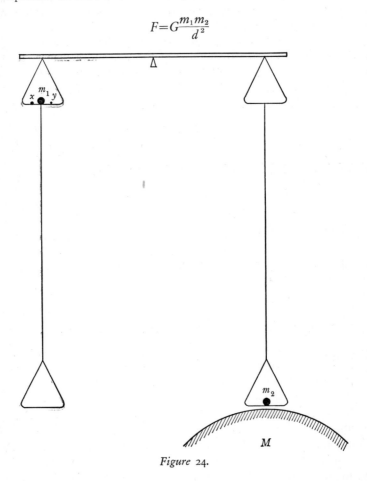

Figure 24.

where F is the attractive force between the two bodies; m_1 and m_2 their masses; d their distance apart; and G the so-called gravitational constant (the attractive force between unit masses at unit distance apart).

Figure 24 shows schematically the apparatus known as Joly's Balance. To the undersides of the two pans of a strong balance is suspended a second pair of pans by long wires: m_1 and m_2 are two spherical bodies of equal mass. When they occupy the same pair of pans, whether the upper or the lower, the beam will be horizontal, since they are equidistant from the earth's center and therefore equally attracted by the earth's gravitation. But suppose that m_2 is placed in one of the lower pans and m_1 in the opposite upper pan, as in Fig. 24. Then m_2, being nearer the earth, will be more strongly attracted by it than m_1. In other words it will weigh more, and the right-hand side of the beam will be slightly depressed. This can be rectified by placing a small additional mass in the pan containing m_1; let its mass be x. When this second equilibrium has been attained a lead sphere of great mass, M, is placed close below the pan containing the mass m_2. Again, the beam of the balance will tilt down on the right, for although the lead mass in attracting m_2 the distance between the two pairs of scales is too great for it to attract m_1 appreciably. To bring the scales back into proper balance a second and even smaller mass, y, must be added to the pan already containing m_1 and x.

It is clear, now, that the attraction between M and m_2 is balancing, and therefore equal to, that between the earth and y. Applying the law of gravitation already stated, we may express this in the form:

$$\frac{G\,M\,m_2}{d^2}=\frac{G\,E\,y}{r^2}$$

where $d=$ the distance between the centers of M and m_2,
   $r=$ the radius of the earth,
and $E=$ the mass of the earth.

That is

$$E=\frac{Mm_2r^2}{yd^2},$$

in which all quantities are known or can be deduced. The result is approximately 5,800,000,000,000,000,000,000 tons (5.8×10^{21} tons) or nearly six thousand million million million tons.

THE IMAGINARY CASE OF A CLOUD-GIRT EARTH

At this point it may prove enlightening to reconsider briefly our knowledge of the earth's motions and physical properties from an entirely hypothetical point of view. Suppose that the earth's atmosphere, instead of being reasonably clear and transparent, were composed of dense cloud-banks similar, let us say, to those that blanket the planet Venus. Under these circumstances—with all the heavenly bodies permanently

invisible and the science of astronomy unknown—how much information should we then be able to deduce concerning the earth we inhabit?
A glance through the two previous chapters will show that a surprising
amount of knowledge could be arrived at even under these unfavorable
conditions; indeed, the earth's circumsolar motion would alone remain
undetected, since it depends on observations outside the earth itself—
stellar observations connected with aberration or with parallactic or
spectral shifts. Of the other terrestrial characteristics which we have
considered, the axial rotation could be proved by Foucault's pendulum,
or the eastward deviation of falling bodies from the vertical; certain
meteorological phenomena might also hint at it though these could not
furnish a rigid proof. The earth's mass could be determined with
Joly's Balance, as explained on pp. 66-7, as well as by other methods not
here described. And finally, a simple calculation based on the results
of the pond experiment (p. 5) would yield the curvature of the earth's
surface, and hence the size of the earth itself.

THE HELIOCENTRIC HYPOTHESIS AND THE STAR SPHERE

If we continue down the list of observations that concluded Chapter 1,
we return to the star sphere. One of our first discoveries was that this
sphere appears to rotate between two diametrically opposed poles, just
as a child's globe rotates between two pivots which must of course be
opposite one another. But since then we have discovered that the earth
rotates on its axis and that it is this motion which causes the apparent
rotation of the star sphere in the reverse direction. The north and south
celestial poles must therefore be the points on the star sphere where the
produced axis of the earth would cut that sphere. It follows from this,
of course, that the celestial poles are directly overhead for observers
situated at the earth's poles; also that if the earth's equatorial plane
were similarly produced, it would intersect the star sphere at the celestial
equator. Now since the ecliptic, which is the plane of the earth's orbit
produced to the star sphere, is inclined to the celestial equator at about
$23\frac{1}{2}°$, the earth's equator must be inclined to the plane of its orbit at a
similar angle. The earth's axis is therefore not perpendicular to the
plane of its orbit, but is inclined to it at an agle of about $66\frac{1}{2}°$. All these
relations should be made clear by Fig. 25.

THE MEANING OF THE ZODIAC

On page 16 it was pointed out that the moon always remains within
a belt around the sky sphere which is known as the zodiac. The central

line of this belt is the trace of the plane containing the earth's orbit about the sun and is known as the ecliptic, or in other words the ecliptic is the path of the apparent motion of the sun about the earth in one year. Examination of the table on page 82 will show that the orbits of all of the planets, except Pluto, are inclined to the ecliptic by less than 9°

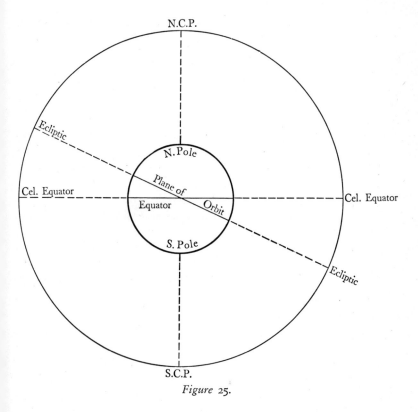

Figure 25.

(the half width of the zodiac). Hence it is to be expected that all of the planets bright enough to be seen with the unaided eye should always be found on the zodiac. It is because of this fact that this celestial highway, with its twelve 'houses' or 'stations,' played such an important part in the astronomy of the ancients. Under certain very particular conditions Venus may be observed from the earth very slightly outside of the zodiac, but this overstepping of the boundary is too slight to be observed without precision instruments. Pluto, a number of the asteroids, and a number of comets are frequently to be found outside of this belt.

III. Spanning the Solar System

The knowledge at which we have so far arrived has been obtained solely with the aid of the human eye, and without recourse to telescopes, spectroscopes, or other instruments. It is true that at several points during the development of the argument appeal has been made to telescopic evidence—the phases of Mercury and Venus, for instance, and the aberrational displacement of the stars—but such appeals were no more than short cuts to conclusions that could be reached without them. For Copernicus conceived his first intimations that the sun and not the earth is the ruler of the solar system before the invention of the telescope; and Kepler, although the telescope was actually being used for astronomical purposes by Galileo and others before he had formulated his three laws, worked throughout on Tycho Brahe's observations which were made with the naked eye.

INTRODUCTION OF THE TELESCOPE

From now onward the naked eye must be assisted by a variety of instruments if the growth of our astronomical knowledge is to continue. At first, the telescope will only be required as a precision instrument—that is, as a means to the more accurate estimation of the positions of bodies than could be possible with the naked eye alone. The optics of the instrument need not detain us here, for even the most skeptical man of common sense will admit (i) that a telescope magnifies, and (ii), that if we see a thing with the aid of a telescope, we are justified in believing in its objective existence even though it may be invisible to the naked eye. He may not have realized, however, that the function of the telescope is twofold. In the first place, it magnifies: it increases the apparent separation of all points within its field. In the second, it increases the apparent brightness of an observed object—at any rate within limits. Thus not only do stars appear to be brighter in the telescope than without it, but stars which are otherwise too faint to be seen at all are rendered visible.

ASTRONOMICAL DISTANCES: PRELIMINARY

One of the most important aspects of the astronomer's work consists of the determination of the distances of remote bodies. In this work he is fortunate in having a number of independent methods at his disposal, and, in theory at least, the discovery of the distances of most celestial objects is comparatively simple. The practical difficulties, on the other hand, are usually great, and except in the case of the nearer bodies such as sun, moon, and planets, the margin of inaccuracy is always undesirably wide; furthermore, the more distant an object is, the wider does this margin of uncertainty become.* The task of measuring the distance of an object 1000 units away is more than twice as formidable as measuring that of an object 500 units away. Not only the practical difficulties but also the effects of instrumental, personal, and systematic errors are increased out of proportion to the increase in distance. Whereas an accuracy of about 0.02 per cent may be expected in the distance of the sun, we cannot hope for better than 20 per cent accuracy in the distance of the remotest members of our stellar system. Expressed in linear units these expectations would represent about 18,000 miles in the case of the sun, but up to as great as perhaps 1,000,000,000,000,000,000 miles (10^{18}) for the remote objects.

There is a further source of inaccuracy which inevitably blurs the clarity of our distance determinations of the more remote celestial bodies, and which may even, without our suspecting it, entirely invalidate them. The basis of all these measurements is the simple trigonometrical method used by surveyors and map-makers. But this can only give a worthwhile degree of accuracy when confined to the nearer stars; for more remote objects, indirect methods must be used. These, though admittedly based upon the results of the fundamental trigonometrical method, nevertheless involve new assumptions, new sources of potential inaccuracy, and the use of analogies whose validity is less certain than it might be. At each successive extrapolation the chances of accurate results are diminished. Thus not only the mechanics

*This statement, and much of the discussion that immediately follows, is not correct for measurement of distance by radar techniques. All that can be said about this at the present time is that radar contact has been made with the moon, and that radar specialists believe that further development of their instruments and methods will yield values of distances within the solar system of an accuracy far greater than anything that we have at present.

of the problem, but also its principles become less accurate the farther we reach out into space. Even the basic method, from which all others are ultimately derived, is not without its tacit assumptions. It has to assume, for instance, that light travels in straight lines—the so-called rectilinear propagation of light. It is only with this proviso that the trigonometrical operations are valid. And although it is within limits a safe assumption to make (and the results of its use likely to be accurate), scientists have nevertheless grown less dogmatic and sure of the infallibility of their fundamental assumptions than were their fathers in the hey-day of cocksure Victorian research, when the universe appeared to be unfolding itself as a structure built upon the principles of the naïve mechanical materialism then in vogue.

For all these reasons the astronomer counts himself fortunate when he has independent methods of unlocking the secret of astronomical distances. When the results obtained by two or more methods are in close agreement he may feel confident that the average value is, in all probability, approximately correct. For although one method may give an erroneous value, it is stretching probability too far to suggest that a second and a third method—quite unconnected but also erroneous—should give practically identical wrong answers.

The purpose of these cautionary remarks is to dispel at the outset any misapprehensions the reader may have nourished as the result of casual readings in 'popular' scientific periodicals or even in popularized approaches to astronomy written by professional astronomers. We have a less exact knowledge of the scale of the universe, of the distribution of the stars and globular clusters, of the dimensions of our galaxy, and of the distances and real spatial distribution of the mysterious spiral nebulae, than the reader of this type of literature (with its inevitable simplifications and avoidance of constant qualifications) might be led to conclude. Or rather, there is a margin of uncertainty associated with all such statements of whose width, or even existence, he may be insufficiently aware. The greater the distance under discussion, the more important is it to bear this in mind if a reliable picture of our present knowledge is to be acquired.

TRIGONOMETRICAL PARALLAX

When a surveyor wishes to determine the distance of a not readily accessible object such as a mountain peak, he does not pace out or measure with a chain the intervening space between the peak and his place of observation. Instead, he measures a convenient baseline with the greatest accuracy (a few millimeters in 10 miles is possible), and then notes the direction of the peak from each end of it; that is, he measures the base angles of a triangle whose sides are the known baseline and the lines joining its extremities and the peak (Fig. 26). Assuming that the light reflected from the peak into the lens of his theodolite is traveling in undeviating straight lines, and that therefore his measurements of the base angles are correct to the limit imposed by the instrument itself, these data permit him to calculate the

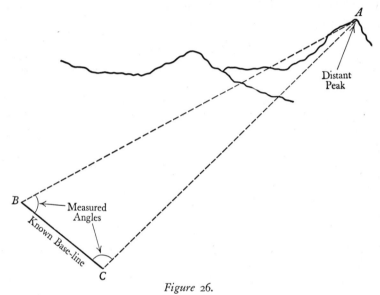

A

Distant
Peak

B

Measured
Angles

Known Base-line

C

Figure 26.

required distance trigonometrically. The great utility of this method lies in the fact that it enables the surveyor to determine the distance of a point without going there. It can be seen from the figure that the greater the distance, the smaller becomes the angle subtended by the baseline at the object. This is the reason for the exaggeration of systematic errors at great distances. Let us suppose, for example, that an instrumental defect such as backlash in the telescope bearing introduced a systematic error of 1'. If the subtended angle were 10° this error would amount to less than 0.2 per cent. But if the peak were so distant that the subtended angle were reduced to ½°, then the error would be 1 in 30, or 3.3 per cent. We can also discern here the reason why trigonometrical parallax cannot be employed on objects whose distance is greater than a certain limiting value. For with any given baseline a limit will eventually be reached at which the angular differences recorded at its two ends are so small as to be swamped by the estimated error, or else are too small for instrumental measurement; in the latter case the lines AB and AC may for all practical purposes be regarded as parallel. The only ways of escape from this difficulty are to increase the length of the baseline, or else to construct a series of triangles from the original baseline towards the peak via a number of intermediate points. Unfortunately the latter course is not open to the astronomer (since he cannot transport himself and his instruments out into space), and the former cannot be followed beyond a certain point.

THE DISTANCE OF THE MOON

These difficulties do not arise, however, in the case of a body as near to the terrestrial observer as the moon, where the direct trigonometrical method based upon parallactic observations from two stations separated by an accurately determined distance, gives results correct to within 0.0005 per cent. Figure 27 represents the earth and the moon. M is the

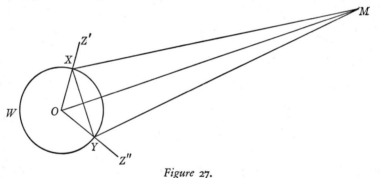

Figure 27.

moon, WXY the earth with its center at O, and X and Y two points on its surface on or near the same meridian of longitude, and widely separated from one another. Since OZ' and OZ'' are perpendicular to the horizon at X and Y respectively, Z' and Z'' must be the zeniths at these two stations. Hence the angles $Z'XM$ and $Z''YM$ are the zenith distances of the moon as observed from X and Y. These distances are measured simultaneously, and with the greatest degree of accuracy possible, at the two observatories. From these data the angles OXM and OYM can be derived, for

$$OXM = 180° - Z'XM$$
$$\text{and } OYM = 180° - Z''YM$$

Since the lengths of OX and OY are known (they are the earth's radii at the two observatories), the quadrilateral $MXOY$ can be solved trigonometrically. Hence the distance OM—that separating the moon and the earth's center—can be deduced.

It is found in this way that the mean distance of the moon is 238,860 miles, the variation on either side of this mean value amounting to some 15,000 miles.

THE FORM OF THE MOON'S ORBIT

In Chapter II we learn it to be an inescapable fact that the moon revolves about the earth. We now know its mean distance. But since the orbit is elliptical and not circular, its distance will steadily vary and can be determined at any given moment either by simultaneous parallactic observations, or else by constructing a 'spider' and thus determining the actual form of the orbit. This simple graphical method involves (i) the accurate determination of the distance that the moon has traveled across the star sphere from a given starting point on a large number of occasions throughout the month, (ii) the accurate measurement of its apparent diameter on each of these occasions. From a point E (Fig. 28), representing the earth, lay off a line EM_1 to represent the direction of the moon at the time of the first observation. If at the subsequent three observations it has traveled 2°, 5°, and 8° from the starting point, lay off EM_2, EM_3, EM_4 such that $\angle M_2EM_1 = 2°$, $\angle M_3EM_1 = 5°$, $\angle M_4EM_1 = 8°$; and so on through the entire lunation. These 'spider's legs' then represent the direction of the moon from the earth on successive occasions; and on each of these its apparent diameter was measured. Now since the moon's apparent diameter is inversely proportional to its distance—the nearer we are to an object, the larger it appears—our table of angular diameters tells us the relative distance of the moon when in positions M_1, M_2, M_3 ... If, then, on each leg of the spider we lay off a length inversely proportional to the moon's angular diameter at the corresponding time of observation, and then join all these points by a smooth curve, we have drawn the true form of the lunar orbit. And since, finally, we already know the linear length of one of the legs (the moon's mean distance, 239,000 miles) we can easily calculate the linear lengths of all the others.

In this way it is established that the moon's orbit is a nearly circular ellipse; and that, as we have been led to expect, the earth lies at one focus while the radius vector describes equal areas in equal times; the mean orbital velocity being rather less than 2300 m.p.h.

THE LUNAR ORBIT AND THE ECLIPTIC

If the moon's path among the stars is plotted on a star map it is discovered that this geocentric path is inclined to that of the sun in the same way that the latter is inclined to the celestial equator (Fig. 7). In other words, the plane of the moon's orbit is inclined to the ecliptic (or the plane of the earth's heliocentric orbit), intersecting it at diametrically opposite points known as the nodes. To discover the degree of this inclination we have only to measure the maximum angular distance of the moon from the ecliptic, for clearly θ in Fig. 7 (the angle in question) is that bounded by the two orbital planes. The inclination is about 5°.

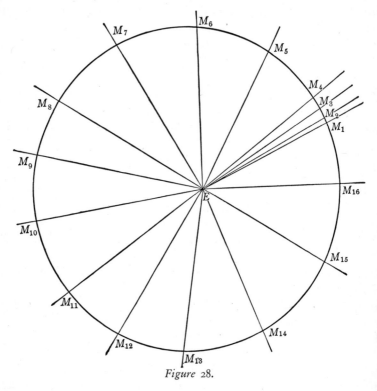

Figure 28.

SUMMARY

Thus by progressive stages we have learned the following facts about the position and motions of the moon:

It travels in a nearly circular orbit, at one focus of which lies the earth.

Its mean distance from the earth is 239,000 miles, and its mean orbital velocity some 2300 m.p.h.

Its orbit is inclined to that of the earth about the sun at an angle of approximately 5°.

RELATIVE SOLAR DISTANCES

This is the first step toward constructing in imagination a scale model of the solar system. Much of the effort preliminary to taking the second step—that of establishing the spacial relationship of the sun to each of the planets—has already been made. In the previous chapter we saw how Kepler first used a geometrical method for determining the relative solar distances of the planets, and thence deduced his much more valuable period-distance relationship. Direct observation gives the synodic period of each planet; the application of the

$$\frac{1}{P} = \frac{1}{E} \pm \frac{1}{S}$$

relationship (see page 59) gives its sidereal period. With the sidereal period known, Kepler's harmonic law gives the heliocentric distance in terms of the earth's distance. The *relative* distances of all of the planets from the sun are thus obtained, but until *one* linear distance is measured our picture of the solar system must remain a perfectly proportioned map lacking a scale of distance. The sun is the most obvious celestial body and we might as well begin with it: for when we have determined its distance from the earth we shall have the one linear heliocentric distance we require.

THE SUN'S DISTANCE FROM PLANETARY DISTANCES

The mean distance of the earth from the sun is one of the most important values in astronomy and is known as the astronomical unit. This quantity cannot be determined with any accuracy by direct trigonometric methods, since the sun, unlike the moon, is too distant for a base line on the earth to yield a satisfactory parallax.

Even though the distance of the sun is too great to permit of satisfactory determination by direct parallax methods, some of the planets are not. For example, at the time of a favorable opposition (see page 198) of Mars, the distance of the planet from the earth is less than 0.4 that of the sun from the earth. An accurately measurable parallactic displacement from widely separated points is yielded for this smaller distance, and the linear distance from the earth to Mars can be determined. From this distance the linear distance from the earth to the sun can be computed. For purposes of illustration let us consider the case of Mars, or any other planet for that matter, assuming, for simplification, that both Mars and the earth are revolving about the earth in circular orbits with radii R and ρ, respectively. Let us assume further that Mars is in opposition and at the node of its orbit so that the sun, earth, and Mars are on a straight line. If d is the distance from the earth to Mars as determined by parallactic methods, we have $R - \rho = d$. Now from Kepler's harmonic law we have

$$\frac{R^3}{\rho^3} = \frac{P^2}{E^2}$$

which may be solved for

$$R = \rho \sqrt[3]{\frac{P^2}{E^2}}$$

in which P and E are the sidereal periods of Mars and the earth respectively. The substitution of this value of R in the equation $R - \rho = d$ will yield a value for ρ, the radius of the earth's orbit. In actual practice none of the assumptions can be made and the computation of the distance of the earth from the sun is a complicated problem.

Some of the asteroids (see page 205) may come even closer to the earth at favorable opposition than does Mars. Eros, for example, may come within 0.15 astronomical units from the earth. This smaller distance, coupled with the fact that the asteriod has a small star-like image as contrasted to the disk of Mars, permits of much more accurate measurement of the parallactic displacement. Another method, involving the parallactic observation of a transit of Venus across the disk of the sun, gives somewhat less accurate results, though it provides a valuable confirmation of those based on the observations of Mars and Eros.

In 1931 a favorable opposition of Eros occurred and observations were made at a large number of observatories scattered over the earth. All of the observational material was forwarded to H. Spencer Jones, Astronomer Royal of England, and in 1944 the result from the 1931 observations, combined with all available results from previous observations, was published. This most recent value of the astronomical unit is 93,005,000 statute miles with an uncertainty of about 9000 miles.

Astronomers frequently use for the astronomical unit not the value of the distance in miles, but instead the angle that would be subtended by the mean radius of the earth from a distance of one astronomical unit. This angle is known as the solar parallax and, on the basis of the above-mentioned value of the astronomical unit, is 8″.790 with an uncertainty, according to Jones, of the apparent angular width of a human hair at a distance of 10 miles.

THE SUN'S DISTANCE FROM THE ABERRATION OF LIGHT

An entirely independent method employs the phenomenon of the aberration of light. We have seen (page 39) that |

$$\tan \alpha = \frac{v}{c} \quad \text{or} \quad v = c \tan \alpha$$

where v is the earth's velocity, c is the velocity of light, and α is the observed displacement of a stellar image situated at right angles to the direction of the observer's motion.

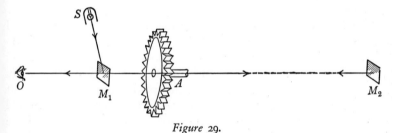

Figure 29.

· The story of Römer's discovery of the finite velocity of light from observations of the satellites of Jupiter will be told in Chapter VII. Two experiments devised nearly a century ago by the French physicists Fizeau and Foucault determined this velocity with a high degree of precision. Fizeau's apparatus is illustrated diagrammatically in Fig. 29. S is a source emitting a narrow beam of light; M_1 is a lightly silvered mirror which, while reflecting the beam from S toward M_2, a second mirror, yet allows the returning beam to pass through it to the observer's eye at O. A is a toothed wheel of known circumference which can be rotated at known velocities; its position is adjusted so that its teeth just intercept the beam between M_1 and M_2. When the wheel is rotated a series of light flashes will be transmitted toward M_2. At high speeds these will appear to coalesce and form a continuous beam, for the same reason (the persistence of vision) that the rapid succession of stationary images on a moving-picture screen gives rise to the illusion of smooth motion. If the speed of the wheel is steadily increased, a certain stage will be reached at which each of the teeth has moved half the distance separating it from its companion during the time required for the light to travel from A to M_2 and back to A. Hence on reaching A each flash will encounter not the gap between teeth which it originally passed through, but one of the teeth themselves. All the returning light will be blocked by the cog teeth and it will appear to the observer at O that the light has been extinguished. The wheel velocity when this occurs, its size, the number of teeth, and the distance between the wheel and the second mirror are all the data required for the calculation of the velocity of light: the first three data will give the length of the interval required for the teeth to move round through half the distance separating them; and this is the time required for the beam to travel twice the known distance AM_2. Carried out under the most stringent experimental conditions, the modern modification of this method yields 299,776 km. per second (186,272 m.p.s.), which is the accepted value of the velocity of light.

A long series of observations for the value of the angle α, the so-called constant of aberration, yields a value of $20''.5$. Hence in the equation $v = c \tan \alpha$ we have only one unknown since $c = 299,800$ km./sec. and $\tan 20''.5 = 0.0000994$. Substitution of these numerical values gives $v = 29.8$ km./sec. or 18.5 mi./sec. for the speed of the earth in its orbit about the sun. If we now assume that this orbit is a circle we can find its circumference since there are 31,560,000 seconds in a year and the earth moves 18.5 miles in each one of them. Hence the radius of this circle, the mean distance of the earth from the sun

$$= \frac{18.5 \times 31,560,000}{2\pi} = 92,900,000 \text{ miles,}$$

a value which is in reasonable agreement with the result of the parallactic methods.

OTHER METHODS OF DETERMINING THE SUN'S DISTANCE

Other means of deriving the solar distance that should be mentioned, though they do not call for detailed descriptions, involve (i) an independent spectroscopic method of determining the earth's orbital velocity which employs the so-called Doppler principle,* (ii) the study of the perturbing effect of the earth's gravitation upon the motions of Venus and Eros, (iii) a somewhat similar study of the inequality in the lunar motion. All these methods permit the determination of the earth's mean solar distance with an inaccuracy not in excess of about 0.013 per

*See page 167.

cent, or 12,000 miles in 93,000,000. Since the orbit is not strictly circular the actual distance varies from midsummer to midwinter by rather more than a million miles on either side of the mean value.

THE MASS OF THE SUN

Because the mass of the sun is a quantity that we shall require later for the determination of certain stellar distances, it will be convenient at this point to see how Newton's work made its derivation possible. Since the force exerted upon one body by a second is proportional to their masses and inversely proportional to the square of their separation, it follows that the relative attractions exerted by the sun (f) and the earth (g) upon a body of unit mass situated at the earth's surface are given by

$$\frac{f}{g} = \frac{\dfrac{M}{R^2}}{\dfrac{m}{r^2}}$$

where M = mass of sun,
m = mass of earth,
R = distance of sun,
r = radius of earth.

Of the quantities in this equation,

M is the unknown,
r we have already discovered (Chapter I),
m we have already discovered (Chapter II),
R we have already discovered (Chapter III),
g, the force of gravity at the earth's surface, can be found from experiments with pendulums, and by a variety of other means,
f is easily calculated from Newton's laws once the earth's orbital velocity is known (Chapter III).

The value obtained for M by this and other methods is approximately 332,000 times that of the earth.

THE ORBITS OF THE PLANETS

Just as in the case of the moon, we may determine the inclination of each planet's orbit to that of the earth, thus completing our three-dimensional scale model of the solar system, some data of which are given in the following table.

Planet	Synodic period in days	Sidereal period in years	Mean distance from sun (earth=1)	Mean distance from sun (million miles)	Mean orbital speed (mi/sec.)	Inclination of orbit to ecliptic
Mercury	116	0.241	0.387	36.0	29.5	7° 00′
Venus	584	0.615	0.723	67.3	21.9	3° 24′
Earth	.....	1.000	1.000	93.0	18.5	.....
Mars	780	1.881	1.524	141.7	15.0	1° 51′
Jupiter	399	11.862	5.203	483.9	8.1	1° 18′
Saturn	378	29.458	9.539	887.2	6.0	2° 29′
Uranus	370	84.015	19.191	1784.8	4.2	0° 46′
Neptune	367	164.788	30.071	2796.7	3.4	1° 46′
Pluto	366.7	248.430	39.518	3675.3	2.9	17° 09′
How derived	Observation	$\frac{1}{P} = \frac{1}{E} \pm \frac{1}{S}$	Kepler's harmonic law	One linear determination.	Mean distance and period.	Observation.

THE SCALE OF THE SOLAR SYSTEM

If the information contained in the fifth column is expressed in a different form it may convey a more concrete impression of the immense size of even our parochial corner of space. Light, traveling with a velocity of 186,000 m.p.s., covers a distance equal to nearly eight round-the-world trips every second. To travel from the moon to the earth it requires rather more than 1¼ seconds; and from the sun to the earth, about 8⅓ minutes. If the sun suddenly 'went out,' we on earth would continue to bask in its rays for a further 8⅓ minutes. The corresponding times for the other planets are given below:

Mercury	3 mins.
Venus	6 mins.
Earth	8 mins.
Mars	13 mins.
Jupiter	43 mins.
Saturn	1 h. 20 mins.
Uranus	2 h. 40 mins.
Neptune	4 h. 10 mins.
Pluto	5 h. 30 mins.

IV. Outside the Solar System

If the reader looks at this page, while rapidly opening and closing alternate eyes, it will appear to him to jerk from side to side against the more distant background, whatever that may be. This simple example of parallactic shift depends upon the fact that the reader is using two viewpoints which are about two inches apart. So small a baseline gives a noticeable shift only for near objects. To produce a parallactic displacement in more distant objects, some bodily movement is required, while the two viewpoints of a body as distant as the moon must be separated by a thousand miles or more. A baseline of this magnitude also gives reasonable displacements for the nearer planets, such as Mars and Eros, but when the stars are studied with a view to determining their distances it is found that their relative positions as seen from the two stations on the earth's surface are indistinguishable, no matter what instrumental refinements are employed.

Clearly, then, the limit that is necessarily associated with every baseline is reached at distances short of even the nearest stars; we have successfully solved the problem of distances within our own local planetary system, but it now appears that the immensely more distant and numerous agglomeration of stars is going to offer even more difficult problems for the astronomer. If the scientific advance is not to be stemmed, astronomers must forge new tools capable of penetrating beyond the limits of our solar system; and then, if necessary, devise new methods for carrying the research out into the remotest depths of space.

HELIOCENTRIC PARALLAX

The tool that was finally used to get outside the solar system had been talked about for centuries before Bessel first used it with success: it is the simple fact that the earth is not stationary in space, but revolves about the sun. Over two millenniums ago, Aristotle had derided the conception of a moving earth, quite reasonably pointing out that such motion of the terrestrial viewpoint would cause apparent displacements among the constellations as between the nearer and the more distant stars. Since it was impossible to detect any displacements of this nature, he argued that the earth must be stationary. The alternative explanation of this lack of visible parallactic displacement, an alternative which Aristotle rejected, was that possibly the stars are so distant that the displacements, though they exist, are too small to be perceptible to the naked eye. It was this alternative that Bessel showed to be the correct one, thus driving another and by now quite superfluous nail into the coffin wherein are interred the remains of the geocentric hypothesis.

Since the earth makes one complete circuit of the sun in one year, it must occupy diametrically opposite positions in its approximately circular orbit at six-monthly intervals. And since the radius of this orbit is 93 million miles, the terrestrial observer's position in space alters by 186 million miles between, say, 1 January and 1 July. It is this longer baseline Bessel showed to be capable of yielding perceptible shifts in the case of the nearer stars; but this achievement involved the use of instruments such as neither Aristotle nor Kepler had dreamed of. When the potentialities of this baseline are exhausted, the terrestrial astronomer has come to the end of his resources so far as the determination of stellar distance by means of trigonometrical parallax is concerned: in order to be able to use this method for the measurement of the distances of stars lying beyond the reach of the 186-million-mile baseline provided by the earth's orbit, he would have to transport himself to one of the outer planets—for there astronomers, if they existed, would have the advantage of still greater orbital diameters. Fortunately, however, once we get outside the solar system by direct parallactic methods, other and more powerful methods are at hand to carry us still farther and to assure us that astronomical investigation will utilize the first steps taken by Bessel to continue on a long journey out through space. These methods will be described in detail later on in this chapter; for the present, let us inquire more closely into the trigonometric method of determining stellar parallax, or the distance of a star.

TRIGONOMETRICAL PARALLAX

Figure 30 represents (i) X, a sheet of glass upon which a circle has been engraved with a diamond, (ii) a small ball, Y, conveniently mounted, and (iii) Z, a screen. If an observer places his eye behind A and looks at the ball, its position as projected against the screen will be a; as the observer moves his eye around the circle toward B, the position of the ball against the screen will change to b; when the observer is looking from C, the apparent position of the ball will be c; and from D, at d. Thus the ball has traced out upon the screen an exact replica of the circle $ABCD$. The size of this circle, $abcd$, will

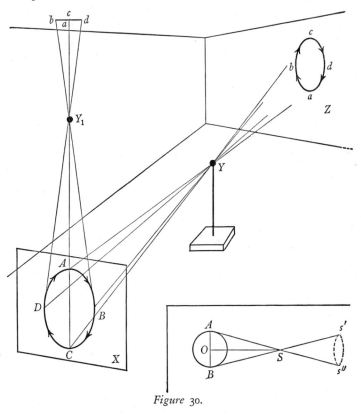

Figure 30.

depend upon the distance of Y from X—the greater it is, the smaller will be the circle. It is further to be noted that the apparent path of Y is only circular (as is the path of the observer's eye) when the line from Y to the center of the circle $ABCD$ is perpendicular to the sheet of glass in which this circle lies. If the ball were moved to some position such as Y_1, situated *in* this plane, then its apparent movement against the screen (which can now be considered as the ceiling) will be a straight line: as the observer's eye travels around the circle *ABCDA*, the path of Y_1 will be from *a* to *b*, back through *c*=*a* to *d*, an equal distance beyond *c*=*a*, and finally back to *a*. Balls situated in positions intermediate between the projected plane *ABCD* and the perpendicular to it will describe ellipses whose eccentricity varies with their position. Finally, it is to be noted that the ball revolves with reference to its background in the same direction as the observer's eye, but 180° in advance of it.

So much by way of introduction. If we now rename *ABCD* the earth's orbit, Y a relatively near star, and Z the background of more distant stars, we have a replica of the mechanism of stellar distance determination by means of parallactic displacements resulting from the earth's orbital motion. Suppose a certain star is observed to shift against the background of stars (which, since most of these are many times more remote, do not themselves shift appreciably) by a distance of 1″ in the course of six months. We then have $s'Ss''=ASB=1''$. Therefore at the star's distance (*OS*) the radius of the earth's orbit (*AO*) subtends an angle (*ASO* or *BSO*) of 0″.5. By trigonometry,

$$OS=\frac{93,000,000}{\tan 0''.5} \text{ miles.}$$

Or, writing *D* for the distance of the star (*OS*),
          R for the radius of the earth's orbit (*OA*),
          p for the star's measured parallax (*ASO*),*

$$D=\frac{R}{\tan p}.$$

Owing to the enormous distances of even the nearest stars, their annual parallactic displacements are excessively minute: the largest are no bigger than a twenty-five cent piece viewed from a distance of about four miles. This accounts both for the flaw in Aristotle's argument, and also for the fact that the displacements were not detected for over two hundred years after the invention of the telescope. It was not, indeed, until 1838 that Bessel detected and measured the first annual stellar parallax, that of the star known as 61 Cygni. He and subsequent workers proved observationally what we have already seen from our model, namely that (i) the annual parallax described by a star at the

---

*The definition of the annual heliocentric parallax of a star is: the angle subtended at it by the semidiameter of the earth's orbit. This is clearly half the *total* annual displacement.

pole of the ecliptic is a small circle, (ii) a star situated on the ecliptic travels back and forth along a short straight line which lies in the plane of the ecliptic, (iii) stars intermediate between these two positions described small ellipses whose eccentricity is inversely proportional to their angular distance from the ecliptic itself. These configurations may be imitated by viewing a penny edge on, when it appears as a straight line, and then by turning it gradually over so that its visible shape becomes, first, a very flattened ellipse, and subsequently a less and less eccentric ellipse, until finally, when viewed at right angles, it is circular. Observation has also shown (iv) that the parallactic orbits are described in the same direction as the earth's motion around the sun, but 180° ahead of the earth. This fact helps us to distinguish between parallactic and aberrational displacements, for it will be remembered that the latter involve a difference in position of 90°.

Another factor that has to be eliminated from the total observed displacement of a star is the component of its real space motion, if any, at right angles to the observer's line of sight: this may be of negligible proportions, but it must nevertheless be considered. The modern method of detecting and measuring parallaxes is photographic, and was initiated by Schlesinger in 1903. Previously to that date the measurements had been made visually at the telescope, a laborious method which had yielded about sixty stellar parallaxes. Schlesinger's method, now universally adopted, is both quicker and more accurate, and also permits the measurement of parallaxes too small for detection by the older methods. Today some 5000 trigonometrical parallaxes have been measured. The procedure is as follows: At an interval of six months two telescopic photographs are taken of the star whose parallax it is required to determine, exceptional practical precautions being observed. The relative positions of the star and the 'background' comparison stars are then measured on the two photographs with the greatest degree of accuracy possible. The movement, relative to the remoter stars of the background, thus revealed, will be compounded of parallactic displacement and actual proper motion. Consequently, a third photograph is taken after a further interval of six months. The parallactic displacement will once again be zero, while any displacement due to the star's motion will have been doubled. In this way the two may be disentangled: it may be necessary to take up to twenty photographs, covering a period of ten years, before satisfaction can be obtained that the effect of the star's motion has been eliminated.

The moment we come to mention the results of these investigations we encounter what can only be called 'astronomical' numbers: that is to say, numbers so large that they are confined in human experience to the realm of astronomy. At this point, therefore, it will be advisable to digress long enough to explain two notations which have been devised for dealing (i) with very large numbers, and (ii) with very great distances.

THE INDEX NOTATION

The function of the first is to express unmanageably large numbers in a compact and easily written form. When a number is multiplied by itself it is said to be 'squared,' and is written with a small 2 above and to the right of it; when multiplied by itself twice, to be 'cubed,' when the index 2 is replaced by a 3. Thus:

$$10 \times 10 = 10^2 = \qquad 100$$
$$10 \times 10 \times 10 = 10^3 = \qquad 1{,}000$$

Similarly
$$10^4 = \qquad 10{,}000$$
$$10^5 = \qquad 100{,}000$$
$$10^6 = 1{,}000{,}000$$

In fact, the index tells us how many ciphers follow the initial unit.

But this notation is not limited to the expression of exact powers of 10. Intermediate numbers can be expressed with equal facility, and nearly as concisely. Consider the number 15,000.

$$10{,}000 = 10 \times 10^3$$
$$20{,}000 = 20 \times 10^3$$

Therefore
$$15{,}000 = 15 \times 10^3$$

By convention, however, the factor not containing the index always lies between 1 and 10. Thus we divide the 15 by 10, making it 1.5, and, in order not to alter the value of the whole expression, multiply the other factor by 10, making it 10^4. Thus 15,000 can be rewritten 1.5×10^4.

The rule to remember when expanding the contracted notation into the longhand form is: move the decimal point to the right a number of places that is indicated by the index. In our example the index is 4; hence the value of the expression is

$$15{,}000.0$$

Similarly, $1.5 \times 10^6 = 1{,}500{,}000$; $7.542 \times 10^9 = 7{,}542{,}000{,}000$, and so on.

The very great convenience of this device will be brought home by the fact that instead of having to write, for example, a 1 followed by enough ciphers to cross the entire page from margin to margin, we may simply write 10^{60}.

ASTRONOMICAL UNITS OF DISTANCE

The second notation is one of distance. When the distances of the first stars were measured it was found that they were so staggering as to render their expression in any unit as small as the mile prohibitively laborious; even the 'astronomical unit' (the earth's mean distance from the sun, or 93 million miles) is in little better case. A very much larger unit had to be discovered, and for all scientific purposes the 'parsec' is now used. This may be defined as the distance at which a star would have an annual parallax of 1″. Though an extremely convenient unit to work in, the parsec is not particularly revealing of the actual distance involved: one may form a clear mental picture of how long a mile is, and even some sort of idea of the astronomical unit, but the parsec is singularly reticent in this respect. For popular works, intended rather for the general public than for fellow astronomers, the 'light year' is accordingly more commonly used. We have already learned something of the velocity of light, that it takes $8\frac{1}{3}$ minutes to travel from the sun to the earth, and a further $5\frac{1}{4}$ hours before it reaches the orbit of Pluto. We may therefore say that the distance from the sun to the earth is $8\frac{1}{3}$ light minutes, and from the sun to Pluto, $5\frac{1}{2}$ light hours. In the same way, 1 light year is the distance covered by light in one year, traveling at an invariable velocity of 186,000 m.p.s. It is as many times greater than the earth's distance from the sun as 1 year is greater than 8 minutes; a quick calculation will prove that it is therefore about 63,300 astronomical units. This fact provides a further way of giving some reality to the conception of a light year, for there are 63,360 inches in one mile. So we can say that there are as many astronomical units in a light year as there are inches in a mile.

A word must now be said of the relation between light years and observed angular parallax. The distance of a star whose parallax is 1″ is 1 parsec, which is equivalent to 3.26 light years. If the parallax is 0″.1, the distance will be 10 parsecs, if 0″.01, 100 parsecs, and so on. Hence, putting D for distance, and p for parallax expressed in seconds of arc,

$$D = \frac{1}{p} \text{ parsecs,}$$

whence $D = \frac{3.26}{p}$ light years.

DENSITY OF STARS IN SPACE

To take an example, the nearest star yet discovered is a faint object in the southern constellation of the Centaur, to which the name Proxima Centauri has been given. Its parallax, the largest yet detected, is only $0''.785$ (this is about the angle subtended by a plate, two feet in diameter, when viewed from a distance of fifty miles).

$$\text{Therefore } D = \frac{3.26}{0.785}$$
$$= 4.2 \text{ light years.}$$

This is equivalent to about 265,000 astronomical units.

It thus becomes clear not only that enormous distances are involved when we come to the stellar system but also that space is exceedingly 'empty.' The distance separating the sun from its nearest neighbor is about $4\frac{1}{2}$ light years, while its own diameter is less than $4\frac{1}{2}$ light seconds, or about one thirty-millionth of that distance. So far, 18 stars have been discovered with distances smaller than 12 light years, though there are very probably other faint neighbors yet undetected. This figure gives a density of stars in the region within 12 light years of the sun of about 1 in every 400 cubic light years!

LIMITATIONS OF TRIGONOMETRICAL PARALLAX

Finally, a word on the accuracy and scope of Schlesinger's direct photographic method of measuring stellar parallaxes. The margin of probable error varies from about 1 per cent for the very nearest stars, to from 10 to 15 per cent for stars at a distance of about 80 light years. Thus the distance of a star, measured as 80 light years with modern astronomical accuracy, would be correctly stated as 80 ± 8 (eighty plus or minus eight) light years: the chance is even that it is between 72 and 88 light years, but it is probably nearer to 80 than to either of these limits. Up to about twice this distance—say to 150 or 200 light years—tolerable results may be expected, but for still greater distances the method is practically useless: the potentialities of the longest baseline available to us have now been exhausted.

PROPER AND RADIAL STELLAR MOTIONS

It has been known for several centuries that the stars have motions of their own: that their relative positions upon the star sphere do not appear to alter from year to year, or even from century to century, when observed with the eye alone is due solely to their very great distances from the observer: with telescopic aid, the angular motions of a great number of stars have been detected and measured. Let us imagine that we are sitting in a captive balloon floating above a field (Fig. 31). Directly beneath us is a man, *A*, at a certain distance from whom is a

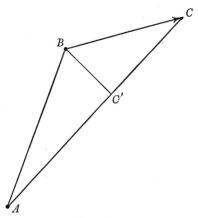

Figure 31.

second man, *B*, who, in the space of time covered by our observations, walks to another position, *C*. It is clear that *B* has moved across *A*'s field of vision by the distance *BC'*, and has at the same time moved directly away from *A* by the amount *C'C*. *B*'s space motion from *B* to *C* may therefore be resolved into two mutually perpendicular components, *BC'* and *C'C*, one of which lies in the observer's line of sight and the other at right angles to it. Supposing that for any reason the observer at *A* were unable to estimate *B*'s true space motion, *BC*, he could nevertheless calculate this distance if he were able to determine *BC'* and *C'C*.

If we call *A* a terrestrial observer and *B* a star whose space motion in a given unit of time is *BC*, then *BC'* is its transverse motion across the star sphere, and *C'C* is its motion in the line of sight, or its radial motion. The former can be measured directly in angular units, the angle *BAC'*, and is referred to as the proper motion of the star. The latter can be deduced from a study of the star's spectrum, as will be explained in detail in Chapter VI. Radial motion, as determined by the spectrum, is given directly in linear units of speed, i.e. in kilometers or miles per second. To convert proper motion from angular to linear units requires a knowledge of the distance of the star from the observer.

An idea of the minuteness of proper motions may be gained when it is learned that the largest proper motion yet detected is that of a faint star (invisible to the naked eye) discovered by Barnard, the annual angular motion of which amounts to 10″.25—roughly 0.02 of the angular diameter of the moon. Among the brighter stars, Arcturus has one of the largest proper motions, having moved across the star sphere a distance equal to twice the apparent diameter of the moon since the time of Ptolemy.

THE POSSIBILITY OF A GREATER BASELINE

Since the stars are in random motion relative to the sun, the sun is clearly moving—in a certain direction and with a certain speed—relative to them. If such motion could be accurately defined, we should have a new and more extensive baseline upon which to base parallactic investigations. For no matter how long we wait, the earth's orbital motion cannot carry us more than 186 million miles (the diameter of the terrestrial orbit) from any previous position. This is the limitation imposed by the fact that the earth moves repetitively in a closed orbit. But if it could be established that the sun is proceeding in a direct course with a velocity of x m.p.s. toward a certain point on the star sphere, the terrestrial observer's spatial displacement due to this motion would increase steadily with the passage of time. If the sun's displacement after one year were insufficient to reveal a parallactic shift for a distant star, it would only be necessary to wait another year (when the shift would be doubled), or a third (when it would be trebled); this could be of course be carried on indefinitely until the observer's displacement were great enough to cause a measurable shift in the star's position. Theoretically there should be no limit to the scope of this method, owing to its indefinitely extensible baseline. One drawback we shall consider in a moment, but first the problem of the sun's motion must be briefly touched upon.

THE SUN'S MOTION

The reader will probably have noticed, while driving at night down a long, straight road on either side of which is a row of street lamps, an 'opening out' effect among the lamps ahead of him; and the reverse effect, that the two rows of lamps are converging upon one another, when he looks out of the rear window. At the same time, the whole panorama of lamps is slipping backward away from the apex of his motion and toward the direction from which he came (the antapex of his motion). This is, of course, an elementary effect of perspective. The existence of a similar effect among the stars may be used to determine the direction and velocity of the sun's motion among them, relatively near stars of known distance playing the role of the street lamps. The problem is complicated, without being essentially altered, by the fact that the stars have peculiar motions of their own—it is as though the street lamps were not fixed in the pavements, but were wandering erratically about. In order to detect the 'opening out' of those stars situated in the direction of the sun's motion, and the 'closing in' of those in the opposite direction, their space motions must first be determined micrometrically and spectroscopically, and these effects eliminated from consideration: if a sufficiently large number of stars is used as the basis of the investigation, individual anomalies will tend to cancel one another out (since the motions are random), and it is possible to arrive at a sufficiently accurate result dependent solely upon the sun's motion.

Herschel, in 1783, was the first astronomer to achieve this, and his first approximate result has been abundantly confirmed and refined by subsequent workers, notably by Boss, Wilson, Campbell, and Moore. The most accurate determination yet made is that of the latter two workers: the sun is moving toward a point on the star sphere on the edge of the constellation Hercules, not far from the first magnitude star Vega, with a velocity of 12·3 m.p.s. relative to the 2,149 stars used as 'street lamps.'

STATISTICAL PARALLAX

In a single year, therefore, the sun's motion displaces the observer by an amount twice as great as the diameter of the earth's orbit. If, now, the stars were stationary with respect to one another (the truly 'fixed' stars of the ancients) the observed proper motion of any star would be due solely to the sun's motion, and its distance could be derived direct from its observed shift. But since the stars all have motions of their own—known as their peculiar motions—it is impossible to disentangle the component of their total observed motion due to parallax from that due to peculiar motion, without first knowing the star's distance;

which is precisely what we hoped to derive. It therefore seems that our proposed new method of determining stellar distance is to be stillborn.

There is, however, a compromise way out of this difficulty. Though it is true that the sun's motion cannot be utilized to determine the distance of *individual* stars (whose peculiar motions cannot be known), it can be utilized to give us the mean or statistical parallax of a *group* of stars. For if a large enough group of stars is considered, the random peculiar motions of its members will tend to cancel one another out, and the larger the group the more nearly true will this be. The drift of the whole group toward the antapex of the sun's way can then be directly related with the mean distance of all the members of the group.

Certain characteristics of such statistical parallaxes are to be noticed:

i. they can be deduced for stars too distant for investigation by either of the methods already described;

ii. they cannot be derived for individual stars, but only as an average for a number of stars;

iii. their accuracy depends upon (*a*) the number of stars for which the motions are deduced, and (*b*) the accuracy with which the proper motions are measured. Thus optimum results would be obtained for a group consisting of a very large number of stars, all of whose proper motions were large enough to be measured with a high degree of accuracy.

THE NEXT STAGE

Statistical parallax, though reaching beyond the limit at which trigonometrical parallaxes are too unreliable to be of any value, is confined to stars far short of the most distant that are known to exist; it is, moreover, not applicable to individual stars. What is required is a method of determining the instrinsic luminosities of the brightest stars, so that even at distances so great that many stars may have faded into invisibility there shall still be tell-tale beacons by whose means those distances can be discovered: this has been achieved, the stars in question being of the types known as Cepheids and Novae.

APPARENT STELLAR BRIGHTNESS

Before we can learn how astronomers have developed this field of inquiry it will be necessary to digress, as briefly as may be, on the subject of the apparent and real brightness of stars. The former is measured in terms of an arbitrary scale of 'magnitudes,' a magnitude being the unit of apparent brightness just as the pound is the unit of human weight or a fathom the unit of water depth. Roughly speaking, the brightest stars in the night sky are of the first magnitude, stars a little fainter of the second magnitude, and so on till we come to those which are only just perceptible with unaided vision; these are of the sixth magnitude. The faintest which are capable of impressing their images upon photographic plates after long exposure with the world's largest telescope are of about the twenty-second magnitude. It is important to realize that 'magnitude,' departing from common usage, has nothing whatever to do with size: it is solely a measure of brightness, as this appears to the terrestrial observer.

Careful visual scrutiny of different stars, notably by Pogson and the younger Herschel during the earlier half of last century, showed (i) that each magnitude is about 2.5 times as bright as the one below it, (ii) an average first magnitude star is about 100 times as bright as an average sixth magnitude star. These two estimations of the relative brightness of different magnitudes differ only slightly from one another; but differ they do, for if each magnitude were exactly 2.5 times as bright as that below it, then a first magnitude star would be $(2.5)^5$ times as bright as one of the sixth—and $(2.5)^5$ approximately equals 95, not 100. It therefore had to be decided which was the more convenient relation on which to base the arbitrary magnitude scale. Herschel's estimate (that a numerical decrease of five magnitudes means a hundredfold brightness increase) was selected. If we write m_a for the magnitude of a star of apparent brightness B_a, and m_b for the magnitude of a star of apparent brightness B_b, then, in accord with Herschel's condition, the ratio of the apparent brightnesses of the two stars,

$$\frac{B_a}{B_b},$$

must be 100 when $m_b - m_a = 5$. It should be remembered that on the magnitude scale the star with the greater brightness has the smaller magnitude, in other words the scale is inverse in character. We must now proceed to find an expression that will give the ratio of brightness of any two stars whose magnitudes differ by any given amount. In the first place we shall assume that the ratio of brightness between two stars whose magnitudes differ by 1 shall be a constant. Our problem now reduces itself to one of algebra, and it may be proved that if the ratio of brightness of any two stars is $\frac{B_a}{B_b}$ and their magnitude difference is m_b

$- m_a$, then

$$\frac{B_a}{B_b} = k^{(m_b - m_a)}$$

in which k is the numerical constant representing the ratio of brightness of two stars whose magnitudes differ by 1. To determine the value of k we use Herschel's criterion that when the magnitude difference is 5 the brightness ratio is 100 and find that $100 = k^5$ or $k = 2.512$ approximately. The substitution of this value for k gives the analytic expression for the magnitude scale as

$$\frac{B_a}{B_b} = 2.512^{(m_b - m_a)}.$$

Those readers who are familiar with logarithmic notation will realize that this expression may be written as $\log B_a - \log B_b = 0.4 \ (m_b - m_a)$ with logarithms on the base 10.

ACTUAL STELLAR BRIGHTNESS

If an observer looks down a long straight street on which there are street lights of equal intensity spaced at equal intervals, he will at once notice that the more distant lights appear fainter than those close at hand. We learn from elementary physics that the apparent intensity of light from any source varies inversely as the square of the distance of the source from the observer. Hence careful measurement would show that a street light 200 yards away would appear to be only one fourth as bright as a light 100 yards away.

The stellar magnitudes that we discussed above referred only to the apparent brightnesses of the stars. This apparent brightness depends upon at least two factors: (a) the actual brightness of the star itself and (b) the distance of the star from the observer. (For the present we are making the assumption that space is transparent.) For the purpose of making comparisons between the stars themselves as individuals, we define absolute magnitude as the apparent brightness that the star would have if it was at a distance of 10 parsecs from the observer, i.e. at a distance or about 33 light years or where the stellar parallax were 0″.1. By proper manipulation of the analytic expression for the magnitude scale and taking into account the decrease of apparent brightness with distance we can determine that the absolute magnitude M of a star is related to the apparent magnitude m by the expression

$$M = m + 5 + 5 \log p$$

in which p is the parallax of the star. If we know any two of the values, M, m, or p we can find the third. Hence if we have any way of discovering the absolute magnitude of a star at unknown distance we can find that distance from a knowledge of the apparent magnitude.

SUCCESSIVE EXTRAPOLATIONS

The superlative importance of being able to determine the absolute magnitudes of stars is therefore evident. Trigonometrical and statistical parallax have provided us with a mass of information concerning the distances of the nearer stars, and the problem is to discover some characteristic of these stars that shows itself to be variable with absolute magnitude. To do this is merely to take one further step in the extended extrapolation represented on the following page. At each new stage in this sequence, data are discovered which transcend that stage, thus establishing a further stage; this in turn contains not only the data from the preceding stage which made possible its determination, but also new data which transcend it and allow a third stage to be established.

In a way, the process is not unlike that whereby a convict, confined in a prison cell, managed to escape from the cell, the prison, and the country, although his initial equipment consisted of nothing more elaborate than a piece of wire: with this wire he was able to pull into his cell the key a careless guard had dropped on the floor outside; once out of the cell he was able to steal a ladder from a storehouse and climb through the window of the warden's bedroom; there to change into civilian clothes, steal a key ring, and let himself out of the prison by the warden's private gate; once outside he was in a position to return to his home and collect his passport and some money; and, thus provided, he boarded a steamer and sailed for South America. Neither the wire, the key, the ladder, the suit, nor the passport would of itself have secured his escape: but, using each in turn to extend the range of his freedom by an amount that placed the next within his grasp, the case was quite otherwise.

At the moment we are in the position of holding the key (statistical parallax)—which the piece of wire (trigonometrical parallax) provided for us—in our hand, and of looking round to see how it can be used to lead us to the next stage in our expansion.

CEPHEIDS

This next stage, which transcends trigonometrical and statistical parallax while at the same time being based upon their results, is known as the period-luminosity relationship of the Cepheids. The importance of statistical parallax in establishing the much more valuable Cepheid method of determining stellar distance will appear in a moment. First, the Cepheids themselves, for a fuller account of which the reader may turn to p. 267. There are in the skies many stars whose brightness is not steady, but fluctuating: the so-called variable stars. If the magnitude of one such star is measured at intervals over a given period and the results incorporated in a curve whose axes represent magnitude and time respectively, this curve will be a 'picture' of the star's light variation, showing at a glance the manner in which the brightness increases

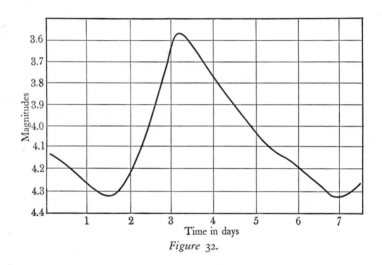

Figure 32.

and fades. The light curves of all variables fall into a comparatively few, easily distinguishable types, each star of a given type behaving in a similar manner to all other members of that type, and differing in obvious respects from variables of other types. The light curve of δ Cephei (the type star which has given its name to the Cepheid variables) is shown in Fig. 32; the steep rise to maximum brightness, followed by a more gentle decrease, is characteristic of all Cepheids.

THE PERIOD-LUMINOSITY RELATIONSHIP

Situated in the southern half of the star sphere and invisible from the latitudes of the United States are two great clouds of faint stars which to the naked eye resemble detached lumps of the Milky Way; they

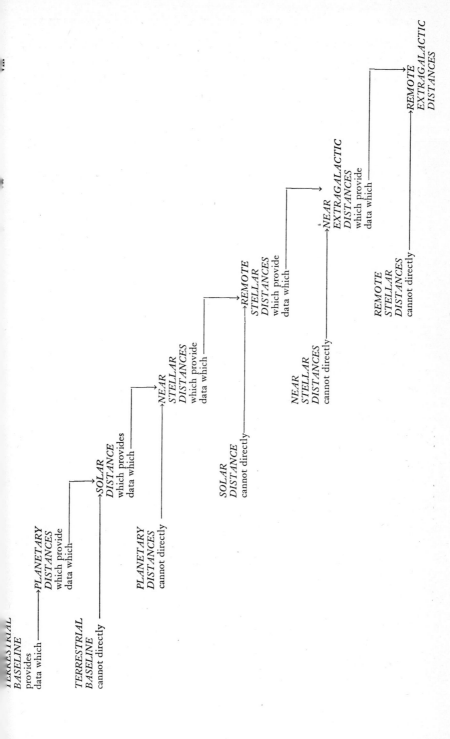

are known as the Greater and Lesser Magellanic Clouds. In 1908 it was discovered that the latter contained a number of Cepheids, and a most surprising connection between their periods (i.e. the interval separating successive maxima) and their mean apparent magnitudes was found to exist: the longer the period of one of these Cepheids, the brighter it was. Since all attempts to detect parallaxes for individual stars in the cloud had proved abortive, it was clear that it must lie at a very great distance from the sun—as had already been suggested by the faintness of its stars. It was thus safe to say that its size was negligible compared with its distance, and that therefore all the stars of which it was composed were at materially the same distance from the observer. Under these circumstances, the apparent magnitudes of its stars would be directly proportional to their absolute magnitudes, and the correlation could be extended to the latter: thus, the period and luminosity of Cepheids are interrelated. But since the distance, and therefore the absolute magnitude, of no single Cepheid had at that date been determined, it was impossible to state the numerical relation between the two; in other words, the curves constructed in 1908 showing the relation between Cepheid period and mean absolute magnitude could not be calibrated. The reason for this failure was that the Cepheids are intrinsically brilliant stars and can therefore be seen at distances too great to be spanned by either the spectroscopic or trigonometrical methods: the nearest Cepheid yet discovered is situated at a distance of about 200 light years from the sun. It was not until 1917 that Shapley made determinations of Cepheid distances, thus enabling him to determine their absolute magnitudes and assign a zero point to the period-luminosity curve. His method was to determine statistically the average parallax of eleven Cepheids possessing unusually large proper motions. Thus a scale of absolute magnitude values was fitted to the uncalibrated curve, and thenceforth Cepheids could be used as celestial milestones wherever they were visible; and owing to their great intrinsic brilliance greater distances were measurable than had ever before been thought possible. The procedure consists simply in measuring the Cepheid's period, reading off the corresponding absolute magnitude from the curve, and comparing this with the observed mean apparent magnitude. This very powerful method has, particularly in the hands of Shapley, provided a great part of our present knowledge of the structure of the universe of stars; this application of Cepheid parallax will be returned to in the next chapter.

There is no reason for doubting the exactness of the relative values (i.e. those derived in 1908), but the absolute values of the calibrated curve are certainly in some error, owing to doubtful fixing of the zero point; and they may be gravely in error. This uncertainty of the zero point results from a variety of causes, among them being: (a) the number of Cepheids used in the determination of the statistical parallax was far too small to insure that the derived value represented the true mean parallax; (b) owing to their great distances, the proper motions of the Cepheids are uniformly small, and even the largest, as selected by Shapley, are small enough for material error to enter into their measurement; and (c) there is the ever-present question regarding the absorption of light in space, for the relationship established between apparent and absolute magnitude assumes that space is perfectly transparent. The estimated inaccuracy from all these causes is of the order of about 0.5 magnitudes. At a later date Shapley and others have been able to refine the original calibration by utilizing a larger number of Cepheids for the fixation of the zero point, although even now there is still a margin of uncertainty associated with all distances determined by this method. This disadvantage is to a certain extent counteracted by the great distances that can be investigated: better to have a rough idea of the distance of a very remote object than none at all. In Shapley's application of the period-luminosity law there is another source of possible error: we shall see in Chapter v that most of his results have been based upon observations of the so-called cluster variables, stars which, though being of the Cepheid type for which the relationship was worked out, nevertheless differ from true Cepheids in certain important respects— and this, also, must be borne in mind when considering Shapley's conclusions.

NOVAE AS SOUNDING LINES

Another type of star that can be used as an approximate sounding line is the Nova.* Novae are stars which, for reasons still not exactly known, suddenly blaze up from comparative obscurity, increasing in brightness by many magnitudes in perhaps no more than a few days: at maximum a nova is often the most conspicuous object in the night sky. Maximum having been attained, a much lengthier and more erratic phase of fading sets in, till finally (usually not for several years) it has sunk to something like its original magnitude. Some of the nearest of these novae have been within the reach of methods of determining parallax already described, and it has been found that at maxi-

*See p. 267 for a fuller account of these objects.

mum they not only appear abnormally bright, but are intrinsically so. Their absolute magnitudes characteristically lie between —5 and —10, the most favored magnitudes being —6 and —7. If, therefore, a nova is discovered which is so faint as to require a large telescope to show it, the reasonable conclusion is that it is many times more distant, not only than the stars visible to the naked eye but also than telescopic stars as bright as, or brighter than, itself. If we assume, as we can with reasonable safety, that its absolute magnitude lies between —5 and —10 we can derive a very rough idea of its distance; and if a number of novae have been observed which are known to occupy the same region of space, we can assume a mean absolute magnitude of —6 or —7 and achieve a considerably more definite result without sacrificing the assurance of at least approximate accuracy.

The reader may object that the Cepheid method has just been criticized for an uncertainty amounting to 0.5 magnitudes, yet we are now thinking worthy of serious discussion a method with an indeterminacy of at least several magnitudes. It must of course be admitted that individual distances derived by this method may be as many as ten times as uncertain as those based upon Cepheid observations. But where several novae in the same region of space are observed, this margin is considerably decreased. Moreover, novae have been mainly utilized in connection with the class of objects known as extragalactic nebulae, concerning whose status there have been, as we shall see in Chapter v, two schools of thought: either they are members of our stellar system and therefore *comparatively* near the earth (their distances being of the order of 100,000 light years or less), or else they are external to it and situated at distances not much less than ten times as great. The value of the novae that have been detected in these nebulae lies in the fact that, even with the wide margin of uncertainty mentioned above, they provide a clear indication of which of these widely different alternatives is to be preferred.

DYNAMICAL PARALLAX

Still another type of star can be used for determining stellar distances: the binary star. Most stars pursue their courses through space in lonely isolation, separated by many light years from their nearest neighbors. But an appreciable percentage of the stellar host are members of duple systems: that is, pairs of stars near enough to one another to be controlled by their mutual gravitation. These binary systems behave like a sun-planet system in that they travel through space together; but since the difference between the masses of two stars is many times less than that between a star and a planet, each will revolve about the other—or, more accurately, each will revolve about the center of gravity of the system. From observations of a binary, coupled with the knowledge crystallized in the laws of Newton (in accordance with which their motions are performed), it is possible to calculate its distance. Parallaxes derived in this way are known as dynamical or hypothetical parallaxes.

Since the mathematics involved is quite simple, and the process is difficult to fathom when described verbally, we shall run through the train of reasoning which starts from the angular separation of the members of a binary system and their period of mutual revolution, and ends with their distance from the observer.

It will be remembered that Kepler's harmonic law was shown by Newton to be strictly accurate only if the planets had no mass whatever; Newton therefore adjusted the equation to bring in the relative masses of the two bodies, planet and sun. From this modified equation it follows that for a pair of stars in mutual revolution

$$\frac{m_1 + m_2}{S + E} = \frac{A^3}{P^2}$$

where m_1, m_2 are the masses of the two stars,

   A, their distance apart (in astronomical units),

   P, their revolution period (in years),

   S, the mass of the sun,

   E, that of the earth.

If A is the stars' linear separation in astronomical units, a their separation as observed (measured in seconds of arc), and p their parallax (also measured in seconds of arc), then

$$A = \frac{a}{p}.$$

We have seen that the mass of the earth is negligible compared with that of the sun; it may therefore be omitted without materially affecting the equation. Making this omission, substituting the value of A in the above equation, and expressing m_1 and m_2 in terms of the sun's mass, we have

$$m_1 + m_2 = \frac{a^3}{p^3 \times P^2},$$

whence, bringing p to one side,

$$p = \dfrac{a}{\sqrt[3]{P^2(m_1 + m_2)}}.$$

Making the assumption that each star is as massive as the sun,* we can substitute $2S$, a known quantity, for $(m_1 + m_2)$:

$$p = \dfrac{a}{\sqrt[3]{P^2 \times 2S}}$$

and solve for p.

By the mathematical 'trick' of successive approximations—use being made of (i) a certain relationship between stellar mass and luminosity which we have not yet discussed, and (ii), the known relation between apparent and absolute magnitude, and distance—this method is capable of giving results with only a small percentage inaccuracy. Though not of wide application, it is useful in that it permits the determination of the distances of binaries which are too remote for trigonometrical investigation. The nearer binaries (those within 30 light years or so) may be dealt with as accurately by the direct method.

GROUP PARALLAX

To round off this account of the means whereby man has conducted his intellectual colonization of interstellar space, we must at least mention one further method of distance determination: group parallax. Since it is of only secondary importance, and restricted in scope, it may be dealt with more summarily than those hitherto described.

Most of the readers of this book will be familiar with the group of stars, visible on winter nights, known variously as the Pleiades and the Seven Sisters. They mark Taurus, a constellation many of whose stars have been shown by a study of their proper motions to be moving in the same direction at the same speed. Further, their paths if produced forward all converge upon a single point on the star sphere. This is to be expected, since parallel lines (and the stars are moving parallel to one another) appear to meet at infinity. Now if the earth were a member of the group, it would also be moving toward this convergent; therefore the terrestrial observer's line of sight to the convergent is parallel to the stars' space motions. If, in addition to its proper motion,

*It is because this assumption has to be made, the true masses of the two stars being unknown, that dynamical parallax is sometimes known as hypothetical parallax. The assumption is well founded, however, for we shall see in Chapter VIII that the stars vary less among themselves as regards mass than in any other respect; the sun, moreover, is a quite 'average' star.

the radial velocity of a star in the group is known—and the spectroscope quickly provides this datum—it is possible to construct a formula linking

the star's parallax,
its space motion,
its proper motion,
its radial motion,
the angle between the observer's lines of sight to the star and to the convergent respectively.

It is to be noted that although this method gives the parallaxes of individual stars, it can only be applied to members of a group whose proper motions are large enough to be perceptible. Though not, therefore, of extensive application, group parallax is a neat and successful method of determining certain stellar distances.

RECAPITULATION

To sum up:

Trigonometrical parallax,
Statistical (mean) parallax,
The period-luminosity relationship of the Cepheids,
The absolute magnitudes of novae at maxima,
Dynamical parallax,
Group parallax—

These are the more important tools with which the modern astronomer has equipped himself for his work in penetrating the more remote regions of the visible universe.* We shall now turn to the results and rewards of this labor.

*A seventh method, known as spectroscopic parallax, is dealt with in Chapter VIII, where the physical conceptions involved in its formulation are discussed. Though it has played an important role in the past, it is today tending to fade out of the picture in favor of trigonometrical and statistical parallax.

V. To the **End of Knowledge**

We are now in a position to inquire what information regarding the organization and extent of the visible universe is provided by the criteria of distance with which we have so far largely concerned ourselves, as well as by such additional methods of specialized application (developed from those already discussed) as we may from time to time devise.

THE NATURE OF THE PROBLEM

During the sixteenth century the belief that the stars were minute points of light equidistant from the earth was shown to be false, but it was not until the end of the eighteenth century that any serious observational attempt was made to replace the outworn cosmology of a bygone age by one in closer agreement with the observational data. The problem to be solved might be stated as follows: Are the stars distributed more or less uniformly throughout the whole of space, or do they form a discrete system which occupies, possibly, only a small corner of space? If the latter, then what are the dimensions, shape and structure of this system? And, it might be added, is the system unique, or has it peers in other regions of outer space? *A priori* theorizing could give no answers to questions such as these, and the only procedure whereby the problem could be attacked with any prospect of success consisted in a careful study of the apparent distribution of the stars upon the face of the star sphere, followed by an attempt to correlate this with some sort of spatial distribution.

THE MILKY WAY

The most noticeable feature of stellar distribution in the moonless night sky is the Milky Way. This is a faint band of light, varying in width from 45° to less than 5°, which traverses the visible half of the star sphere from horizon to horizon. A trip round the world proves that the Milky Way girdles the entire star sphere, forming a continuous, or nearly continuous, belt about the heavens. Furthermore, it is very nearly a great circle; that is to say, it divides the star sphere into two almost equal sections. One of the earliest discoveries of the telescope was that the Milky Way, or galaxy, consists of vast hordes of stars too faint and too closely crowded to be individually distinguishable by the naked eye, although their integrated light is visible as a misty band. More detailed study shows that the richness of the Milky Way varies along its length: one area may be almost starless, while near by the stars are so congested, so piled upon one another, that they present a 'solid' wall of light.

It is also noticeable with the naked eye, and still more so in long-exposure photographs, that the Milky Way is materially richer in one direction—roughly in the direction of the constellation Sagittarius—than in the opposite direction. Finally, although there is a colossal piling up, or concentration, of the fainter stars in the galactic regions, the brighter stars show a less marked crowding.

STRUCTURE OF THE MILKY WAY

The stellar concentration toward the galactic plane, with progressive avoidance of the regions approximating to the galactic poles, can be explained in one of three ways. We may suppose, in the first place, that the sun is surrounded by a ring of stars within which the star density is higher than elsewhere. Since this ring, the Milky Way, apparently bisects the star sphere, the sun must lie near its median plane. Since there is no reason why the ring should not be very distant, this theory can account for the observed fact that the brighter stars (in general, the nearer ones) are less restricted to the galactic regions than the fainter. According to this explanation, the apparent concentration of stars within the boundaries of the Milky Way is a reflection of a real spatial crowding: the average distance separating two adjacent stars within the ring is less than that separating adjacent stars outside it. This conception of a ring is, however, artificial to a degree, and bears no relation to any configuration of stars known to exist elsewhere within the boundaries of the observable universe.

The appearance of the Milky Way can also be reproduced without recourse to any actual concentration of stars within a certain spatial zone: the laws of perspective alone could achieve it. Suppose that the stars form a disk-shaped system similar to a biconvex lens, within all regions of which the star density is uniform. Suppose, further, that the sun lies in the median plane of this system but at some distance from its center. Then a terrestrial observer will, in gazing out into space, be looking through a greater thickness of stars when he is facing the periphery of the disk than when he is looking toward either of its poles. In the former direction, therefore, the stars will appear to be more closely crowded together than in the latter, and the observed effect will be that of a Milky Way separating two relatively starless regions. The eccentric position of the sun within the galactic plane will, furthermore, produce the effect of greater star density in one direction along the plane (toward its center) than in the opposite direction, where the edge of the system is nearer.

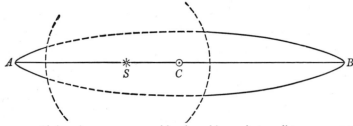

Figure 33. If the telescope were capable of reaching only to a distance represented by the dotted circle, star counts would give an apparent shape of the galaxy as bounded by the dotted line and circle. Furthermore, the sun would appear at the center of the system.

A third possibility is a combination of the two just considered; the stars do not indeed permeate all space, but are concentrated into a roughly lenticular system, in whose median plane the star density is higher than on either side of it. This was the conclusion at which the elder Herschel arrived in the early years of the nineteenth century. He was led to this result by the simple observational method of star-counts: he divided the entire celestial sphere into a large number of equal adjoining areas, and then, using the most powerful telescope at his disposal, proceeded to count the number of stars visible in each area. Only one assumption was made—that his telescope was capable of penetrating to the confines of the star system in all directions. Were it incapable of achieving this, the derived shape would inevitably be to a greater or less extent misleading (as shown in Fig. 33), since he regarded it as axiomatic that the distance to the edge of the system in any direction was proportional to the number of stars per unit area in that direction. At the outset of his surveys he made the further, and not entirely unconnected, assumption that the system was homogeneous;

later, he was forced to conclude that this assumption was not strictly justified, and that, as is now known to be the case, the star density is not uniform throughout the system. Nevertheless, the results of his survey convinced him that the observed star crowding in the Milky Way was very largely optical.

DISTRIBUTION OF THE BRIGHTER STARS

Herschel's star counts showed clearly that there is an immense piling up of the fainter stars toward the median plane of the Milky Way— known shortly as the galactic plane, or galactic equator—but that, as is proved by a glance at the night sky with the naked eye, the brighter stars are not similarly restricted. Indeed, what slight degree of crowding there is among the brighter stars is not about the galactic plane but about a plane inclined at some 15° or 20° to it. This second plane— known as Gould's Belt of Bright Stars, after the astronomer who first drew attention to it—is most clearly seen in winter, when the bright stars of Canis Major, Orion, and Taurus, all components of the belt, are above the horizon during the night time and are conspicuously aslant the Milky Way itself. For many years this freedom of the brighter stars from galactic concentration was held to constitute a conclusive argument against the validity of Herschel's disk theory, for if the appearance of the stellar universe is due entirely to its shape and to the position of the sun within it, then it is to be expected that the brighter stars as well as the fainter would be subjected to the laws of perspective and would therefore exhibit galactic concentration.

THE LOCAL STAR CLOUD

More recent work has resolved this difficulty and has at the same time vindicated Herschel in the main outline of his universe-picture, though his early assumption of approximately uniform stellar distribution is very wide of the mark. Telescopic examination of the Milky Way shows that its structure is far from homogeneous (see Plate 1). It consists of vast star clouds in which the individual stars appear to be so closely crowded as to merge into an undifferentiated haze of light, interspersed with areas of lower star density or even of apparent absence of stars altogether. Also there are in galactic regions many small clusters or clouds of stars, humble and more localized editions of the vast star clouds. It has been established as the result of work on star motions that the sun itself is a member of one such minor star cloud, all of whose members are—compared with the faint stars of the Milky Way—

close neighbors of the sun. For this reason they are to be seen in all directions about the sun and, since the terrestrial observer is inside the cloud, are exempt from galactic concentration. In point of fact, the median plane of this Local Star Cloud—for, like the galaxy, it is a flattened lens-shaped structure—is inclined at some 12° to that of the galaxy, and is closely coincident with Gould's Belt of Bright Stars, all of which are members. In general, it is true to say that all the brighter stars of the constellation figures are members of our Local Star Cloud. Shapley and Charlier have shown by their studies of the distribution of the brighter blue* stars that these also characterize the Local Star Cloud and consequently show a tendency to crowd around a plane inclined at about 12° to that of the main galaxy. This is true of blue stars down to the sixth magnitude, it being statistically correct to say of the brighter stars of any type that they are nearer than the fainter. Blue stars fainter than magnitude 7.5 congregate about the galactic plane in the normal way of faint stars, while those of intermediate brightness show a preference between those of the galaxy and the Local Star Cloud.

Using criteria of distance already described, Charlier has discovered that the Local Star Cloud is a flattened spheroid with a diameter of some 2000 light years, and a thickness, measured perpendicularly to the median plane, of perhaps 600 or 700 light years. The sun is located slightly to one side of the median plane at a distance of about 300 light years from its center. Charlier's Cloud may be the nucleus of a larger conglomeration which measures, according to Seares, some 20,000 by 7000 light years.

METHODS OF PLUMBING THE GALAXY

The discovery of the Local Star Cloud—a minute galaxy within the galaxy—was made possible by the study of apparent stellar distribution and of stellar motions and distances. Owing to its comparatively small

---

*Stars are classified into a number of types, each possessing distinctive spectroscopic features. These types are more fully described in Chapter VIII, after the functions of the spectroscope have been systematically set forth. Here it will be sufficient for the reader to note that the correspondence between the colors and spectral types of different stars is roughly as follows:

Type	Type
B: blue stars	G: yellowish-white stars
A: blue-white stars	K: yellow stars
F: white stars	M: red stars.

dimensions it was practicable to use distance determinations based upon individual stars, as already described. The rough outlines of the galaxy as a coherent, isolated, roughly lenticular system were traced by Herschel purely from studies of star numbers in different directions. When the problem of scale-mapping the star system arises—discovering the distances to its edges in different directions—the solution is less easy than in the case of the Local Star Cloud, owing to the very much greater distances involved. Even the brightest stars are invisible at distances of a galactic order (mainly owing to the existence of amorphous absorbing material within the galaxy) and although Cepheids and novae have provided a partial solution, single stars are in the final analysis of little value except for approximate statistical purpose. To probe the galaxy to its limits we must fall back upon the clusters and groups of stars, first evolving distance criteria for these objects.

EVIDENCE OF SINGLE STARS

Before proceeding to a description of the clusters, their appearance, their classification, and the distance criteria that have been elaborated for them, let us first see what light has been thrown upon the scale of the galaxy by such sounding lines as Cepheids, novae, and other individual stars of great intrinsic luminosity.

Cepheids in the galactic plane have been detected in all directions to distances of about 20,000 light years, their average distance on either side of the plane being less than 500 light years. At such distances they are extremely faint and difficult of detection, and it is not to be supposed that none fainter and more distant exist. This is borne out by the evidence of other types of variable whose distance can be approximately determined from an only narrowly varying mean absolute magnitude. Such variables have extended the minimum distance to the edge of the galaxy in the direction of Sagittarius to over 30,000 light years.

This is the limit to which we are led by single stars. That even this is not the end of things is clearly indicated by figures, the results of detailed star counts, which show the numbers of stars visible at each successive magnitude level. For when star numbers are arranged in this way it is found that in the regions of the Milky Way—but not of the galactic poles—their numbers are still increasing rapidly at magnitude 21, which is about the limit of photographic detection. A star similar to the sun would have to be removed to a distance of 50,000 light years before sinking to this threshold; so far, then, the evidence indicates that within the galactic plane and at least in one direction stars are to be encountered for more than 50,000 light years.

ECCENTRIC POSITION OF THE SUN

This question of direction is of some interest: even if the sun is centrally placed within the galaxy (we have seen that it must be near the central plane, i.e. near the line *AB* in Fig. 33, since the Milky Way is approximately a great circle) the edge of the system will lie at different distances in different directions. This depends upon the fact that the galaxy is not spherical but lenticular. But if, in addition, the sun is eccentrically placed within the median plane, the distance to the edge will vary with different directions even within this plane. It has been found that the most distant variables yet detected are confined to one hemisphere of the Milky Way, and congregate particularly in the constellation Sagittarius, where the star clouds are also densest. Furthermore, the faintest novae show an identical distribution. Finally there is the evidence of the globular clusters; these will be described later in the present chapter, and it will suffice to say at this point that they likewise appear to be centered upon the Sagittarius region. We may therefore assume, at any rate until contrary evidence appears, that the galaxy is deeper in this than in the opposite direction, since the faintest objects characterize it; in other words, the sun is not as Herschel thought, situated at, or even very near, the center of the galaxy. Figure 33 shows how this misconception is liable to arise if the telescope employed for the star counts is incapable of reaching the edge of the galaxy in all directions. That Herschel's great reflector was able to plumb the galaxy in the direction of its poles is demonstrated by the fact that more powerful instruments show very few more stars per unit area in this direction than did his. This, however, is not true of those directions which lie in the galactic plane.

PRELIMINARY RESULTS

These preliminary results, together with considerations based upon Shapley's studies of the globular clusters which we shall consider later suggested 200,000 light years as a very provisional diameter for the galaxy, its thickness being perhaps one sixth as great. It is true that this early figure has been whittled down by Trumpler, van de Kamp Stebbins, and others by something like one half, but even with these revised figures the galaxy remains a structure built to a scale immeasurably greater than that of the solar system or even of the Loca

Star Cloud. A ray of light takes eight minutes to reach the earth from the sun; five hours later it crosses the orbit of Pluto, while four and a half years are required for it to reach the nearest star. Yet a ray of light leaving one edge of the stellar system would not reach the diametrically opposite edge for something like a thousand centuries.

MOVING CLUSTERS

Stars show a marked proclivity for going about in groups; one such group, the Local Star Cloud, we have already mentioned. Since the sun is an internal member of the Local Star Cloud, and is therefore surrounded on all sides by other members, this grouping does not appear as a cluster to the terrestrial observer. In fact, as we have seen, its existence avoided detection until comparatively recent times, when astronomical methods of probing behind the mask of appearances had reached a considerable degree of finesse. This is also true of star groups which, though not actually containing the sun, are nevertheless comparatively near to it in space. The smaller the distance of two objects from the observer, the wider is their angular separation. Hence the members of a comparatively proximate grouping appear to be widely dispersed upon the star sphere. They do not in fact look like a star cluster, and their coherent nature can only be demonstrated by proving a community of motion among them. If a number of stars—no matter how great their apparent separation—are found to be traveling in the same direction with the same velocity, the only alternative to supposing them to constitute a single, gravitationally coherent group is to appeal to coincidence, assuming them to be in reality so remote from one another that they cannot be affecting one another gravitationally to any appreciable extent. The greater the number of stars that are found to share a particular motion, the more fantastic becomes the coincidence. Though the study of proper and radial motions is necessary before the true nature of a cluster of this type can be proved, it can nevertheless sometimes be guessed. The stars of the Big Dipper, for instance, look as though they might form a single system, and the same may be said of the Orion stars; but before this can be shown beyond doubt to be the case, a very careful investigation of their motions must be carried out.

In the case of the nearest groupings, however, it may be quite impossible even to guess that the individual stars are gravitationally connected. The stars Sirius, β Aurigae, δ Leonis, α Coronae, and, among others, five of the stars of Ursa Major form such a cluster.

Since their true nature can only be discovered through a study of the motions of their components, these clusters are known as moving clusters. Though they are described as 'comparatively near' the sun, it must be remembered that the most distant stars in the galaxy are perhaps 100,000 light years distant, so that a cluster 130 light years from the sun (as is the Taurus moving cluster of eighty known members), though inconceivably remote by terrestrial standards, is yet a next-door neighbor compared with the whole galaxy.

OPEN CLUSTERS

Clusters that are more distant than these moving clusters appear to be more highly concentrated; the angular separations of their components are smaller, and their cluster-nature can be perceived visually. Clusters of this category are known as open clusters, and the Pleiades is a prominent example. It is to be noted that a closer crowding of the stars within the confines of the cluster would give the same appearance as greater distance, but it is probable that the majority of the open clusters appear to be more condensed than moving clusters because they are more distant and not because of greater spatial concentration. A moving cluster at 100 light years, in fact, would be an open cluster at 10,000. The angularly largest of the open clusters are visible to the naked eye, and in some cases, though not all, the individual stars may be seen without instrumental aid. An example of an open cluster whose individual stars are invisible to the naked eye, though its integrated light allows it to be seen as a faint misty spot, is the great double cluster in Perseus; the telescopic appearance of this object is illustrated in Plate II. The more distant clusters, however, are not visible to the naked eye. Telescopically they are seen to be clouds of faint stars, whose arrangement is characteristically random, the cluster as a whole having no obvious structural symmetry, although this generalization is not universally valid.

APPARENT DISTRIBUTION OF THE OPEN CLUSTERS

About 400 of these clusters are known. Their distribution upon the star sphere is characteristic and has given them their most usual name of galactic clusters, for they share with the fainter stars a strong galactic concentration. Their distribution in galactic longitude is more or less irregular and in general follows that of the fainter stars: the galactic clusters, in other words, while being confined almost exclusively to the region of the Milky Way, occur haphazardly along its length.

DISTANCES OF THE OPEN CLUSTERS

The problem of their distances and spatial distribution was attacked systematically by Trumpler some fifteen years ago, and his researches uncovered facts whose significance extends far beyond the realm of the open clusters. The first distances of the nearer clusters were discovered by determining the spectroscopic parallaxes of the involved stars. Trumpler's technique was to single out the twenty or thirty brightest stars in a cluster and to determine their spectroscopic type. As we shall see in Chapter VIII, stars of each spectroscopic type are closely similar to one another in a number of respects—mass, temperature, size, luminosity, and so on. Thus a fairly precise correlation is to be established between a star's spectroscopic type and, among other things, its luminosity; hence from the type of each of Trumpler's forty-odd bright stars in each cluster its intrinsic luminosity or absolute magnitude could quickly be derived. Since, in completely transparent space, apparent brightness decreases with the square of the distance, the distances of each of the selected stars could now be calculated in a few seconds. And since each star is, within the limit of the inaccuracies inherent in the method, situated at the same distance from the observer, it is only necessary to average the results, omitting any stars that give values differing widely from the mean (probably background or foreground stars unconnected with the cluster) in order to derive the cluster's distance with a probable error of about ± 10 per cent.

The farthest clusters, however, are so remote as to preclude the accurate determination of the spectroscopic types of even the brightest components, and in order to bring these particularly important clusters within his scheme Trumpler had to evolve a further distance criterion based upon observations of those clusters whose distance he had already determined. He found that the galactic clusters, although at first glance their linear dimensions varied within wide limits, were nevertheless susceptible of classification according to their structure—degree of central condensation, numbers of stars comprising the cluster, degree of symmetry, et cetera—and that members of each group of this classification were much more nearly of equal linear dimensions. Thus for the most distant clusters, to which the spectroscopic method is inapplicable, it was necessary to determine by close examination to which group of the classification they belonged, to measure their angular diameter, and then to compare this with the linear diameter already derived for the group by a study of the nearer clusters whose distances had been determined by the independent spectroscopic method.

EVIDENCE OF LIGHT ABSORPTION IN SPACE

The preliminary survey of one hundred clusters yielded distances with a probable maximum inaccuracy of 10 per cent to 20 per cent for about three quarters of them. From this survey an extremely interesting fact emerged, a fact whose significance has necessitated the reviewing of all previous work on the size of the galaxy and the distances of individual components of it. Knowledge of the distance and angular diameter of each cluster gave its linear diameter, and hence the average linear diameter of all the clusters included in the survey could be calculated. When this was done, and the clusters arranged in order of distance, the further fact came to light that the nearer clusters were systematically smaller than the average, while the most distant were systematically larger. It appeared that, on the scale of distances derived, the more distant a cluster is from the sun, the larger it must be—an altogether fantastic proposition. Obviously, some systematic error had crept into the distance estimates. After considering various possibilities, Trumpler came to the following conclusion. Interstellar space is not entirely transparent, and therefore apparent brightness decreases more rapidly than with the square of the distance; therefore all the distance determinations were too large, the error being inappreciable at small distances, but growing to measurable proportions at greater distances—in short, the greater the distance the greater the error. It was found that the degree of light absorption in space that it was required to hypothesize, in order to remove the discrepancy between distances and diameters, amounted to about 0.8 magnitudes per 3,250 light years. In other words, a cluster which is situated at this distance from the observer appears to be 0.8 magnitudes fainter than it would if space were perfectly transparent. When this correction is neglected the derived distance will be larger than the true distance and the cluster will therefore appear to be larger than in fact it is.

SPATIAL DISTRIBUTION OF THE OPEN CLUSTERS

The survey was then extended to include all of the 350-odd known open clusters; the light absorption correction was applied to the distances and the results were correct within a probable error of 10 per cent to 12 per cent. The following facts emerged. The galactic clusters form a flattened system similar in shape to the supposed shape of the galaxy itself, but exhibiting a degree of concentration upon their median plane even more marked than that of the fainter stars upon the galactic plane two thirds of all the open clusters are situated within 325 light years of the median plane of the cluster system. This plane of symmetry is nearly, though not quite, coincident with the galactic plane. The diameter of the system is something like 40,000 light years, its maximum thickness something over 3000 light years, although the outer regions are very sparsely populated. Within it, there is a strong concentration of clusters, not only upon the median plane, but also toward the center of this plane. The sun is situated at something over 1000 light years from the center of the galactic cluster system as at present defined.

The bearing of these results upon the structure and dimensions of the Milky Way itself—the star system in which the clusters are embedded, like currants in a cake—must be shelved until we have learned something of the next type of cluster, the globular cluster.

GLOBULAR CLUSTERS

The globular clusters, though having some obvious points of resemblance with the open clusters, differ from them in appearance in much the same way that the open clusters differ from the moving clusters. They resemble the more distant open clusters in their faintness and small angular diameter, but differ from all open clusters in their extremely high central condensation and in the definiteness of their shape and structure. Plate III shows a typical globular cluster and a comparison of it with Plate II will immediately reveal both the resemblances and differences between the two classes of object. All globular clusters are spherical—some are very slightly oblate—whereas the open clusters have no definite shape, or, rather, a variety of more or less asymmetrical structures. The globular clusters are strongly condensed centrally—the average distance separating two adjacent stars is smaller in the center of the cluster than in the outskirts—while a trace of central condensation is shown by only a minority of open clusters. Furthermore, the star density does not fall off steadily from the center of a globular cluster toward its periphery, but rapidly at first and then more slowly.

These clusters are faint objects, only a few of the hundred-odd that are known being visible to the naked eye: we shall see shortly that this feature is dependent upon their great distances, for they are the most remote class of object in the galaxy. An interesting characteristic is that they are all roughly the same size; their average diameter is about 100 light years, while that of the condensed central portion is normally little more than one tenth of this figure. Shapley, who is responsible for the greater part of our knowledge of the globular clusters, established this fact in the following manner. Most of the clusters contain variables in great numbers, and a very careful study of these has shown that their light curves are of the typical Cepheid variety. By their means Shapley was able to determine the distances of a number of clusters; once this was done their linear size could of course be deduced from their angular size.

APPARENT DISTRIBUTION OF THE GLOBULAR CLUSTERS

We shall return to this point in a moment, but first something must be said of the distribution of the globular clusters about the star sphere. This distribution has two outstanding features.

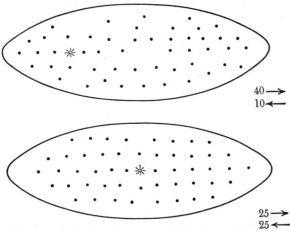

Figure 34. That more globular clusters are visible in one direction than in the opposite direction indicates an eccentric position of the sun within the system.

In the first place, the clusters are confined almost exclusively to one hemisphere of the heavens. The pole of this hemisphere, which contains over 80 clusters, lies in the Milky Way in the Sagittarius region; in the other hemisphere there are only four. The only conclusion to be drawn from this, if the clusters are scattered through space with any degree of uniformity, is that the sun is eccentrically placed both with regard to the system of the stars and to that of the globular clusters. Figure 34 shows how such a location of the sun within the system would result in the asymmetrical distribution of the clusters in the sky.

Secondly, although clusters are to be found on both sides of the Milky Way, they are wholly absent from the mid-galactic regions: their distribution in galactic latitude shows a concentration in two zones lying approximately alongside the Milky Way, outside which they occur with diminishing frequency and between which they are almost completely absent.

DISTANCES OF THE GLOBULAR CLUSTERS

Shapley's main objective was to discover the shape and size of this system of globular clusters, and the first step toward accomplishing it was the accurate determination of as many of their distances as possible. We have already encountered three methods that he had at his disposal: Cepheids; the fact that the clusters are all of about the same size, which size can be determined initially through Cepheid observations; and thirdly, the absolute magnitudes of the brightest stars in each cluster, for he found that the average absolute magnitude of the apparently brightest stars in a number of different clusters was much the same. It seems reasonable to assume that if this law held good for those clusters whose distances had already been determined, it would also apply to those clusters whose distances were yet unknown. For, the mean absolute magnitude of, say, the dozen brightest stars being known, it required only the sufficiently accurate determination of their mean apparent magnitude for their distance to be calculated.

Before we proceed to an account of the results of this investigation, it would be advisable to glance a little more closely at the various assumptions inherent in the three distance criteria employed by Shapley, for upon their validity depends the validity of the results. The foundation of his series of criteria is the Cepheid method, for the subsequent discoveries of the uniformity of the size of the clusters and of the luminosity of the brightest stars were the result of applying this method to those clusters in which Cepheids were visible. The period-luminosity relation of these stars has been confirmed time and time again, and results based on it may be considered absolutely reliable within the small margin introduced by inexact fixing of the zero point. But the variables in the globular clusters differ from true Cepheids in one important respect, and it has been suggested that this difference vitiates the results derived by applying the period-luminosity law to them. Though the shape of their light curves is that of true Cepheids their periods are in every case very much shorter—less than one day. Despite this divergence of the cluster variables from typical galactic Cepheids, Shapley considered that the striking similarities between the two justified his assumption that the period-luminosity law held for both.

His use of the cluster variables has been attacked from a somewhat

different direction by Kapteyn and van Rhijn. Cepheids are known
to be giant stars. Now these workers showed that cluster variables
have large proper motions, and from this they argued that they must
be considerably nearer the sun than Shapley supposed. Hence, since
their apparent brightness is that of a giant at Shapley's distance, they
and the clusters in which they occur must be both fainter and nearer
than Shapley supposed. Although it is now known that this is indeed
the case, the particular argument under consideration is not to the
point. Shapley retorted quite correctly that large proper motions are
characteristic of variables in general, and Lindblad appears finally to
have clinched the matter by showing that the spectra of at least some
of the cluster variables are those of giants.

The assumptions involved by the other two criteria have already
been indicated: that because some of the clusters are about the same
size they all are; and that because the mean absolute magnitudes of
the brightest stars in some of the clusters are the same this uniformity
applies to all clusters. Yet not only are these assumptions prima facie
reasonable but they also appear to be justified by the close concordance
between the results that are yielded by different methods. The odds
against this being so in a large number of cases, if one or all of the
assumptions are invalid, are so great as to be unacceptable.

One further assumption that Shapley unhesitatingly made, since at
that time there was no known reason why it should not be, was that
space is absolutely transparent and that therefore the brightness of a
source falls off in proportion with the square of its distance. The implications of this inverse square law possibly being inoperative were
not considered at the time that the distances mentioned in the next
paragraph were being derived.

The nearest cluster is ω Centauri, which is also the largest (angularly)
and the brightest; its distance from the sun was derived by Shapley as
22,000 light years. That of the furthest, N.G.C. 7006, is in the neighborhood of 200,000 light years, nearly ten times as great. It will be
recalled that the most distant galactic clusters, which are objects showing no preference for one hemisphere of the star vault, are distant about
20,000 light years from the sun, or just about the same distance as the
nearest globular clusters.

SPATIAL DISTRIBUTION OF THE GLOBULAR CLUSTERS

If we accept as the explanation of the one-sided distribution of the
globular clusters that the sun is eccentrically placed within the system

we have immediately at hand a logical explanation for the different distributions of the open and the globular clusters. The open clusters—all of which are nearer than the nearest globular clusters—are too close for any 'piling up' effect to be noticed in the direction of the galactic center, whereas in the case of the more distant globular clusters this is not the case. Figure 35 may help to clarify this distribution.

The second feature of the distribution of the globular clusters—their avoidance of a zone stretching for about 10° on either side of the galactic plane—at once reminds us of Trumpler's discovery that the light is absorbed by, presumably, diffuse dusty or gaseous material permeating the central plane of the Milky Way. His experience of the distribution of the open clusters led him to believe that this material constitutes a thin sheet, probably of varying density and light-absorbing powers, probably not more than 600 to 1000 light years thick, and extending centrally through the system of galactic clusters—that is, with a minimum diameter of something like 40,000 light years. This stratum of obscuring matter would effectively mask any globular clusters lying in its plane at still greater distances, and result in the observed bilateral distribution of these distant objects.

Evidence is not lacking that this account is in the main true. According to Trumpler, the heaviest absorption would occur within 10° of the galactic plane, the very region from which the remote globular clusters are missing. The fact that the vast majority of visible globular clusters lie outside this region explains why they are free from the color excesses that characterize the remoter galactic clusters within it.

MECHANISM OF LIGHT ABSORPTION

At this point a few words on the mechanism of light absorption must be interpolated in order to make the meaning of the last sentence plain. Material particles in the form of a rarefied cloud affect light passing through it in one of two ways, according to whether the particles are larger or smaller than a certain critical value. This threshold is about the wave-length of light:* if the diameter of the particles is larger than this value, they will scatter light of all wave-lengths to an equal extent, so that the source will appear to be dimmer than in fact it is; if, on the

*Because of the systematic description of the nature and behavior of light given in the next chapter, it will suffice to state the following facts in elucidation of the present account: (1) light behaves as though it were a system of waves; (2) the distance separating the crests of adjacent waves is different for light of different colors; (3) the wave-length of red light is longer than that of blue.

other hand, the diameters of the particles are on the whole smaller than the wave-length of light, the absorption will be selective, the degree of scattering varying inversely with λ^4 where λ is the wave-length of the incident light. Thus, blue light will be scattered more than the red— just as the sun's light is scattered by the molecules of the terrestrial atmosphere, giving us a blue sky, and a red sun at sunrise and sunset— and the light from the source will appear to be redder than it actually is. Absorption by small particles, as against absorption by large particles, changes the observed color of light from a source beyond them.

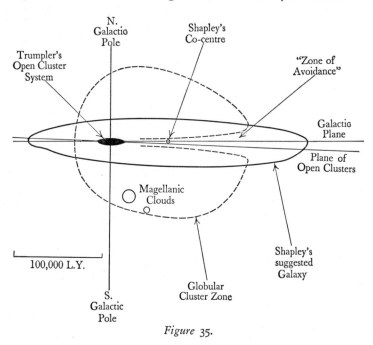

Figure 35.

Now the color of a star may be expressed in the form of the color index, or c/i. Photographic plates and the human eye are sensitive to slightly different wave-length ranges, the eye being comparatively more sensitive to red light and less sensitive to blue; hence the apparent brightness of a star as shown by a photographic plate may be greater than, less than, or the same as recorded by the eye; a red star photographs fainter, compared with a blue star, than it appears visually. The difference between the photographic and visual magnitudes of a star depends upon the color of the star—it is, in other words, an index of the star's color. If we write m_p and m_v for the photographic and visual magnitudes respectively, we have $c/i = m_p - m_v$.

Since stars of different spectroscopic types are of different colors, the c/i of each type is distinctive and has been established carefully by using near-by stars that are not materially affected by interstellar absorption. If the light of a distant star is subjected to selective absorption in transit to the terrestrial observer, its c/i will be altered, and this difference between the observed c/i of a star and the normal c/i for stars of its spectroscopic type is called its color excess. If, then, the absorption detected by Trumpler is of this type, the stars of the more remote open clusters should have noticeable color excesses, and the excess should be a direct function of the distance. This has actually been found to be the case, adding one further buttress to the edifice raised by Trumpler.

LIGHT ABSORPTION AND THE SYSTEM OF GLOBULAR CLUSTERS

It was noted on p. 121 that the majority of globular clusters are free from color excesses, although more distant than the open clusters, for the reason that light passing to the terrestrial observer from an object outside the 20°-wide band centered on the galactic equator would travel through only a negligible thickness of the absorbing medium. This interpretation is borne out by the fact that the few globular clusters that have been detected within 10° of the galactic plane do show the effects of the same absorption to which similarly situated open clusters are subjected. For these globular clusters are measurably fainter than their distance, as determined by their diameters, would warrant.

Shapley's estimates of the distances of the clusters lying far from the galactic plane are therefore not largely affected by the new light that has been thrown on the question of interstellar absorption. But whereas his globular cluster system was originally thought to be a flattened structure, drawn out to a diameter of fully 300,000 light years in the direction of the edges of the 'zone of avoidance,' it now appears that the distances to clusters in this region of the system have to be pulled in to counteract the effects of absorption upon the original distance measurements. The result is that the globular cluster system—unlike both the galactic and the open cluster systems—is more or less spherical, with a diameter of some 80,000 to 100,000 light years. Figure 35 gives some idea of this; both the scale and the outlines are necessarily uncertain at the present stage of our knowledge, but are likely to be approximately correct at least.

THE GLOBULAR CLUSTERS AND THE STELLAR SYSTEM

The point at issue at the present time is whether the known galactic clusters are coextensive with the galaxy, or whether the latter is not coextensive but concentric with the system of globular clusters. That the globular clusters and the galactic system are not coextensive in all directions seems highly probable, for whatever the extent of the galaxy in its median plane beyond the star fields of Sagittarius, it apparently is (as Herschel suggested nearly one hundred and fifty years ago) a highly flattened structure. The farther globular clusters in high galactic latitudes seem almost certainly to be extragalactic objects—satellites of the galaxy, if we like, or flies hovering above a cake whose embedded raisins are the galactic clusters.

But though the globular clusters may not be coextensive with the star system, the latter will be of very different dimensions if it is (i) exclusively coextensive with the system of known open clusters or (ii) concentric with the globular cluster system. If the latter, the center of the galaxy lies at a distance of perhaps 30,000 light years in the direction of Sagittarius and will be of the order of 100,000 light years in diameter (see Fig. 35).* If, on the other hand (i) represents the true picture, then the sun is much more centrally placed in the star system, whose diameter is at the same time reduced to something like 40,000 or 50,000 light years. These opposing schools of thought are championed, respectively, by Seares and Shapley on the one hand, and by Trumpler on the other. The pros and cons may conveniently be tabulated as follows, their statement in such a forthright form being justified by the fact that at present one man's guess is as good as his neighbor's.

THE STELLAR AND GLOBULAR CLUSTER SYSTEMS ARE CONCENTRIC

i. That the position of the sun within the galaxy is eccentric is suggested by

(*a*) the comparative richness of the Milky Way in the direction of Sagittarius, as against the direction 180° away in galactic longitude,

(*b*) the unilateral distribution of the globular clusters, also centered upon the Sagittarius region,

(*c*) the preference shown by the most distant types of galactic object, such as novae, for the galactic hemisphere centered on Sagittarius.

*Before correction for absorption, Shapley's figures were 300,000 and 100,000 light years for the diameter and the eccentricity of the sun respectively.

ii. Since the globular clusters are disposed with approximate symmetry about the galactic plane, it is assumed by Shapley that the two centers are coincident.

iii. This center, in the case of the globular clusters, lies in the same direction as that suggested by the foregoing considerations for the galactic center, at a distance of very roughly 30,000 to 50,000 light years.

THE STELLAR AND OPEN CLUSTER SYSTEMS ARE COEXTENSIVE

i. More significant than the roughly symmetrical distribution of globular clusters on either side of the galactic equator, is the entirely unstellar distribution of these objects. Whereas the stars are concentrated into a flattened, pancake-like system, the clusters occupy a more or less spherical volume of space.

ii. The distribution of the galactic clusters, on the other hand, is pre-eminently stellar in character. The concentration of the open clusters upon the galactic plane (or one very close to it) is, in fact, even more marked than that of the fainter stars.

iii. The closeness of the correspondence between the two systems is indicated by the closeness of the correspondence of their respective median planes.

iv. Mere inspection shows how intimate is the association of the galactic clusters and the star clouds of the Milky Way.

v. Other stellar systems are known, and are shortly to come under discussion. Shapley's estimate of the size of our own stellar system makes it about five times as large as these similar star systems. One of the nearest of these 'island universes' is about 40,000 light years in diameter, an approximate figure which agrees well with Trumpler's figure for the diameter of the open cluster/galactic system. That this nebula (M. 31) is known to be exceptionally large, accentuates the discrepancy in Shapley's figures, although, as we shall learn later, not too much reliance must be placed on this analogy.

THE REALM OF THE EXTRAGALACTIC NEBULAE

The objects referred to in the last paragraph are the extragalactic nebulae, or so-called 'island universes.' They are exceedingly numerous, the positions of some 20,000 having been specifically determined, this perhaps representing one tenth of the number whose images are recorded on existing plates. Hubble, the foremost authority in this branch of astronomy, has estimated that were the galaxy perfectly transparent, something like 100,000,000 extragalactic nebulae would be within long-exposure photographic range of the Mt. Wilson 100-inch reflector—within, that is to say, a distance of about 5×10^8 light years. The recently completed 200-inch reflector should, theoretically, double this distance. Thus the observable region of space is a sphere centered upon the earth whose present diameter is of the order of 10^9 light years (cf. the distance to the remotest galactic objects—probably of the order of magnitude of 10^5 light years).

These myriad, faint, enigmatic objects have been the subject of energetic speculation for the better part of two centuries, and the idea that they may be stellar systems similar in general outline to our own—i.e. true 'extragalactic' objects—is far from new. In the time of Kant (mid-eighteenth century) the conception of 'island universes' was already considerably developed and bandied about as a philosophical speculation. The conception remained in this category of human ideas until little more than twenty years ago, when the distances of some of the nearer nebulae were at last determined, and the theory of external systems elevated from the plane of speculative fancy to that of ascertained fact.

APPARENT DISTRIBUTION OF THE EXTRAGALACTIC NEBULAE

Before we can describe in any detail the methods whereby this most important advance was achieved, however, something must first be said of the distribution of the extragalactic nebulae. Their disposition upon the star sphere is even at first glance peculiar and unlike that of any class of object that we have yet studied.

Briefly, the spiral and elliptical nebulae (see Plates xvii, xviii, xix, and xx) are oriented upon the Milky Way, a fact that was for many years held to indicate that they were dependent to some extent at any rate upon the galaxy, and therefore probably not extragalactic; from the Milky Way itself they are completely absent; they are of rare occurrence for some distance on either side of it; and it is only in the regions nearer the galactic poles than the equator that they are encountered in large numbers. Thus they reverse the usual procedure as exemplified by the galactic clusters, faint novae, and distant variables, and star clouds, all of which congregate about the galactic plane and are conspicuously absent from the regions of the galactic poles. Before the first extragalactic distances were incontrovertibly established this aspect of their distribution was the usual rejoinder of adherents of the 'extragalactic school' to the intragalactic argument just mentioned. Although the extragalactic objects of all types share with the globular clusters an avoidance of the galactic plane, they differ from them in occurring with equal frequency in all galactic longitudes. Thus in the matter of distance, the globular clusters might be expected to represent a sort of halfway house between galactic objects on the one hand and the extragalactic objects on the other.

Methodical and painstaking surveys have filled in the details of this rough outline. Three distinct zones may be distinguished. The first is an irregular strip, from 10° to 40° wide, circumscribing the star sphere; the median line of this strip is the galactic equator. This zone is one of complete avoidance. The second zone, or rather pair of zones, consists of a fringe along either side of zone 1, and is one of partial avoidance. The last pair of zones consists of the rest of the star sphere: two polar caps extending from the galactic poles down to the edges of zone 2. It is in this third zone that the spirals and elliptical nebulae are found in their myriads, but even here their distribution is not precisely uniform: area for area, progressively larger numbers of nebulae are encountered the farther one moves the direction of observation from the lower galactic latitudes toward the poles. The precise nature of this numerical increase is peculiar and its significance will be discussed shortly.

EFFECT OF INTERSTELLAR ABSORPTION ON APPARENT DISTRIBU- TION OF THE NEBULAE

We have determined the apparent distribution of the extragalactic nebulae but it now remains for us to account for its pecularities in terms of three-dimensional or space distribution. The clue to this translation has already been placed in our hands by Trumpler. Not only is the piling up of star clouds and diffuse nebulosity in the plane of the galaxy apparent from any photograph of the region, but the spectroscope and the investigation into the linear diameters of the open clusters both indicate the existence of an absorbing layer, probably somewhat thin, extending throughout the galactic plane. It is this galactic absorption, then, that is responsible for the first zone in the apparent distribution of the extragalactic nebulae: the zone of total avoidance is rather one of 'total obscuration,' the galaxy itself hiding from our eyes those extragalactic objects that lie beyond it in the extension of its median plane.

The second zone, the fringe along either side of the 'zone of avoidance,' derives from the gradual thinning of the absorbing layer along its limits. But what of the third zone, that extending from the second toward the poles? Since obscuration, rather than a graded spatial distribution, is the cause of the apparent anomalies of distribution within the first and second zones, it is natural to look for a similar cause here. And that this is correct is shown by the fact that the number of nebulae visible in successive galactic latitudes from the edge of zone 2 up to the poles themselves increases in the same manner that the visibility of faint stars increases as they move from the horizon toward the zenith in their diurnal revolution of the star sphere. In other words, the particular increase in numbers visible in increasingly higher latitudes is of such a nature as indicates a progressively smaller degree of absorption by some gaseous or dusty medium, the relative degree of absorption in different latitudes being proportional to the respective lengths of the light paths through the absorbing medium. Not only, therefore, is there a heterogeneous and relatively dense layer of absorbing matter in the galactic plane, but also a tenuous absorbing cloud probably coextensive with the whole star system.

Hubble has estimated that the optical thickness of the galactic absorbing layer is about half a magnitude, and when allowance is made for this absorption, the apparent dependence of extragalactic distribution upon galactic latitude vanishes. The large-scale distribution of the nebulae is seen to be uniform in different galactic latitudes, and at the same time no appreciable systematic variation of numbers with galactic longitude is to be detected. Furthermore, the distribution of the nebulae throughout the two polar caps is, within the limit of error, identical, indicating that the sun is approximately centrally placed relative to the minor axis of the absorbing layer, and that this layer is indeed coincident with the galactic plane.

LARGE-SCALE SPATIAL DISTRIBUTION OF THE NEBULAE

This important result—that, when the effects of galactic absorption are allowed for, the large-scale distribution of extragalactic objects is the same in all directions—was reached by means of surveys of nebula-numbers down to a limiting magnitude of 20 in over 1000 sample areas distributed over the whole star sphere. But in addition to a 'surface' survey of this sort, it is possible to carry out surveys in depth. Granted the assumption, certainly justified, that *in general* a faint nebula is more distant than a bright one, it is possible to plot their numbers in successive concentric spheres all centered upon the earth and each associated with a particular limiting magnitude; simply to count the numbers of nebulae brighter than each limiting magnitude is to provide us with invaluable information regarding their distribution in depth.

When this is done, the same spatial homogeneity is encountered. The whole of the present observable region, perhaps 10^{27} cubic light years, appears to be uniformly and impartially populated with nebulae. Nor is there any indication that the present limit of observation is anywhere near the limit of the system of extragalactic objects, for with their numerical increase in magnitude their numbers increase steadily and (when corrections for the red-shift are made)* exhibit no appreciable falling off as the limits of the observable region are approached. This is in striking contrast with the stars; we know that, in the direction of the galactic poles, our present instruments can probe almost, if not quite, to the confines of the galaxy, for fewer of the faintest stars are visible than would be expected were there no thinning out of stars in these distant regions. Since the extragalactic nebulae show no such thinning out, it follows that with numerically increasing magnitude the nebulae catch up with the stars in number. From magnitude 1 down to magnitude 21 there are at the galactic poles more stars than nebulae, area for area, though the numerical superiority of the former decreases with each successive magnitude. At magnitude 21.5, however, stars and nebulae are equally numerous. This happens to be the limiting magnitude of the Mt. Wilson 100-inch reflector. Observations are now being made with the new 200-inch, which may show that at magnitudes lower than 21.5 the extragalactic nebulae are actually more numerous than the stars.

Whereas present equipment can reach to the limits of the galactic system in the direction of the poles, the system of extragalactic nebulae stretches out beyond our reach; there is no observational indication that they do not 'go on forever.' It is worth noting that this clear distinction between the extragalactic nebulae and the stars in the matter of their distribution in depth is a conclusive demonstration of their true extragalactic status and remains so independently of any linear distance determinations.

SMALL-SCALE SPATIAL DISTRIBUTION OF THE NEBULAE

Although the large-scale spatial distribution of the extragalactic nebulae is uniform in all directions and at all depths throughout the observable region—the average separation one from another being 2×10^6 light years—their small-scale distribution is highly irregular. Apart from

*Red-shifts, a spectroscopic phenomenon which will be discussed later, tend to make the more distant nebulae appear fainter than they really are; hence they appear to be more distant than they are, which in turn produces a spurious effect of thinning out.

single nebula and small groups consisting of several members, there is also a number of giant clusters each containing some 500 nebulae.

Of the former the 'local group,' consisting of 13 known members all within about 10^6 light years of the galaxy, may be taken as tolerably representative. The largest member of this sub-family of 'extragalactic' systems is the galaxy itself. The Magellanic clouds (see Plate VI), on account of their nearness, small size, and unusual structure, may probably be regarded as extragalactic 'satellites' of the galaxy rather than extragalactic nebulae in the accepted sense of the term. Their distances from the sun are about 85,000 and 95,000 light years respectively; and their diameters 12,000 and 6000 light years. The giant M.31 of Andromeda (the central portion of which is shown in Plate VII) is to northern terrestrial eyes the most striking member of the group. It is distant some 760,000 light years. M.33, a late spiral, is the most distant of the 'local group.' It was to this group of nebulae that the initial Cepheid observations were confined.

The giant clusters are of infrequent occurrence, only about twenty having been definitely established so far. The largest and nearest is situated in the constellation Virgo at a mean distance of some 7×10^6 light years; that of the most remote yet studied is about 2.4×10^8 light years. The proof by distance determinations that these are true spatial clusterings is reflected in the fact that the members of any one cluster are mostly of the same type: in one, for instance, spirals predominate, in another the globular and early elliptical types. But the diversity of types within any given cluster is considerable enough for the interesting fact to be established that there is a continuous increase in size from the early globular nebulae to the late-type spirals. It is not even required to know the linear distance of a cluster of nebulae in order to establish this fact, for all its constituent nebulae are at substantially the same distance from the observer and consequently linear diameters are directly proportional to apparent diameters.

DISTANCES OF THE EXTRAGALACTIC NEBULAE

The ground is now cleared for a discussion of the linear distances of the extragalactic nebulae. The problem has been attacked and solved from a number of angles; their extragalactic nature is now established beyond possibility of reversal—less by any single and conclusive proof than by the uniform consistency of results derived by independent methods.

It was not until the early 'twenties of the present century that individual stars were finally and incontrovertibly detected in an extragalactic nebula; but before that time—indeed, as long ago as 1889—there had been indications of the stellar nature of certain regions in the larger spirals. Photography had effected partial resolutions, but whether the quasi-stellar points whose images were imprinted upon the plates were stars or unresolved clusters, or possibly some form of stellar progenitor, was not certain. Again, novae had been found in some nebulae, but the evidence of these was to a certain extent contradictory and the significance of the observations difficult to evaluate, owing primarily to incomplete knowledge of these objects. The status of the 'extragalactic' nebulae was, in fact, a matter for speculation, but, on the incomplete data then available, for speculation only.

EVIDENCE OF INDIVIDUAL STARS

In 1923, however, the whole complexion of the controversy was changed. The Mt. Wilson 100-inch reflector not only carried resolution of M.31 further than had been achieved previously but for the first time established that the doubtful stellar points were indeed stars: for some of them exhibited Cepheid variation. As so often happens in the progress of science, the breaching of a long unassailable barrier was quickly followed up by a spurt of new developments in the same direction, and by the end of the decade forty Cepheids and well over eighty novae had been discovered in the Andromeda nebula, while Cepheids had also been detected in other spirals. The maximum magnitude of the first Cepheid in M.31 was only 18.2; yet its period of about one month indicated an absolute magnitude of -4, or 7000 times that of the sun. For a star of this luminosity to be reduced to an apparent magnitude of 18.2 it must be removed to a distance of some 900,000 light years from the observer. Subsequent investigations involving the absorption of light in space have reduced this distance to approximately 760,000 light years. At such a distance it would be well beyond the farthest frontier of the galactic system. On the evidence of a single star, abundantly confirmed later, the Andromeda spiral was thus shown to be truly extragalactic: a hypothetical observer on an imaginary planet revolving about a star in the nebula M.31 would call our stellar system an extragalactic nebula—probably of late spiral type.

Parallel investigations confirmed this general order of distance. The brightest stars visible in the nebulae to which these early examinations were confined would, at such distances, have absolute magnitudes comparable with those of the most intrinsically luminous stars in our galaxy. Having established the distance of some of the nearer nebulae—all of the general order of one million light years—it became possible to transcend this scale and by successive extrapolations extend the sphere in which distance determinations were possible beyond that in which Cepheids were visible. Cepheids are not the brightest stellar objects that may be distinguished in the spirals, just as they are not the most intrinsically brilliant galactic objects: they are surpassed by novae, by the abnormally bright novae known as supernovae, by certain irregular variables, and by the stars known as blue giants (of which we shall learn more in Chapter VIII).

With increasing faintness of the nebulae it is found that these objects fade into invisibility in the order of their normal luminosity as exemplified by galactic counterparts which have been exhaustively studied. Not only does this fact demonstrate that apparent brightness of the nebula as a whole can be employed as a general criterion of its distance—a criterion that, once established, remains valid after the final traces of resolution have become impossible—but, in addition, each class of object can have assigned to it an absolute magnitude from which it is known (as a result of close-range investigations within the galaxy) not to deviate widely. Even, therefore, in the case of those nebulae which are too distant for Cepheids to be detected, these further classes of star allow the distance to be determined, though admittedly with a wider margin of probable error.

APPARENT BRIGHTNESS AS A DISTANCE CRITERION

Yet even when we have passed the limit at which the last blue giants and supernovae have faded from sight, and have reached the borders of the vast realm of nebulae which show no trace of stellar resolution whatever, we are still in the close neighborhood of the galaxy—close, at any rate, by comparison with the whole observable region. Does this mean that the distances of only our nearest extragalactic neighbors can be plumbed? Emphatically not, for our knowledge of the latter distances has already provided us with the key to the next leap outward. Though stellar resolution is possible in only about 125 nebulae —just reaching to the nearest of the great clusters, that in Virgo at a distance of about 6.7×10^6 light years, or $1/80$ of the radius of the observable region—this nevertheless represents a fair enough sample upon which to base the next extrapolation. Examination of those nebulae whose distances had been determined by observations of involved stars showed that though the linear size of a nebula is dependent upon its type and position in the sequence, yet its luminosity remains tolerably constant at all stages from globular to late spiral. Thus a new method of calibration is established—a correlation between distance and the nebula's total apparent brightness. The permitted range of luminosity among the extragalactic nebulae was quickly discovered to be small: the luminosities of half the near nebulae whose distances had been established by observations of involved stars lay between one half and twice the mean value of 8.5×10^7 times that of the sun. With this new weapon, the distance of any visible nebula may be estimated with a probable error not in excess of 20 per cent to 30 per cent—an incredible achievement, as will readily be acknowledged when it is reflected that the frontier of the visible universe is something like 1000 million light years distant.

THE RED-SHIFTS AS A DISTANCE CRITERION

It has already been remarked that inner consistency is the main justification for confidence in the scale of distances revealed by the extragalactic nebulae. The correctness of the extrapolation from the Cepheid and other stellar determinations of the nearer nebulae to the brightness determinations of all nebulae within the observable region is strikingly confirmed by the so-called 'distance-velocity' relation, or, more prudently, the red-shifts. This phenomenon—the happy hunting ground of popular-science writers in the press, and the subject of much loose and illegitimate speculation by the scientifically minded man in the street—remains one of the foremost enigmas of the fundamental pattern of the universe as at present discerned.

The reader is already familiar with the fact that radial velocities— i.e. velocities in the observer's line of sight—are revealed and measured by the spectroscope. When the source is approaching the observer, the wave-length of the radiation is shortened, and the whole spectrum shifted toward the blue end; when receding from the observer, the wave-length is lengthened, and the shift is consequently toward the red.* In the former case, the radial motion of the source is said to be negative, and in the latter positive.

The measurement of the radial velocity of an extragalactic nebula was first accomplished by Slipher in 1912; the nebula was the great Andromeda spiral, and the radial velocity derived was —190 m.p.s., i.e. a velocity of approach. This was followed by results for other of

*The mechanism of velocity shifts will be more circumstantially described in the next chapter.

the nearer nebulae, and by the time that the first distances of the spirals were being determined, some forty radial velocities had been measured. A few of these, which had been derived for the brighter and therefore presumably the nearer spirals, had been negative, but as the determinations accumulated, positive radial velocities quickly predominated. Some of these were of a high order of magnitude, strikingly contrasted with the velocities of various galactic objects with which astronomers had, at the time, been solely familiar: another clear indication of the galactic independence of the spirals. The limiting velocities of the group of 45 known in 1925 were —190 and +1,125 m.p.s., the mean being +375 m.p.s. At this time, too little reliable knowledge of the distance criteria had come to light for any correlation of distance with radial velocity to be attempted, but by the end of the decade the startling discovery had been made that the size of the red-shift of the spectrum of any nebula was dependent upon that nebula's distance: the more distant the nebula, the greater the shift.

All measurements made thus far indicate that the relation between distance and the red-shift is direct and linear. As the distance increases by millions of light years, the velocity of recession apparently increases by hundreds of miles per second. More precisely, every increase of 10^6 light years in distance adds 107 m.p.s. to the positive radial velocity. We may express this relation in the analytic form $v=107\ d$ where v is the velocity in m.p.s., as indicated by the red-shift, and d is the nebula's distance in 10^6 light years. At once we are furnished with an additional distance criterion which provides an independent check on those already derived. The distances as derived from the red-shifts, combined with the apparent magnitudes of the nebulae, led to their intrinsic luminosities by a simple calculation, brightness decreasing with the square of the distance. Intrinsic luminosities of a number of nebulae had also been calculated on the basis of distance determinations by means of involved stars. And it was found that there was a good correspondence between the two sets of results. The validity of both lines of approach to the problem of extragalactic distances was thereby strengthened, for it would be quite beyond the bounds of probability that an identical numerical error was involved in each.

Humason, using the 100-inch telescope and the most sensitive photographic materials, has carried the distance and radial velocity determinations out to about 2.4×10^8 light years and finds the radial velocity of recession to be about 26,000 m.p.s., or one-seventh the velocity of light! If we assume that this linear relationship holds to the present limit of observation we should expect to find these objects receding with velocities of the order of 50,000 m.p.s., while it is at a distance only three times as far as we can explore with the 100-inch that the velocity of recession reaches the velocity of light. This is a problem of tremendous importance to all present-day philosophy of the physical sciences. While the 200-inch will not reach out to the distance where a velocity of recession is equal to the velocity of light, nevertheless one of the early problems with this new instrument will be to determine whether the relation between distance and the red-shift remains linear to the limit of observational distance.

RECAPITULATION

In brief outline, the foregoing account represents the extent of our present knowledge relating to the dimensions of the extragalactic universe, and of our galaxy as a member of that universe. From naked-eye observations of the diurnal and annual behavior of the star vault we have, by a series of overlapping bounds, reached a limit—1000 million light years distant—at which our knowledge is finally arrested.

The initial step of this journey was to establish the true figure of the earth. This necessary preliminary was followed by the disentanglement of terrestrial from extraterrestrial motions, and the discovery that the veil of delusive appearance that distorts our vision of reality is largely the creation of the earth's own motions—its axial rotation and circumsolar revolution, neither of which is directly apprehended as such by the senses.

Man's progress in cosmological understanding was then traced from Ptolemy, to Copernicus and Kepler, and on to Newton; it was shown that Kepler's laws of planetary motion were corollaries of the single law of universal gravitation.

The true spatial arrangement of the various members of the solar system was thus established, but it was still a map without a scale. The first object to be surveyed in was the moon, by means of trigonometrical parallax from widely separated stations on the earth's surface. To determine the sun's much greater distance, however, required new principles of distance determination. Of these, the most important is the prior determination by trigonometrical parallax of the distance of a near planet such as Eros, whence the solar distances of all the other planets (including the fundamental earth-sun distance) can be derived by the harmonic law.

The leap from the solar to the stellar system involved yet another search for new and more powerful distance criteria, interstellar distances being incomparably greater than those between planets. The successive extrapolations, by means of which further and further reaches of the stellar universe are brought within the astronomer's grasp, were then described; this led to a discussion of the stellar system as a whole, and of its structure and size as revealed, in particular, by studies of the clusters.

Again a gigantic leap had to be taken—from the realm of the stars to that of the extragalactic nebulae. And once again, the discussion was restricted to the problem of their spatial distribution, including their distances.

But of the nature of these various bodies—planets, stars and nebulae—next to nothing has been said. The picture that has been drawn is no more than a geometrical diagram. It is now necessary, therefore, to retrace our steps and to reconsider the heavenly bodies, not merely as stepping stones across the observable region, but as things in themselves.

PART II

QUALITY—THE NATURE OF THINGS

VI. Entry of the **Spectroscope**

The man in the street will believe the evidence of his eyes—little realizing what a fallible criterion of the truth this may be—provided that such evidence is, so to speak, direct and not in need of interpretation. Thus he does not regard the astronomer as trangressing the bounds of reason when he states that the existence of mountains on the moon is proved by the fact of their being visible with a telescope. A photograph of the moon, taken with the aid of a telescope, requires no more interpretation than does 'common-sense' everyday experience: there are the mountains, plain and clear for anyone to see.

But presented with a spectrogram of the sun—a photograph taken with a spectroscope in addition to a telescope—and told that it constitutes conclusive proof (i) that the sun is rotating on its axis in a period of some four weeks; (ii) that its surface temperature is in the neighborhood of 6000° C.; (iii) that it is in early life; (iv) that it is possessed of an atmosphere whose temperature is lower than that of the radiant surface; and (v) that this atmosphere contains calcium, iron, hydrogen, and nearly sixty other elements, all of which are also found on the earth—told all this, and our 'common-sense' man may well be skeptical. For the spectrogram seems to be—and, without proper interpretation, is—totally unconnected with any of these facts; this will be appreciated from Plate viiia. A considerable degree of interpretation of the spectrogram is necessary before this information emerges: the fact of the sun's surface temperature does not stand out from the spectrogram in the same obvious way that the fact of the moon's mountainous surface stands out from a photograph of the moon.

It is the ultimate purpose of this chapter to show that such interpretation of spectroscopic data is valid: that, for example, the existence of solar calcium is as indisputably proved by the spectroscope as is the existence of lunar mountains by the telescope.

THE ROLE OF LIGHT

The connecting link between any celestial body and the astronomer's instruments is light. A body is visible when light is reflected from it to the observer's eye, as in the case of the moon and planets, or radiated from it as in the case of the sun. In the latter case we know, incidentally, that the source of the light must be hot, since a body has to reach a tolerably high temperature before it incandesces; we know this of the stars also, although their great distances render their heat imperceptible without the intervention of delicate instruments.

It must be our first concern to discover what we can about this radiation, by whose agency all our knowledge of the heavenly bodies has been derived—to learn why some bodies radiate light while others do not, what form the radiation takes, the manner in which different forms of radiation are related to one another, and, most important of all, what changes are actually occurring within a substance while it is radiating—in other words, the physical operations underlying the process.

In order to tackle this last point, the crux of a vast amount of the physical research of the past few decades, we have to readjust our mental focus from the gigantic cosmic distances of the last chapter to those most minute, ultimate particles of which the material universe is constructed. Whereas we have up to now been dealing with distances measurable in thousands or millions of light years, we have to turn to the realm of the ultramicroscopic, in which one hundred thousandth of a centimeter is a handy unit of measurement.

THE ACTION OF THE PRISM

A few simple experiments will serve to make clear some of the fundamental characteristics of the behavior of light. The scene of the first of these is a darkened room; a small crack in the shutters admits a narrow beam of sunlight. If this beam is intercepted by a white screen it will be observed that there is a thin line of colorless light upon the screen's surface. Now interpose a glass prism between the screen and the shutter (Fig. 36), in such a position that the beam falls obliquely upon one of its faces. The appearance of the line of light upon the screen is immediately changed. The narrow streak of white light is drawn out laterally to form an elongated band of color. It is of the same height as the original streak but many times wider; from one end to the other of this band there is a steady gradation of color from red, through orange, yellow, green, and blue to violet.

Since the prism is only acting upon the light that is already there—upon the beam of white light—and is not adding colors of its own, it follows that the lights of different color now separated upon the screen were originally constituents of the white beam. The prism's action on this beam is merely to disentangle the various components which, when blended, constitute white light. The inference is that white light is polychromatic, i.e. that it is composed of many different colors.

It will be seen from Fig. 36 that the prism bends or refracts the incident polychromatic beam, and, furthermore, that it refracts the violet constituents through a larger angle than the red. It is this property of refracting lights of different colors in varying degrees that enables the prism to form the colored band known as the spectrum.

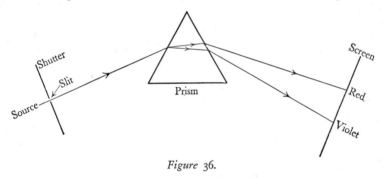

Figure 36.

CORPUSCULAR AND WAVE THEORIES OF LIGHT

The experiment with the prism and narrow slit was performed by Newton in 1665 and he then began a truly scientific study of reflection, refraction, and dispersion of light. Newton was able to explain all of the phenomena that he observed on the basis of a hypothesis that light is composed of minute particles of matter, known as corpuscles, which travel through space with a finite velocity and produce the sensation of light when they impinge on the retina of the eye. This corpuscular hypothesis was by no means original with Newton, for it had been discussed, in various forms, by many of the ancient natural philosophers. However Newton was the first to subject the hypothesis to truly scientific experimentation and analysis. The weight of Newton's opinion was so great that the corpuscular hypothesis was accepted for many years following the announcement of his results. Before the end of the seventeenth century Christian Huygens, a Dutch physicist, advanced a theory of light which held that the energy is transported across 'empty space' in the forms of transverse waves (i.e. waves whose direction of vibration is perpendicular to the direction of velocity of the light). In 1801 Thomas Young, an English physicist, experimented with various phenomena involving the so-called interference of light and showed that these effects could be explained only on the basis of a wave theory of light. The defenders of the corpuscular hypothesis refused to accept Young's explanation of interference and it was not until about fourteen years later that Fresnel was able to prove by additional experiments that, if the corpuscles did exist, they must be vibrating back and forth perpendicular to the direction of propagation of the light in such a manner that they made up waves. About the middle of the nineteenth century Clerk Maxwell attacked the problem from the point of view of theory and advanced the so-called electromagnetic theory of light, which postulates that light is made up of waves traveling through space in a medium known as the luminiferous ether. Maxwell's hypothesis received strong support from the later experiments of Hertz, a German physicist, who was able to produce by electrical methods electromagnetic waves, which had many of the properties of light but did not produce the sensation of light on the human eye. These so-called Hertzian waves have since become known as radio waves. During the first quarter of the twentieth century one series of experiments cast serious doubts about the existence of the luminiferous ether which is necessary to carry the electromagnetic waves of Maxwell and Hertz. Another series of experiments on the so-called photoelectric effect could not be explained on the basis of any simple wave theory, but required that the energy of light must be moving through space in finite particles, or corpuscles. The problem in regard to the validity of either the corpuscular or the wave theory of light is not completely settled at the present time, but we can say with some confidence that the ultimate solution will require both wave motion and also finite particles of matter or energy. In the discussion that follows we shall employ the general terminology and symbolism of the wave theory, but we do this merely as a matter of convenience.

WAVE-LENGTH AND FREQUENCY

Suppose that at the center of a pond there is a source of disturbance which breaks the surface of the water at regular intervals: it might be a succession of pebbles dropped into the water at one-second intervals. Let us assume that each time a pebble hits the surface a single wave travels out from the source toward the banks. A cork floating on the pond somewhere between the bank and the center of the wave system will bob up once a second. Now, the point where the pebbles strike the surface may be considered analogous to a source of radiation—the sun, for example, or the filament of a lamp—in which energy sets the light waves in motion. These travel out through three-dimensional space just as the waves of the pond spread out across its two-dimensional surface. Finally, we may consider the energy that causes the cork to move on the surface of the pond analogous with the energy of the light waves that produces the sensation of light in the retina of the eye.

If the fall of the pebbles is manipulated in such a way that the surface of the pond is disturbed at regular intervals, it will be found that the distance separating adjacent wave crests or wave troughs is the same in all directions. This distance is known as the wave-length of the particular wave system and it will depend upon the interval of time between disturbances of the surface and the speed with which the waves move over the surface. If, instead of at one-second intervals, the pebbles are dropped at intervals of half a second, it will be noticed (i) that the wave-length has been halved and (ii) that the cork will now make two oscillations per second. Twice the number of waves now occupy a given distance and therefore twice as many pass a given point in a given length of time provided the speed of the waves has remained constant. In other words the greater the wave-length the smaller the frequency, and vice versa. This relationship may be expressed in analytic form by

$$f = \frac{c}{\lambda}$$

in which f is the frequency in vibration cycles per second, λ is the wave-length, and c is the speed of the wave. In the case of light waves we have seen that $c = 3 \times 10^{10}$ cm. per sec., and it may be proved by a variety of experimental methods that this is the same for all electromagnetic waves traveling through 'empty space.'

THE ELECTROMAGNETIC SPECTRUM

By a variety of instrumental methods the wave-lengths of different radiations may be measured with great accuracy. It is found that the only difference between red light and violet light is one of wave-length (and with it, of course, frequency). Red light is found to have a longer wave-length than violet, but they are both examples of electromagnetic radiation. The wave-lengths are very short in comparison with the distances used in describing the structure of the universe, being about 8×10^{-5} cm. for red and 4×10^{-5} cm. for violet. These correspond to frequencies of about 3.75×10^{14} vibrations per second for the red and 7.5×10^{14} for the violet.

These values represent the extreme limits within which electromagnetic radiation can be detected by the human eye. But there are electromagnetic radiations whose wave-lengths lie beyond these limits of visible radiation and which are detectable by instruments other than the eye. If the wave-length is slightly shorter than 4×10^{-5} cm., the radiation is invisible to the eye but leaves its imprint on the photographic plate; such radiation is known as ultra-violet. If it is slightly longer than 8×10^{-5} cm. the radiation is known as infra-red, or radiant heat, and can be detected as heat by the human skin or measured quantitatively by various types of radiometers. If the wave-length is still longer it is capable of detection by electronic circuits and this radiation, with wave-lengths from about 1 cm. to about 2.5×10^6 cm., is utilized in radio transmission. At the other end of the scale that radiation with wave-lengths shorter than the ultra-violet is known as X-rays, gamma rays, cosmic rays, and other types.

This vast range of radiation, known as the complete electromagnetic spectrum, is of the same general nature throughout, although the human organism uses different senses to perceive different sections of it or even has to fall back upon special and complicated instruments for its detection. These different sections are differentiated from one another solely by difference in wave-length and by the effects which they produce.

Returning now to the action of the prism upon the visible white light —that section of the electromagnetic spectrum with wave-lengths between 4×10^{-5} cm. and 8×10^{-5} cm.—we are now in a position to say that this action consists in refracting the various radiations through angles that depend upon their wave-lengths. Thus to any point in the visible spectrum, or the invisible for that matter, a definite wave-length can be assigned. For convenience in discussing wave-lengths, particularly in the visible region or in the near ultra-violet or infra-red, a unit of wave-length known as the Angstrom unit is employed by scientists. The Angstrom unit is equal in length to 1×10^{-10} meters and on this system of units the visible spectrum is from about 4000 Angstroms to 8000 Angstroms.

DISCOVERY OF THE FRAUNHOFER LINES

In 1801 Wollaston repeated Newton's experiment with sunlight passing through a prism, but he used a much narrower slit than that used by

Newton. Wollaston noticed that the band of color was not absolutely continuous, but that it was crossed by some dark lines. He failed completely to recognize the importance of his observation and merely assumed that the five strongest lines marked the boundaries of the simple colors.

About fifteen years later Fraunhofer developed an instrument for observing the solar spectrum that employed lenses as well as the slit and the prism. He found the dark lines and published a careful map of the solar spectrum showing the positions of several hundred of the lines. He lettered the more prominent lines, and his original designations are still used. Subsequently many more lines were found by other observers but they are all referred to as Fraunhofer lines in recognition of the pioneer observer. In 1883 Rowland began an accurate and systematic study of the solar spectrum, using photographic methods, and he listed, with accurate wave-lengths, about 20,000 Fraunhofer lines in the region from 2975 to 7330 Angstroms. The improvement of photographic emulsions for work in the infra-red has permitted photographs of the solar spectrum to be obtained out to 13,500 Angstroms and about 5000 lines have been added to Rowland's list.

KIRCHHOFF'S EXPERIMENTS

We may next turn to the brilliant work of Kirchhoff, which was brought to its culmination in 1859. At that time there was no acceptable theory regarding the method of radiation of spectra, but this in no way detracted from the practical value of his results: fortunately one does not have to know the technical details of the locksmith's art in order to be able to use a key for unlocking a door. Nevertheless, the significance of Kirchhoff's observations has only been appreciated in comparatively recent years.

The apparatus used in these experiments is almost the same as that required for Newton's demonstration of the polychromatic nature of white light. On a bench in a completely darkened room is placed a prism; to the right of it stands the screen on which the spectrum is to be cast (actually, a small telescope for direct viewing of the spectrum); to the left of the prism stands another screen, in which is cut a fine slit. The relative positions of the prism and the two screens are adjusted so that the spectrum of a light source placed behind the slit is cast upon the right-hand screen. If a lump of iron is placed behind the slit and heated to incandescence, a continuous spectrum is formed: it consists of a band of color, red at one end, violet at the other, with orange, yellow, green, and blue between. Clearly, the source is emitting radiation of all wave-lengths within the visible range. No matter what solid is used as source—it may be copper, lime, tin, zinc, or what you will—the same continuous spectrum is produced. Furthermore, liquids give identical continuous spectra, as also do gases when subjected to sufficiently great pressures; thus mercury vapor has been made to yield a continuous spectrum when subjected to a pressure of some 20,000 pounds per square inch in the laboratory.

Kirchhoff therefore formulated his first law, which states that *any incandescent solid, liquid, or dense gas emits radiation of all visible wave-lengths;* in other words, their spectra are continuous and mutually indistinguishable, no matter what the chemical constitution of the source may be.

A volatilized solid is now placed behind the slit. If, for example, the spectrum of sodium is to be studied, a colorless Bunsen flame is placed behind the screen and a few grains of common salt (which contains sodium) are blown into it; alternatively a piece of sodium may be held in the flame on the end of a platinum wire. In either case the flame is colored a livid yellow, and a spectrum quite unlike that in the last experiment is produced. Instead of a continuous polychromatic background there is now nothing but a pair of fine, closely adjacent, bright yellow lines on a dark background; nothing else is visible. This clearly indicates that no visible radiation of wave-lengths other than these two is being emitted; the lines are yellow because they lie in the yellow region of the (invisible) continuous spectrum, i.e. they have the wave-lengths of yellow light. This can easily be demonstrated by marking their positions on the screen, and then, taking care not to alter the relative positions of the prism and the two screens, replacing the sodium flame by a solid source. It will then be found that the marks indicating the original positions of the sodium lines lie in the yellow region. No matter how often the experiment is repeated, the two lines are always produced and always in exactly the same positions, so long as the source contains sodium vapor: in other words, sodium in a volatilized state always emits radiation of these two wave-lengths and never emits radiation of any other wave-lengths. Therefore, if we find these lines in the spectrum of a star, for example, we know beyond a shadow of doubt that the visible portions of that star consist partially of sodium. Experiments with numerous other elements prove that the bright-line emission spectrum of each is invariable and unique.

Kirchhoff also demonstrated that incandescent gases likewise yield bright-line spectra when they are not under pressure, and that the spectrum of every gaseous element is unique. When the source consists of a gaseous or volatilized compound—whose ultimate particles are molecules, or closely knit groups of atoms—the bright lines are extremely numerous and crowded into groups which appear as bright bands. These complex-band spectra are, like the line spectra of elementary substances (whose ultimate particles are single atoms), unique for each compound.

Kirchhoff's second law therefore states that *the spectrum of a glowing rarefied gas or volatilized solid consists of bright lines only; if the source is molecular, the lines are more numerous and crowded together into bands.*

Kirchhoff next tried combining the two foregoing experiments. He placed an incandescent lump of some solid behind the slit, and between it and the slit itself interposed a sodium flame. The result was, to him, somewhat startling, for although a composite spectrum was formed, the sodium lines were not bright but dark; they stood out against the yellow region of the continuous spectrum as two fine black lines. If the source of the continuous radiation is removed or screened, the dark lines are immediately replaced by bright ones in precisely the same positions; the dark lines, in fact, become bright with the removal of the continuous background. Since the two vertical strips of the continuous spectrum that underlie the dark lines would be bright were the sodium vapor not interposed between the prism and the incandescent solid, it follows that this vapor is absorbing from the polychromatic radiation passing through it just those two wave-lengths which it itself emits. The significant point in this experiment is that the sodium vapor is at a lower temperature than the source of the mixed radiation producing the continuous spectrum, and it is only under this condition that it absorbs its own wave-lengths. When it is hotter than the incandescent solid the sodium lines appear bright once more, and are superimposed upon a less bright continuous background. The same phenomenon is observed if the volatilized solid is replaced by a gas. The third law may therefore be stated as follows: *a gas will absorb from mixed radiation passing through it exactly those wave-lengths that it itself is capable of emitting, provided that the source of the radiation is at a higher temperature than itself.*

BLACK-BODY RADIATION LAWS

Following the anuouncement of Kirchhoff's empirical laws a tremendous amount of research, both theoretical and observational, was undertaken in the field of radiation analysis. It had been noticed for many centuries that the color of a bar of iron changes as it is heated to higher and higher temperatures. When first heated the bar appears black, as the temperature is raised the bar appears to glow with a dull red color, as the temperature is increased the bar becomes bright cherry color, next orange, and finally, just before melting, the bar appears to be white hot.

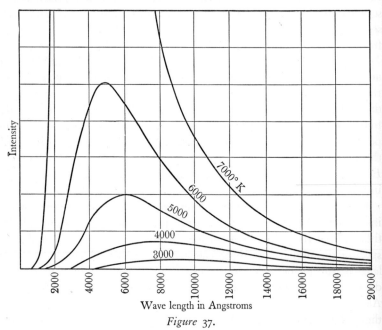

Figure 37.

A blacksmith can make a good estimate of the temperature of his work by merely noticing its color. Careful study of the radiation from a bar of metal at different temperatures showed that the rate of radiation in all wave-lengths increased as the bar was heated, but that the relative intensities of the various wave-lengths varied with the temperature. Figure 37 shows several curves in which the relative intensity of radiation is plotted against wave-length for several different temperatures. It will be noticed that the wave-length of maximum intensity of radiation shifts toward the violet with each increase of temperature of the source.

By purely empirical methods Wien determined that this wave-length of maximum intensity of radiation was inversely proportional to the temperature of the source. This may be expressed analytically by what is now known as Wien's law

$$\lambda_{max} = \frac{A}{T}$$

in which A is a constant whose numerical value depends upon the units in which λ and T are expressed. Most modern scientists express temperatures on what is known as the Kelvin scale. The degree divisions on this scale are the same as those of the centigrade system, but $0°$ on the Kelvin scale is $-273°$ centigrade. On this modern scientific scale water would freeze at $273°$K and boil at $373°$K.

A further study of the relation between rate of radiation of energy and temperature indicated that the total energy radiated, i.e. the sum of the rates of radiation for each particular wave-length, is proportional to the fourth power of the temperature on the Kelvin scale. This was found by Stefan while working by purely empirical methods, and independently by Boltzmann, who had attacked the problem from the theoretical point of view. The Stefan-Boltzmann law is given by $E=BT^4$ in which B is a constant whose value depends upon the units in which E is expressed.

Wien's law and the Stefan-Boltzmann law give us much important information, but they do not tell the whole story. While they do give us the wave-length of maximum intensity of radiation in the continuous spectrum and also the total rate of radiation of energy of all wave-lengths as functions of the temperature of the source, nevertheless they do not give us the rate of radiation at each individual wave-length. At the very beginning of the twentieth century Max Planck, a German theoretical physicist, attacked this problem from the purely theoretical point of view, using as his source what is now known as the black body. This black body is a purely theoretical object that is both a perfect absorber and also a perfect radiator, i.e. it will absorb all energy incident upon it and will re-emit all of this energy as radiation. The closest approximation to this theoretical object that can be used in the laboratory for experimental purposes is a small hole in a relatively large box whose surfaces are thoroughly blackened both outside and in.

Prior to the twentieth century all scientists had assumed that radiation was due to the vibrations of atoms and that these vibrations could be of any frequency. The emission of radiant energy from such a system was assumed to be a steady process analogous to a stream of water at constant pressure coming out of a pipe. Planck assumed that the emission of energy from the vibrating atoms must be in finite amounts, which he referred to as quanta. This assumption was so radical that few scientists of his time would even consider it, but it was destined to become one of the most important principles of modern physical science. The assumption is equivalent to saying that a set of brass tuning forks can be constructed only with certain definite frequencies, say 5, 10, 15, 20, et cetera vibrations per second, and that all intermediate frequencies, say 7 or 18, are impossible. Classical mechanics did not put any such restriction on the frequencies of vibrations of tuning forks and it seemed highly improbable that there should be any such restrictions on the vibrations of atoms. Furthermore Planck assumed that the quanta of energy radiated by the atoms must be directly proportional to the frequency of the radiation or, of course, inversely proportional to the wave-length. In other words, the loss of energy from any atom must be an integral multiple of a fundamental quantum or

$$e = nh\frac{c}{\lambda}$$

where e is the rate of radiation, h is a fundamental constant of nature, c is the speed of light, λ the wavelength of radiation, and n is any integer 1, 2, 3, 4, etc. This implies that radiant energy is not emitted like water out of a hose, but in a manner more analogous to a stream of machine-gun bullets. However, it must not be imagined that these quanta are the so-called corpuscles used by Newton in his theory of light, since unlike the corpuscles they are further assumed to have a vibratory nature. It should also be noted that the energy of a quantum of violet light is greater than that of red light.

On the basis of the quantum theory of radiation Planck was able to derive a general law of radiation giving the rate of radiation of energy at any particular wave-length from a black body in terms of the temperature of the source. This law may be expressed analytically as

$$E_\lambda = \frac{a\lambda^{-5}}{e^{\frac{b}{\lambda T}} - 1} .$$

In this expression E_λ in the rate of radiation at wave-length λ, T is the temperature of the black body on the Kelvin scale, e is 2.718 . . . , and a and b are numerical constants depending upon the units of λ and E_λ.

This equation will yield the curves shown in Figure 37. Wien's law and the Stefan-Boltzmann law may be shown mathematically to be special solutions of Planck's general equation. Planck's law has been tested in the laboratory for temperatures between 300°K and 1700°K and there is no evidence of failure at much higher temperatures. The question of the practical value of Planck's law may very well be raised, since it was derived for a black body and no such object exists in nature. At this point it is sufficient to say that there are many objects that, in spite of the fact that they are not black bodies but gray, satisfy Planck's equation to within a few per cent.

EARLY STUDIES OF LINE SPECTRA

During the period that so much work was being done on Kirchhoff's first law of spectral analysis, the second and third laws were by no means neglected. Immediately following the announcement that the wave-lengths of the spectral lines, either of emission or of absorption, were characteristic of the chemical elements or compounds involved in the production of the lines, careful investigations of the spectra of various elements and compounds were begun. Identification tables of the various lines characteristic of the elements and compounds were compiled and these tables were used for qualitative analysis of both laboratory and celestial sources.

A study of the spectrum of the element hydrogen, a photograph of which appears in Plate VIIIb, indicated that the wave-length difference between successive lines becomes smaller and smaller as the violet end of the spectrum is approached. In other words the lines are apparently arranged in some form of converging series. The point of convergence was found to be at about 3647 Angstrom units. In 1885 Balmer, a Swiss scientist, made the first determination of an empirical formula for the prediction of the wave-lengths of the spectral lines due to hydrogen. He found that the wave-length of each line could be computed by the formula

$$\lambda = 3647 \frac{n^2}{n^2 - 4}$$

in which n is any integer greater than 2. For example if $n = 3$ in this Balmer formula, we obtain $\lambda = 6565$, which is the wave-length in Angstroms of the red line of hydrogen known as H_α; when $n = 4$ we find $\lambda = 4863\ A$, which is H_β, and so on for all of the lines in what is now called the Balmer series of hydrogen.

Following the announcement of Balmer's formula for hydrogen a number of studies were made of the wave-lengths observed for other elements, and other series relations were discovered and their formulae determined. For the heavier chemical elements several formulae are necessary for the representation of all of the observed lines.

THE STRUCTURE OF MATTER

From the earliest days of natural philosophy, that branch of learning which has been divided, since the early nineteenth century, into the various fields of science, there has been the fundamental hypothesis that all matter is composed of fundamental particles which cannot be subdivided. These particles were known originally as atoms, but as science advanced this term was reserved for the fundamental particles that make up the different chemical elements. Atoms are now assumed to combine to form the individual particles of the various chemical compounds and these particles are known as molecules. By suitable methods the molecules may be broken down to the individual atoms composing them. The atoms and molecules were assumed to be too small to be observed by any known instrumental methods, but various experiments indicated that they did exist, that they were of different masses and sizes, and that they were in rapid and random motion. It was further proved that the speeds of the particles increased with an increase in the temperature of the material.

The year 1853 may be said to mark the dawn of modern atomic physics or, perhaps, the atomic age. In that year Masson, a French scientist, connected a high-voltage induction coil to electrodes inserted in a tube containing gas at low pressure. Instead of the spark that would pass between the electrodes in air at normal pressure, he observed that the tube was filled with a colored glow. As vacuum pumps were improved, Masson's experiment was repeated with gas at lower and lower pressures. This is not the place even to outline in any detail the entire subject of conduction of electricity through gases and we must content ourselves by stating that two types of particles are separated out from the gaseous material in the tube.

One type of particle carries a negative charge and is found to be the same no matter what type of gas is used in the low-pressure tube. This negatively charged particle is known as the electron and its characteristics have been determined from the brilliant experimental researches of Sir J. J. Thomson, R. A. Millikan, and a number of other scientists. At the present time the accepted values for the mass and charge of the electron are:

Mass$=9.1066\times10^{-28}$ grams
Charge$=4.8025\times10^{-10}$ absolute electrostatic units.

The other type of particle is positively charged. The amount of this positive charge is usually equal in magnitude to the charge on the electron, but it may be some integral multiple of this value. The mass, however, is characteristic of the gaseous material in the tube. The smallest mass of the positively charged particle is found when pure hydrogen is used in the tube, and this particle, assumed to be the unit particle, is known as the proton. The mass of the proton is found to be 1.6765×10^{-24} grams or equivalent to about 1834 times the mass of the electron. When a gas other than hydrogen is used in the tube, the positively charged particle has a mass approximately equal to the mass of the proton multiplied by the atomic weight of the gas.

THE RUTHERFORD NUCLEAR ATOM

The results of the researches on the particles produced by the passage of electricity through gases indicated that the atom could be broken up into small negatively charged particles known as electrons and much larger positively charged particles whose masses are proportional to the atomic weight of the gas used in the tube. However, until the beginning of the twentieth century there was no satisfactory theory or model to explain how these particles were distributed in the atom, or the mechanism by which they are separated by external energy.

In 1895 Roentgen found that if a solid inside a vacuum tube was bombarded by a stream of high-velocity electrons, some form of very penetrating rays appeared outside the glass of the tube. These rays were called x-rays and were thought to be a stream of uncharged particles. Subsequent experiments proved that x-rays are a form of electromagnetic radiation of wave-length much shorter than the shortest known ultra-violet light. The important feature of this radiation for our immediate problem is that when x-rays are passed through air, or any other gas, at atmospheric pressure electrons are released. This means that high-energy electromagnetic radiation, as well as electricity, can break up the atom. It was later found that visible light, or energy in any form, can drive electrons out of atoms.

In 1896 Becquerel discovered by accident that radiation, capable of fogging a photographic plate enclosed in black paper wrapping, was given off from a salt of uranium. This was further investigated by Madame Curie, who found that the atoms of a previously unknown element, radium, were breaking up without the application of outside energy. Investigation of the particles given off by this spontaneous disintegration of the radium atom showed that three types of rays were given off. These were known as α-rays, β-rays, and γ-rays. The β-rays were found to be streams of electrons, the γ-rays were found to be electromagnetic radiation of a slightly shorter wave-length than x-rays, but the α-rays were found to be made up of particles of an entirely different character from anything that had previously been observed. These α-rays, or α particles as they are called at present, have a positive charge twice that of the proton and a mass four times that of the proton.

In 1903 P. Lenard, a German physicist, after a long series of experiments with positively charged particles, concluded that the mass of a solid body is not distributed through an object uniformly but is concentrated in small particles. During the next few years Sir Ernest Rutherford and a number of co-workers carried on an epoch-making series of experiments on the scattering of α particles in passing through thin sheets of various materials. As a result of these experiments Rutherford was able to announce that the atom is nuclear in nature and has the following characteristics: (i) all of the positive charge of an atom is confined to a particle smaller than 10^{-12} cm. in diameter; (ii) the amount of this positive charge, using the charge on the proton as a unit, is equal to half the atomic weight; (iii) practically all of the mass of the atom is contained in this particle, or nucleus of the atom. Rutherford assumed further that electrons are arranged in some manner about this nucleus with the number of electrons equal to the number of unit proton positive charges on the nucleus. Hence the negative charges on the electrons just neutralize the positive charges on the nucleus.

THE BOHR ATOM

In 1913 Dr. Niels Bohr, a young Danish physicist, proposed certain specifications for the Rutherford nuclear atom. These were so radical that at first physicists in general would not accept them but they actually mark the beginning of a new era in the history of physical science. Chemists had been able to make considerable progress in the theory of chemical reactions by using various models for the nuclear atom, and several physicists had proposed that the electrons might be revolving about the nucleus in circular orbits. However, neither the geometric models proposed by the chemists nor the planetary models proposed by the physicists could adequately explain the origin of the line spectra, either of emission or absorption, which were believed to be due to changes within the atom itself.

Bohr considered first the simple case of the hydrogen atom with one proton in the nucleus and one electron outside. In common with several other physicists he assumed that this electron could revolve about the nucleus in a number of circular orbits with the centrifugal force balanced by the electrostatic and gravitational attractions between the charges and masses of the two particles. For the atom to be in a stable condition there is one and only one value for v, the speed of the electron in its circular path, for each value of r, the radius of the circular orbit. Bohr introduced the condition that there are only certain particular orbits possible for the electron, and that the radii of these orbits are subject to certain quantum conditions. In other words, Bohr introduced to atomic structure the quantum theory used by Planck in his theory of continuous spectra. After making the assumption of quantum conditions Bohr proceeded by perfectly standard methods and found that the radius of any particular electron orbit in the hydrogen atom is determined by

$$r = \frac{n^2 h^2}{4\pi^2 m e^2} \qquad \text{(i)}$$

In this expression h is Planck's constant, m is the mass of the electron, e is the charge on the electron, and n is any integer. The numerical values for h, m, and e are all known from experimental determination and when we set $n=1$ we find r to be approximately 5×10^{-9} cm. as the radius for the innermost orbit that the electron may occupy in the hydrogen atom. The next orbit will have a radius four times that of the first, the third will have a radius nine times that of the first, and so on. In the Bohr model the electron may occupy any one of these orbits and may move from one to any other, with a corresponding change in the internal energy of the system. Bohr's fundamental assumption is that the electron can never occupy the space between any two of the orbits.

Under normal conditions the electron is assumed to occupy the innermost orbit. To 'lift' the electron to any outer orbit energy must be put into the atom and, under such conditions, the atom is said to be excited. If a sufficient amount of excitation energy is supplied the electron will jump out to a relatively infinite distance from the nucleus and the atom will be said to be ionized. With the atom in an excited state it will tend to return to the normal condition. The electron may return to the innermost orbit in one jump, or it may go back by a number of successive jumps from orbit to orbit, always moving closer to the limiting position in the innermost orbit. If an ionized atom comes relatively close to a free electron the electron will be captured and will go to the innermost orbit either by a single jump or by a number of successive hops. As the electron returns toward the innermost orbit, energy is given out by the atom. Since the electron must move by specified jumps from orbit to orbit and never occupy the spaces between orbits there must be certain definite energy levels in the atom. The existence of these energy levels in atoms other than hydrogen had been demonstrated experimentally before the announcement of the Bohr atomic model, but there had been no logical explanation for them.

Bohr's final postulate concerning the hydrogen atom is concerned with the absorption or emission of radiant energy by the atom. If E' represents the energy level in the atom for the electron in one orbit, and E'' represents the energy level with the electron in another orbit, Bohr postulated that the wave-length of the electromagnetic radiation absorbed or emitted is inversely proportional to the energy change. Expressed analytically we have

$$E' - E'' = h\frac{c}{\lambda}$$

in which c is the speed of light and λ the wave-length of the radiation, both expressed in centimeters.

Mathematical analysis enabled Bohr to show that the value of the energy E in any energy level is inversely proportional to n^2, the square of the quantum number for the particular electron orbit involved. Hence the wave-length of the radiation absorbed or emitted by the hydrogen atom can be computed from

$$\frac{1}{\lambda} = K\left(\frac{1}{n'^2} - \frac{1}{n''^2}\right) \qquad \text{(ii)}$$

The value of the constant K can be computed by the use of the same physical quantities previously mentioned and is found to be 109,678. If we now take the reciprocal of (ii) we obtain

$$\lambda = \frac{1}{109,678}\left(\frac{n'^2 n''^2}{n''^2 - n'^2}\right) \qquad \text{(iii)}$$

As an example let us assume that $n' = 2$, i.e. that the electrons are moving from outer orbits toward the second orbit for the emission of radiation, or from the second to outer orbits for the case of absorption of energy. Then we have from (iii)

$$\lambda = \frac{4}{109,678}\left(\frac{n''^2}{n''^2-4}\right) = 3.647 \times 10^{-5}\left(\frac{n''^2}{n''^2-4}\right) \text{ cm.}$$

or $3647\left(\dfrac{n''^2}{n''^2-4}\right)$ Angstrom units.

Reference to page 151 will show that this is the empirical formula derived by Balmer for the previously observed lines of hydrogen. Thus Bohr's introduction of the quantum-theory conditions to the nuclear atom seemed to accomplish for the emission and absorption spectra of hydrogen something approximating what Newton's enunciation of the law of universal graviation did for the structure of the solar system —it placed an empirically determined law on a theoretical foundation.

The final step toward the establishment of a physical hypothesis is to predict phenomena that have not previously been observed. With this in mind Bohr computed the wave-lengths of the lines to be expected when n' takes on values other than 2, the value that gave the previously known Balmer series of lines. When the electrons in an excited atom return to the innermost orbit, or, in other words, when the energy levels settle down to normal condition, n' has the value 1. Substituting this in (iii) yields

$$\lambda = 911.75\left(\frac{n''^2}{n''^2-1}\right)$$

or a series of lines converging on $\lambda = 911.75$ A. Substituting in this expression the values 2,3, etc. for n'' we find that the wave-lengths of the individual lines should be at about 1216 A., 1026 A., et cetera. Air is opaque to radiation in this extreme ultra-violet region but Lyman, after enclosing all of his apparatus in a vacuum chamber, was able to observe and verify the wave-lengths of the predicted lines in the extreme ultra-violet, now known as the Lyman series of hydrogen. When n' is given the values 3 and 4 the predicted lines are found to be in the extreme infra-red region. The lines were found at the predicted wave-lengths and make up what are now known as the Paschen and the Brakett series of hydrogen.

The Bohr model of the nuclear atom seemed well established for hydrogen and the next step was to determine the orbits, or energy levels, for the atoms of the other elements. The helium atom, on the basis of the nuclear model, has two protons in the nucleus and two electrons outside. Each of the electrons will have its particular set of orbits, but the computation of the constant in (iii) is complicated by the fact that there will be electrostatic forces between the two electrons as well as the increased attractions of the nuclear particles on the electrons. The first case attempted was to consider that the helium was in a strong enough energy field that the atom was singly ionized, i.e. one of the electrons is forced out of the atom. We now have an approximation to the hydrogen atom with one electron, but with two or more particles in the nucleus. However, the computation of the constant for (iii) is not difficult for the singly ionized helium atom and, as might be expected, the series of lines predicted were arranged in a group of series not unlike in appearance the various series for hydrogen. Some time before these computations were made Pickering, an American astronomer, had observed a series of lines in the spectrum of the star Zeta Puppis which were arranged in a manner similar to those in the Balmer series for hydrogen. However, the wave-lenghts of these lines did not agree with those of the Balmer series but did agree with those which were subsequently computed for the spectrum of singly ionized helium. This was a great triumph for the Bohr atomic model and spurred workers on to determine the necessary constants for the heavier atoms.

When the attempt was made to extend the simple Bohr model of the nuclear atom to include the atoms of the heavier elements almost insurmountable complications were encountered. Furthermore continued improvements in spectroscopic techniques permitted determinations of wave-lengths to a very high order of precision, and slight variations from the wave-lengths predicted by the Bohr model were found. Within recent years the early quantum theory and certain details of Bohr's atomic model have come under considerable suspicion and to an extent have been superseded. Regarding the latter, it remains firmly established that atoms can and do exist in various energy levels, or stationary states, and that they pass from one to another of these in the processes of emitting and absorbing radiation. It is doubtful, however, if Bohr's actual model of the atom with electrons revolving about the nucleus in circular or elliptical orbits corresponds to any objective reality. The original quantum theory has come under graver suspicion, and although it was undoubtedly a very great advance on any previous conception, it has been tentatively replaced by the matrix mechanics of Heisenberg and the wave mechanics of Schroedinger. These are only susceptible of discussion in mathematical terms of an advanced order, and in an account of this nature the work of Bohr and Planck may be accepted as a reasonably satisfactory account of the theoretical background.

THE NUCLEUS OF THE ATOM

In the discussion of the Bohr atom we were interested primarily in the electrons outside of the nucleus, which are believed to give rise to the energy levels so important in the theory of spectra. We were interested in the nucleus only in so far as it provided the necessary positive charges to attract the electrons and hold them in their various stationary orbits or states. The number of these electrons and hence the number of positive charges on the nucleus is believed to be the characteristic factor of the individual elements and is known as the atomic number Z of the element.

If the elements are arranged in order of increasing atomic number it will be noticed that the order of arrangement is that of increasing atomic weight. It will also be noticed as we pass down through the list that the rate of increase of atomic weight is not any direct function of the atomic number. The atomic numbers and approximate atomic weights for a few elements are given in the following table:

Element	Atomic number Z	Atomic weight.
Hydrogen	1	1
Helium	2	4
Lithium	3	7
Carbon	6	12
Silver	47	108
Gold	79	197
Mercury	80	201

It is assumed that the nucleus of the hydrogen atom consists of one proton which carries unit charge and is assumed to be of unit weight. Since the value of Z for helium is 2 there should be 2 protons in the nucleus to provide the necessary positive charges to neutralize the two electron charges, and if the protons contained all of the mass the atomic weight should be 2. The atomic weight of helium is actually 4 and it is assumed that there must be something other than 2 protons in the nucleus to provide for the observed atomic weight. It was assumed that in addition to protons atomic nucleii contain particles that have no electric charge but do have mass equal to that of the proton. These particles were known as neutrons, and when in 1932 Chadwick, an English physicist, was able to isolate these particles the whole field of modern nuclear physics was opened.

It is now believed that the atomic number Z is characteristic of the element itself. The number of neutrons in the nucleus may vary slightly for different atoms of the element, thus giving rise to what are known as the isotopes of the element. For example, in the case of the element iron $Z=26$, indicating 26 protons in the nucleus and 26 electrons outside. The number of neutrons in an iron atom may be 28, 30, 31, or 32, providing for four isotopes of iron of atomic weights 54, 56, 57, and 58 respectively. Of the various isotopes of any element, one is the most common in nature and this one strongly influences the value of the atomic weight determined for a relatively large sample of the element. In the case of iron the isotope of atomic weight 56 is the most common and the average atomic weight of iron is given as 55.84. Furthermore certain of the isotopes may be unstable in nature, as is the case with the iron isotope 58.

The amount of energy bound up in the nucleus of an atom is very great; we shall have occasion to return to this subject in connection with the discussion of the source of radiant energy in the sun and in the stars (see page 271).

FORBIDDEN LINES

A further class of spectral lines must now engage our attention—the so-called 'forbidden' lines. This is somewhat of a misnomer, for under exceptional circumstances forbidden lines do make their appearance in astronomical as well as in laboratory spectra. The forbidden lines of an elementary may, however, be defined as those lines that do not appear in the normal spectrum but make their appearance when the radiating material exists under peculiar and uncommon physical conditions. Examples of such conditions are, in the laboratory, intense electric fields; and in the astronomical sphere, exceptionally low densities such as involve widely spaced atoms among which collisions will occur only at very much longer intervals than obtain in gases at even the lowest experimentally produced pressures.

The conception of stationary states goes far toward an elucidation of the forbidden lines, and the mechanism of their production. Figure 38 shows in diagrammatic form some of the stationary states of sodium. These are shown on the left in a single column of ascending energy-values. To the right they are sorted out into four separate columns, S, P, D, and F. From a study of the sodium spectrum it is possible to determine what transitions are responsible for the individual emission lines, and each such transition is shown in the diagram by an arrow linking the two stationary states concerned: for example, three lines in the spectrum result from transitions between the states 2S, 3S, 4S, and 2P. It will be observed that the states in columns S, P, D, and F have been chosen so that normal transitions—i.e. those producing lines observed in the normal spectrum—occur only between states in

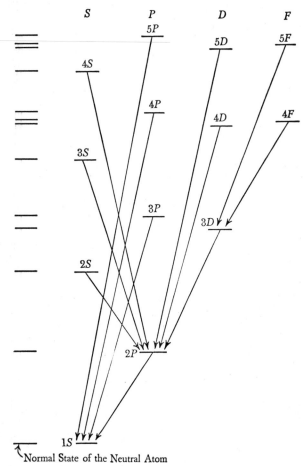

Figure 38. (Modified from Darrow) Normal transitions within the sodium atom.

adjacent columns. That this is not entirely arbitrary, but does in fact reflect some significant facet of the structure of the atom itself, is shown by the ordered disposition of the levels in each of these columns.

This principle of selection is, however, violated by certain lines, which result from transitions between states in the same column or between states separated by one or more columns. These are the forbidden lines. Viewed in this way they can be seen to depend upon transitions within the atom which are 'forbidden' under normal conditions, but which become permissible under certain special laboratory conditions, as well as under some celestial conditions (such as ultra-low density) which cannot be paralleled in the laboratory.

Even at this stage, then, the spectroscope has vastly increased our powers of investigating bodies that are not directly accessible. Merely by inspecting the spectrum of, say, a star, we can tell (i) if it, or part of it, consists of a solid, a liquid, or a dense gas; (ii) if it consists wholly or partially of vaporized solids or liquids, or of rarefied gases; and (iii) what the chemical constitution of these is. And this is only a beginning.

TEMPERATURE FROM SPECTRA

In the first place, it will be remembered that Kirchhoff's third experiment gave information regarding the relative temperature of the sources of a composite spectrum; we can tell by inspection only which of the two is the hotter.

Bright-line and absorption spectra give us detailed and accurate information regarding the chemical composition of the source, but continuous spectra (those of glowing solids, liquids, or dense gases) give us no information of this sort since, whatever the chemical composition of the source may be, they are always a continuous band of color. Nevertheless, continuous spectra can give us valuable information about the temperature of the source. As has been pointed out already in our discussion of black-body radiation, the relative intensities of the light at different wave-lengths are not the same in a continuous spectrum. The measurement of the relative intensities is made by the methods of spectrophotometry and curves can be obtained that show the observed values of intensities plotted against wave-length. The determination of the wave-length of maximum intensity from such a curve will give a value of the temperature of the source by a direct application of Wien's law. A comparison of the shape of the plotted curve with those computed theoretically from Planck's general radiation formula (Fig. 37), plotted for different temperatures, may be made and, when a matching curve is found, the temperature of the source is determined. If we can determine the total energy radiated at all wave-lengths from the source producing the continuous spectrum, either by direct measurement or by integrating the area under the plotted curve from spectrophometric data, we can determine the temperature of the source by application of the Stefan-Boltzmann law.

All three of these methods of temperature determination from the continuous spectrum are based upon the assumption that the source is a black body. Since the black body is a purely theoretical object and does not exist in nature, corrections to the determined temperatures must be made to allow for the grayness of the object. This grayness is a more or less uncertain quantity but an approximation to it may be obtained by comparing the shape of the curves determined by spectrophotometric methods with the curves computed from Planck's law. From the differences in shape the grayness corrections may be determined approximately and then applied to the determinations of temperature made on the assumption of the black body. The final value of the temperature may be accepted as moderately accurate, as will be shown by the numerical determination of the temperature of the sun in Chapter VIII.

The approximate temperature of the source may be determined spectroscopically in other ways. The line spectrum of an element (whether bright or dark—emission or absorption) consists of a series of lines, whose number may vary from only one or two to several hundred, which are relatively widely spaced; widely enough, at any rate, to show as separate and individual lines. But the spectra of compounds, as we have seen, consist of one or more bands which high magnification and wide prismatic dispersion reveal to consist of innumerable lines crowded closely together. Compounds can be identified by their spectra as surely as elements, and are at the same time easily distinguishable from them. Now all chemical compounds are dissociated by high temperatures—i.e. are split into their constituent elements—and the dissociation temperature of each compound is only variable within narrow limits, which can be discovered experimentally. Thus if, for instance, the spectrum of a particular region of the sun shows the banded spectrum of a certain compound, it is certain that the temperature of that region is lower than the compound's dissociation temperature as determined in the laboratory. This, we shall see, is the method whereby the temperature of sunspots has been measured.

Still another means of determining the temperature of the source from the appearance of the spectrum is available to the astronomer. Although the line spectrum of each element is unique, it does itself undergo characteristic modifications with varying temperature. Thus the temperature not only of an incandescent solid, liquid, or dense gas, but also of a volatalized solid, liquid, or rarefied gas, may be determined by spectral analysis. In the laboratory three ranges of temperature in particular are available for study: the temperature of the flame, such as the Bunsen burner (about 2300°K), that of the electric arc (about 4000°K), and the high-tension electrical discharge (effective temperature up to about 20,000°K). Experiments carried out at these temperatures have proved that the number and relative intensity of the spectral lines of each element differ to some extent in the flame, arc, and spark spectra. Those lines which can be produced in the labortory only by the high-tension discharge are known as enhanced lines. Thus, if the spectrum of a star shows the enhanced lines of calcium we can assign a minimum temperature to that part of the star containing the calcium. In point of fact this technique is capable of giving more detailed results than the foregoing account might lead the reader to suppose; for the gradual emergence and subsequent strengthening of the enhanced lines is a direct function of increasing temperature, and a close correlation between the two has been established.

IONIZATION

With the development and modification of the Bohr model of the nuclear atom the reason for the correlation between the enhanced lines and the temperature of the source was established. We have seen that under conditions of strong excitation one electron is driven out of the atom and the atom is said to be singly ionized. The partially stripped atom carries a positive charge and is known as an ion. When the excitation conditions are sufficiently intense for an appreciable portion of the atoms to be ionized the lines due to the ionized atoms make their appearance in the spectrum along with the lines due to the normal atom. As the strength of the field energy increases, which is frequently due to a rise in the temperature of the region, more and more of the atoms become ionized and the normal lines fade in intensity at the expense of the enhanced lines. If the strength of the field energy is increased still further another electron may be driven out of the ionized atoms and they are said to be doubly ionized. Other spectral lines due to the doubly ionized atoms make their appearance and the intensity of these lines increases with the strengthening of the field energy. The temperatures at which the atoms of the various elements become ionized (singly, doubly, triply, et cetera) can be computed from atomic theory and have been verified in the laboratory. Accordingly if a mass of gas contains a number of different elements the numbers and relative intensities of the normal and ionized lines of the different elements may be used to obtain a very good value for the temperature of the gaseous mixture.

PRESSURE AND DENSITY FROM SPECTRA

Two other important physical conditions of a source, which may be millions of miles distant, can be measured spectroscopically. The first of these is pressure, which modifies the spectrum in certain recognizable ways. The most important of these modifications has already been noted: a gas under great pressure behaves spectroscopically like a solid, giving a continuous spectrum, while a rarefied gas gives the characteristic line spectrum. But line spectra themselves are modified by pressure, just as they are by temperature. In general, the effect of decreasing the pressure of a gas or vaporized solid is the fading and finally, with great rarefaction, the disappearance of all but the strongest lines. Conversely, high pressures tend to widen the lines of the normal spectrum, with the possibility of adjacent lines merging if sufficiently great pressures are applied, and sometimes to shift them slightly toward the red. Reduction of the quantity of a radiating gas likewise produces the gradual disappearance of all but the strongest spectral lines; the very fine lines that remain even under great rarefaction of the source are called *raies ultimes,* and a consideration of the number of these ultimate lines relative to the other lines of the normal spectrum allows a fairly close estimate of the source density to be made. In the same way, the pressure-shifts and the widening of the lines can be related to an approximate quantitative scale.

MAGNETIC FIELDS AND SPECTRA

It has been proved by laboratory experiments that if the source of a radiation is placed between the poles of a strong electromagnet a curious spectroscopic effect results. In a relatively weak field the spectral lines are thickened, and if the field is strong enough they are split into pairs and triplets. The extent of this doubling and trebling of single lines allows the strength of the field to be calculated with considerable accuracy. One application of this effect, known as the Zeeman effect, will be described when we deal with that section of our knowledge of the sun which has been gained spectroscopically.

RADIAL MOTION AND SPECTRA

One further application of the spectroscope must be mentioned before we can proceed to a more detailed description of the instrument in its astronomical form. Probably everyone has at one time or another noticed the effect that motion has upon the pitch of a sound. An observer standing on a station platform will notice that the whistle of an express train passing through the station not only increases in volume as the train approaches, but also rises in pitch; once it has passed and is receding from him, the pitch drops again. The reason for this alteration of pitch is that while the train is approaching the observer it is all the time catching up the sound impulses which it is emitting; they are therefore crowded closer together than they would be were the whistle stationary. Since they are closer together, more of them pass a given point in a second, and more therefore impinge upon the observer's tympanum in that time. Since the pitch of a note is determined by the frequency of its impulses (a small tuning fork gives a higher note than a large one because it vibrates more rapidly), the pitch of the whistle will appear to rise. In the same way, when the source of the sound is traveling away from the observer the distance between consecutive impulses is lengthened, and a lower note is heard.

This can be demonstrated quite simply:

Suppose that S is the sounding body, that it is emitting n impulses per second, and that in one second they travel the distance from S to O, where there is an observer. The space between S and O will therefore be occupied by n impulses. Now suppose that S is in motion toward O, and that in one second it covers the distance Ss. The distance sO will now be occupied by n impulses; hence they will be closer together (sO being shorter than SO); hence a greater number will pass O in a second; hence he will hear a note of a higher pitch than that emitted by S when stationary. If S is moving away from O the reverse effect will obviously result.

Sound and light affect different human senses because they are phenomena of a fundamentally different character; sound waves, to cite one example, require a medium (normally the air) in which to travel, whereas light and other electromagnetic radiations are propagated *in vacuo*. Nevertheless, the term 'light waves' may be substituted for 'sound impulses' in the foregoing account without invalidating the argument, and it is found that analogous alterations in the wave-length and frequency of a system of electromagnetic radiation are caused by movement of the source relative to the observer. If S, now a source emitting light, is moving toward O, more waves will pass O per second than would be the case if S were stationary. Hence—since wave-length and frequency are inversely proportional to one another—the wave-length of the radiation is shortened. Let us suppose, to take an example, that the radiation is monochromatic and that its spectrum consists of a single line in the red; the wave-length of the line can be accurately determined with the interferometer. If the source of the radiation is moving toward the observer, the wave-length will be shortened, with the result that the line will be displaced toward the violet, or short wave, end of the spectrum; were the source receding from the observer the displacement would be toward the red. In either case the amount of the displacement would depend directly upon the velocity of this motion in the line of sight. The size of the displacement, or the amount by which the wave-length has been altered, will be given by the simple relation

$$\Delta\lambda = \frac{v \, \delta \lambda}{c}$$

where $\Delta\lambda$=difference between displaced and normal wave-length of the line,

v=line-of-sight velocity of the source,
c=velocity of light,
λ=the wave-length of the undisplaced line.

$\Delta\lambda$ can be accurately measured, and since the other two terms in the equation are known the velocity of the source can quickly be calculated.

As a numerical example of the application of this so-called Doppler principle let us assume that the hydrogen line with $\lambda = 4863$ A. is observed in the spectrum of a certain star to have a wave-length of $\lambda = 4862$ A. Then, in the analytic expression for the Doppler principle, $\lambda = 4863$ and $\Delta\lambda = 1$. Substituting these values in the equation we have

$$1 = \frac{v}{3 \times 10^{10}} \times 4863$$

hence $v = \dfrac{3 \times 10^{10}}{4863}$ cm./sec. $= 6.169 \times 10^{6}$ cm./sec. $= 61.69$ km./sec.

or about 38.4 mi./sec. Since the observed value of the wave-length is shorter than it would be if the source and the observer were relatively at rest, we can say that the line-of-sight, or radial, velocity of the star is 38.4 mi./sec. toward the observer.

We may now tabulate the varied information that the spectrum of, say, a star gives us about the visible regions of that star:

    i. Its physical nature: whether it is liquid, solid, volatilized solid, dense gas, rarefied gas, or a combination of these.

    ii. Its chemical composition, and whether compounds as well as elements occur.

    iii. The relative temperatures of the component sources of a compound spectrum, e.g. a continuous spectrum with superimposed absorption lines.

    iv. Its actual temperature, ascertained by independent methods.

    v. Its density.

    vi. The presence or absence of a magnetic field.

    vii. Its line-of-sight velocity.

The spectroscope, as an astronomical instrument, is essentially the same as the apparatus on the work bench in the experiments already outlined. The three components, or their equivalents, are combined in a single instrument which can be attached to a telescope. The construction of the prismatic spectroscope is shown diagrammatically in Fig. 39. The tube *a* is known as the collimator, whose function it is to prepare the light of the observed object for the prism. It screws into the drawtube of the telescope at *f*, and at *g* there is a fine slit through which a narrow beam of light passes to the lens *e*. The light emerges from *e* as a parallel beam which falls upon one face of the prism. The emergent, refracted beam then encounters the object lens of the view telescope, *c*,

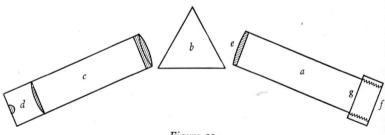

Figure 39.

the spectrum being viewed direct instead of being cast on a screen as before. This lens focuses the spectrum upon the eyepiece *d,* where it is magnified and observed. The view telescope is pivoted at the center of the instrument so that it may be directed at different regions of the spectrum.

This is the basic type; two modifications must be mentioned, but need not be described in detail. To secure wider dispersion, thus increasing the length of the spectrum and securing greater separation of closely adjacent lines, a train of several prisms may replace the single prism shown in the figure. Alternatively, an entirely different principle may be utilized, the formation of the spectrum resulting from the diffraction instead of from the refraction of the incident light. The position of the prism or train of prisms is now occupied by a small sheet of glass or metal upon which are engraved many thousands of fine lines to the inch. When a mixed radiation is reflected from such a surface the different wave-lengths are sorted out, as with a prism. A crude example of a diffraction grating can be provided by a phonograph record. If the disk is held up slantwise against the light from a window, it will be seen that the band of light reflected across it contains some of the spectral colors. The dullness of these colors and the poor quality of the spectrum are due to the coarseness of the grating, the disk having comparatively large and few ridges to the inch.

It is usually more convenient to photograph spectra than to study them visually, for not only is a permanent record made in this way but the measuring of the positions of the lines and the comparison of unknown lines with spectra obtained in the laboratory are greatly facilitated. For this purpose a photographic plate is exposed in the focal plane of the lens of the view telescope, where normally the eyepiece would be.

VII. The Moon and the Planets

The moon is the nearest body to the earth that is comparable with the planets in size: its diameter of 2,162 miles is rather more than one quarter of the earth's. We have seen in an earlier chapter that it revolves about the earth in a somewhat eccentric orbit, completing one circuit in about twenty-seven days at a mean distance of 238,857 miles.

THE MOON'S ORBIT AND MASS

Its mass, which is less than one eightieth that of the earth, may be determined by means of an interesting application of Newton's law of universal gravitation. Up to this point we have always envisaged the earth as describing a perfectly elliptical orbit about the sun, and the moon as revolving about the earth. This is not strictly true, for the earth and moon constitute a single gravitational unit, and it is the center of gravity of this system which describes the elliptical circumsolar orbit; the earth and moon each describes an orbit about the center of gravity whose size is inversely proportional to the body's mass. The phenomenon is somewhat similar to that of a pair of exhibition dancers performing one of those athletic maneuvers in which the man turns rapidly over the same spot, with his partner, held at arms length, flying through the air around him. If such an exhibition is watched carefully it will be observed that it is an incorrect description to say that the man is rotating on his axis, while his partner revolves round him: in fact, both partners are revolving about a point between them, but this point is much nearer the man than the woman.

If, to employ more accurate terms, M in Fig. 40 represents the moon, and E the earth, the center of gravity of the system would be at some point C such that were the two bodies connected by a rigid, weightless rod, the system would balance at this point. If we write

M_e for the mass of the earth,

M_m for the mass of the moon,
D_e for the distance of the earth's center from the center of gravity,
D_m for the distance of the moon's center from the center of gravity,
then,

$$M_e \times D_e = M_m \times D_m$$

Though small, the movement of the earth about the center of gravity of the two bodies is large enough to cause observable parallactic displacements of the nearer planets such as Mars or Eros when they are in the vicinity of the earth. Measurement of these displacements allows the distance of the earth from the center of gravity to be determined,* from which M_m can be calculated by means of the equation just given.

Figure 40. (Not to scale)

THE LUNAR SURFACE

The naked eye shows that the moon's surface is patched and mottled, and observations extended over a period of time prove that the same lunar hemisphere is always turned toward the earth, a fact which must be held responsible for the anonymous housemaid's memorable lines:

> O Moon, when I gaze on thy beautiful face,
> Careering along through the boundaries of space,
> The thought has often come into my mind
> If I ever shall see thy glorious behind.

Telescopically the moon is a wonderful sight, especially when a comparatively narrow crescent. At this time the sun's light falls obliquely upon the whole of the visible surface, and throws its innumerable ridges, craters, valleys, and mountains into sharp relief against their jet-black and unfathomable shadows. At full it is a much less spectacular object, because there is then no terminator on the disk, and the terminator is, as we have seen, the line of sunrise or sunset where the illumination is necessarily most oblique. The shadows which gave an appearance

---

*The parallactic displacement of the sun, for example, amounts to about $12''.5$. At the sun's distance of 9.3×10^7 miles, $12''.5$ is subtended by 5.760 miles. Hence the radius of the earth's orbit about the center of gravity of the earth-moon system is 2,880 miles. This indicates that the point C in Fig. 40 should be inside the surface of the earth.

of such stark grandeur to the crescent moon are absent, and the general effect is of flatness, lack of relief, and unalleviated glare.

THE MARIA

The most obvious lunar surface features are the dark plains, or maria, which are easily visible to the naked eye. They are seen telescopically to be vast smooth, or nearly smooth, plains, sprinkled with minute craters, low ridges, and occasionally mountain peaks and larger crater rings. The name 'mare' is a misnomer, since these flat areas are not seas and almost certainly never held water. Our knowledge of the physical conditions prevailing upon the moon proves that they cannot be areas of water, but at this point it will be a good enough demonstration of this fact to point out that the sun is never observed to be reflected in the maria, as it would be were they seas. It will be noticed at first glance that the maria are approximately circular and that they are largely confined to the northern hemisphere, the southern being much rougher and more broken up, consisting largely of crowded and often contiguous crater rings and walled plains. The largest of the maria, Mare Imbrium, has an area of about 350,000 square miles.

THE CRATERIFORM OBJECTS

The most numerous type of lunar surface formation is the so-called crater. The name 'crater' is perhaps unfortunate, since they cannot be likened to the volcanic craters of this planet, as regards either origin or appearance. They vary in size from small, wall-less pits a few hundred feet across, to huge plains 150 miles in diameter and rimmed with mountain walls many thousands of feet in height. The larger craters frequently have a central mountain mass and a floor bearing much detail in the way of craterlets, rings, ridges, and isolated mountain peaks. In general, the smaller a crater is, the more regular are its shape and ramparts, but apart from this and such minor details as the presence or absence of a central mountain, they differ very little among themselves. One almost universal characteristic is that the floor of the crater is at a lower level than the surrounding terrain; thus the drop from the summit of the rampart is greater within the crater than on the outer side.

THE LUNAR MOUNTAINS

Like the earth, the moon possesses several great mountain ranges and masses; these, when seen under oblique illumination (when near the terminator, that is), are perhaps the most arresting features of the telescopic view of the moon. The height of a lunar mountain or other feature may be determined quite easily by measuring the angular length of its shadow. From this datum its height can be calculated since the moon's distance, and hence the linear length of the shadow, is known, and the only other factor in the problem, the angle of illumination, may be derived from the mountain's distance from the terminator at the time the observation was made. An alternative method is to determine its distance from the terminator at the moment when the sun's light first catches its summit, making it shine like a star from the darkness beyond the terminator.

In this way it has been found that the highest of the lunar mountains are comparable with the earth's most notable examples. But taking into account the size of the body on which they are situated they far outstrip any terrestrial mountains, since the diameter of the moon is only about one quarter that of the earth. The Leibnitz Mountains, situated on the moon's southern limb, rise in places to 30,000 feet, the equivalent of well over 100,000 feet on the earth.* For the most part, however, the great lunar ranges are confined to the northern hemisphere where they are commonly the bulwarks separating adjacent maria.

THE BRIGHT RAYS

The maria, the crateriform objects, and the mountain ranges are the most important of the lunar surface formations. The telescope reveals in addition a multitude of minor features such as ridges, valleys, faults, and clefts. These are all topographical or 'geological' features, objects of rock and soil; but perhaps the most interesting and certainly the most baffling of all the objects visible on the moon are the bright streaks, because they have no terrestrial counterpart. These rays, which occur most prolifically in the southern hemisphere, are well illustrated in Plate ix. They are apparently surface markings only, for they cast no shadows and are invisible under low illumination when all objects in relief cast the longest shadows; on the contrary, they are characteristically a feature of the full moon. At this time they contribute appreciably to the glare already referred to and even render invisible whole ring formations which happen to lie on the territory that they

---

*It must be remembered, however, when comparing the heights of lunar and terrestrial mountains, that whereas the latter are measured from sea level, the former are measured from a plane of reference that is roughly equivalent (on the earth) with the ocean bed.

cross. For the most part they are not distributed haphazard over the whole lunar surface but are grouped into definite systems which usually radiate in all directions from a central crater. One of the most important of these systems is that connected with the crater Tycho; the longer of the rays from this center cover hundreds of miles. Besides their shadow-lessness, their invisibility under a low sun, and their grouping into separate systems, a notable characteristic of the bright rays is their inflexibility. They proceed for hundreds of miles across broken, mountainous, and crater-strewn terrain without suffering the slightest deviation or interruption from these formations. When a ray encounters a large crater ring or mountain range it is not deflected, but merely stains the whole formation with its whiteness. In only about one known instance does another formation cause any deviation of a bright streak.

The markings and formations of the lunar surface present two major problems, as yet virtually unsolved. The first concerns these bright streaks. What is their nature, and (when that has been answered) what was their origin? If the first question could be answered conclusively, the answer to the second would probably follow. But even their nature is veiled in mystery, chiefly because of the lack of any terrestrial analogy. Since the systems radiating from central craters bear a superficial resemblance to the splashes formed when a viscous object or a squirt of liquid is projected at a hard surface, or when a solid object is thrown at a viscid or liquid one, it has been suggested by Würdemann that the streaks may be the 'splashes' of meteors that impacted with the lunar surface when it was still in a semi-liquid state. Again, it has been suggested that they may mark cracks in the lunar surface which strike out radially from the central craters and through which some white substance at a past epoch oozed up from the interior. The drawback of these theories is that they cannot explain the observed fact that in no instance does a streak throw a shadow under a low sun—that they are, in fact, flush with the surface.

Perhaps the most ingenious and attractive theory is that developed by Stewart and Buell, and supported experimentally at Princeton Observatory. It has been known for a number of years that moonlight is polarized in a manner that can be most nearly matched among terrestrial materials by powdered pumice. If the surface of the moon does largely consist of this volcanic material, it is probable that it is in a broken and shattered condition, owing to the rapidly fluctuating extremes of temperature to which it is subjected. Stewart and Buell suggested that the bright rays consist of more finely powered (and therefore more highly reflective) material that has been expelled from the central craters, either by volcanic action or as the result of meteoric impact. This fine dust would settle between the coarser grains of the surrounding lunar surface, and in this position would only be visible under a high sun; under oblique illumination it would be hidden from view in the multitudinous small shadows of the larger particles of which the surface consists.

THE MOON'S PAST HISTORY

No instrument is more powerful in the hands of scientists than mathematics. Newton generalized the laws of Kepler, showing the nature of the 'why' that underlay his 'how,' and all subsequent work has gone to ratify the universality of the law of gravitation. By its means the behavior of bodies in space can be calculated for almost any set of conditions. The physical constitution and behavior of matter, investigated in the laboratory by means of experiments which the reader can find described in any textbook of physics, also allow of mathematical expression and investigation. Thus it was that G. H. Darwin was able to proceed from premises generally believed to correspond most closely with the past condition of the solar system to a mathematical demonstration that the moon was very probably 'born' of the earth.

Before describing the results of his investigation a word must be said of the currently accepted picture of the earth's origin; it is well to bear in mind, however, that this account of the birth of planets is entirely lacking in anything approaching proof. At some epoch in the past a star is said to have swung out of the depths of space, passed comparatively near to the sun, and once more receded into the unknown. As the distance separating the two bodies—sun and star—grew steadily smaller their increasing gravitational attraction raised gigantic tides in their plastic bodies; for a similar reason the moon today raises tides in the earth's oceans. The solar tides increased in volume as the two bodies drew nearer to each other, until a point was reached when equilibrium could no longer be maintained, and a jet of solar material was drawn out toward the star. From this liquid or gaseous filament the planets later condensed.

It follows from this hypothesis that at some period in the past—the study of radioactive minerals in the earth's crust suggests some two thousand million years ago—the earth was a plastic body with a temperature of several thousand degrees; it also follows that its rotation period was very much shorter than it is today. It was from this stage in the earth's supposed early history that Darwin began his deductions. He proved that this body would contract and that the contraction would be accompanied by a steady acceleration of its rotation. Then came the crucial stage of the demonstration in which it was proved that if this acceleration increased beyond a point when the earth was rotating once in about three hours, then it would disrupt with the formation of two bodies of unequal size. At first these would be in contact and in rapid revolution about their common center of gravity. But just as the moon now raises tides in the terrestrial oceans, and as the earth's two 'parents' are supposed to have raised tides in one another, so each of the two bodies would cause enormous tides in the semi-plastic body of the other. It was shown that the immediate effect of these tides would be to put a brake upon their axial rotations: and since the angular momentum of the whole system must be conserved, this would result in the two bodies moving further apart. The moon would continue to recede from the earth until continued cooling resulted in the cessation of the tides and the assumption of their present relative positions. Observational confirmation of a single point in this hypothesis is possible. Darwin proved that not only would the tides affect the lunar orbit, but that they would also decelerate the moon's rotation until its axial rotation and its circumterrestrial revolution occupied the same period. As can be observed, this actually is so; the moon rotates on its axis in the same period as it revolves, and therefore always turns the same hemisphere to the earth. Furthermore, the oceanic tides must have a similar retarding effect on the earth's rotation, and though the effect is slight it is large enough for detection: the day is steadily but very slowly lengthening.

Thus we have sound cause to believe—it is generally regarded as proven—that at some past epoch the moon was a plastic body at a very much higher temperature, and a very much smaller distance from the earth, than at present. These facts have been made use of in one of the many attempts that have been made to solve the second great problem propounded by the moon's surface features: that of the origin of the maria and crater rings.

ORIGIN OF LUNAR 'CRATERS': METEORIC THEORY

Only two of the more interesting suggested explanations of the existence of lunar craters will be discussed here; even so, the treatment must be unsatisfactorily brief. The first supposes that the moon was once subjected to a prolonged meteoric bombardment. At this epoch it is envisaged as having lost whatever atmosphere it may once have possessed, but as having developed, through cooling, a solid crust. At each point of impact between a meteoric fragment and the lunar surface an intense temperature would have been instantaneously generated by the translation of the meteor's kinetic energy into heat energy. The resultant explosion, given a meteor of considerable mass, would have made the atom bomb look like a cap-pistol. Assuming meteors of dimensions comparable with the asteroids,* there is no difficulty in envisaging the formation of even the greatest of the walled plains by this means.

Other points in the theory's favor are the satisfactory explanation it provides of the astonishing circularity of formations often 150 miles in diameter, and its provision of a mechanism for the expulsion of jets of pulverized material called for by recent suggested explanations of the bright rays.

Two of the commoner objections that have been leveled against the meteoric theory are easily disposed of: that the earth also should be pockmarked with craters, and that since not all of the impacts would be in a vertical plane a large proportion of the craters should be elliptical. The former neglects the fact that the earth's atmosphere provides a protective screen with the moon lacks, and also that erosion and sedimentation are terrestrial smoothing agencies not to be found on the moon. The latter makes the false assumption that an oblique impact must cause an elliptical crater: if the impact were explosive, as it would be, the crater would always be circular. This fact is well known to readers who have had experience of aerial or artillery bombardment.

It is, however, a valid criticism of the meteoric theory that it cannot account for the maria, and it seems probable that these do represent areas of subsidence such as are envisaged in the seismic theory.

ORIGIN OF LUNAR 'CRATERS': SEISMIC THEORY

The seismic or tidal theory proceeds from entirely different premises. According to this hypothesis, the first age of crater formation occurred when the moon had a thin solid crust over a still molten interior which was scoured by gigantic tides raised by the comparatively near earth. The progressive cooling of the moon would result in the contraction of this crust, strain being set up in it, and the final collapse of points which were either weaker or thinner than the surrounding surface.

*See p. 205.

Each time the internal tide swept past such a rupture, the molten material would be forced up through it, enlarging it and leaving a cooling deposit round its edge. Since each vent-hole would be continuously growing, the older craters would be larger than the more recent. Finally, the crust, cooling gradually throughout this period of crater formation, would grow sufficiently thick to prevent the periodic uprushes. The maria are represented as areas of subsidence and secondary crater formation at a later epoch. The fact that they are darker than the areas of initial crater formation is explained by supposing that the less dense materials which would float to the molten surface were of a lighter hue than the denser substrata. The subsidence theory of the maria receives support from the observed fact that they contain many reduced and partially melted ring plains of a light color, relics of the primary stage which escaped complete destruction at the time of the formation of the maria.

Against the seismic theory it may well be urged that such geometrically circular formations could not invariably have resulted from the 'eating away' of the periphery of the original vent or subsidence.

It seems reasonably safe to believe that for the true explanation of the origin of the craters and maria we must look to one of these two theories, or more probably to some modification or combination of them. On the other hand, it would be invidious in a book of this nature to support one against the other: all that can be said is that the case for neither is yet proved, and that the debate continues.

THE LUNAR ATMOSPHERE

Perhaps the most striking feature of the lunar landscape, as seen telescopically, is its unrelieved starkness. Shadows are dead black, and land and surface markings hidden from the direct rays of the sun by the terminator are completely invisible. The definition is as sharp as that of a steel engraving, and half tones, gray shadows, blurred details, and soft distances are conspicuously absent. This alone would lead one to suspect that the moon has no atmosphere, for these are characteristically atmospheric effects. Still more important, objects near the limb are seen with a stark clarity which is in no way inferior to that of objects near the center of the disk. Such a dimming would inevitably result from the existence of any but an extremely rare atmosphere.

General appearances, then, lead one to suspect that the moon has no atmosphere. But this is not enough, and more specific observations can be found to confirm this conclusion. Several times a month, on the average, the moon passes in front of a tolerably bright star. Because the moon's motion is eastward the star disappears at the eastern limb and reappears at the western. If the moon had no atmosphere, the disappearance (and the reappearance) of the star would be instantaneous— at one moment the star would appear to be perched on the moon's limb and the next it would be gone. If the moon had an appreciable atmosphere the light from the star would pass through it just before reaching the limb of the moon. The star's light would gradually fade out, its color would change, and the apparent rate of approach of the star toward the limb would be changed. Many hundreds of occultations of stars by the moon have been observed and in every case the disappearance of the star has been instantaneous with no observable change in the brightness or appearance of the star just before it disappeared. Hence it is concluded that the moon has no *appreciable* atmosphere.

Observation of the occulted star cannot tell us that the moon has *no* atmosphere: on this point it can give us no information. All we are justified in concluding is that if there is an atmosphere at all, it is below a certain threshold density at which the occulation phenomena referred to would be sufficiently marked to be noticeable with our most accurate instruments. This threshold is 10^{-4} of the terrestrial; the atmospheric pressure at the surface of the moon cannot therefore be greater than one ten-thousandth of that at the surface of the earth, or 0.076 mm. of mercury. Rare though such an atmosphere would be, it would not be nonexistent.

The second pointer which indicates that the moon has not a dense atmosphere is the absence of lunar twilight. On earth darkness does not fall the instant that the sun is obscured by the horizon; higher levels of the atmosphere are still lit by the direct light of the sun for an hour or more after sunset, and the molecules of this atmosphere reflect and scatter the light, thus preserving the indirect illumination known as twilight. An observer looking at the earth from outer space would not see a sharply defined terminator separating night from day, such as we see on the moon, but a zone of appreciable width which is neither day nor night, but an insensible shading into each. It has been estimated that a lunar atmosphere with a density exceeding 10^{-5} that of the earth would cause an observable twilight effect in the cusps.

The spectroscope clinches the matter. Since the moon shines by reflected sunlight, its spectrum is a faint replica of the solar spectrum. But should the moon possess an atmosphere, it would be betrayed spectroscopically by the presence of absorption bands, provided its density is sufficiently high. For the solar light when reflected from the moon's surface would have to pass twice through its atmosphere, once before reflection and once after. Yet the lunar spectrum is identical with that of the sun, and no lines that might be attributed to lunar atmospheric absorption can be detected. There are non-solar lines, it is true, but these have all been established as telluric, i.e. caused by absorption in the earth's atmosphere. The lunar atmosphere, then, if it exists at all, does not exceed one ten-thousandth of our own in density.

THE LUNAR TEMPERATURE

From the point of view of life, the next most important environmental factor is temperature. The earth's atmosphere contains considerable quantities of water vapor, and acts as a blanket wrapped round the day-warmed hemisphere which retards the radiation of its heat into the night sky; it is well known that a clear, starlit night is colder than one that is overcast and cloudy. But whether or not the moon does possess an atmosphere 10^{-4} or 10^{-5} as dense as our own, an atmosphere of lower density than this would certainly be incapable of performing this blanketing function. Hence the lunar surface must not only get very much hotter than the earth's during the day, but also become very much colder during the night. Still more so, since the lunar days and nights are equal in length to fourteen terrestrial ones.

The measurement of the moon's temperature would be impossible were it necessary to do so directly. The measurement of very minute units of heat presents considerable practical difficulties. It is fortunate, therefore, that heat can be converted into electricity, for minute electric currents can be detected and measured more easily than minute units of heat. The galvanometer (an instrument that performs this operation) is a very much more delicate and sensitive piece of apparatus than the thermometer. If two pieces of metal—one, say, of iron and the other of copper—are soldered together and then heated, an electric current will flow between them. It has been discovered that the metals that give the strongest current for a given temperature are antimony and bismuth. A number of these antimony-bismuth units, known as thermocouples, are joined in series and connected with a highly sensitive galvanometer. Then the light and other radiation from the moon is allowed to pass through a telescope of large aperture and is focused on the bolometer; the galvanometer is read, and a simple calculation (based on data derived from laboratory experiment) permits the

temperature of the source to be deduced. It is found that the temperature of the night side of the moon is very low indeed, and different
workers are almost unanimous in their estimate of a temperature near
to absolute zero (—273° C.). This is the absolute cold, the complete
lack of heat, which characterizes interstellar space.

Unfortunately, estimates of the temperature of the sunlit side that
have been made by different workers and at different times do not agree
so closely. But the most reliable recent work on the subject makes it
probable that the temperature at the center of the sunlit hemisphere is
some 30° above the boiling point of water (130° C.); it falls off rapidly
during the long afternoon, freezing point being reached shortly before
sunset. During even the few hours that the sun is obscured at lunar
eclipse, the temperature may fall to the neighborhood of —120° C.

Thus the moon, judged by terrestrial and human standards, is not
a hospitable place. It has an atmosphere which is at best almost non-
existent, and the surface temperature fluctuates between about 200°
below zero and that of superheated steam. It is hardly surprising,
therefore, that the moon has generally been regarded as a dead world.
Within the last fifty years, however, some doubt has been cast upon this
easy assumption, notably by W. H. Pickering. Even before this time
it had been known that the face of the moon is not entirely change-
less, though such minor changes as had been noticed were consistent
with a 'topographical' explanation—that is to say, were probably in
the nature of landslides, subsidences, and the like.

TOPOGRAPHICAL CHANGE ON THE LUNAR SURFACE

The most famous case of such lunar change is that which occurred to
the crater Linné. This is a small, wall-less crater situated on the flat
expanse of Mare Serenitatis. It first figures in the map of Riccioli, constructed in 1651, where it appears as a deep crater some 4½ miles in
diameter. At the end of the eighteenth century Schröter described it as
a doubtful crater consisting of a small, brilliantly white spot. Not only
do these two accounts conflict with one another, but had the crater
been no larger during the seventeenth and eighteenth centuries than
it is today neither Riccioli nor Schröter would have been able to detect
it with their relatively primitive instruments. In 1823 Löhrmann
described it in terms reminiscent of Riccioli, and in 1831 Mädler, as
the result of several observations, stated that it was a deep, bright, and
distinct crater 6 miles in diameter. Twelve years later Schmidt confirmed this general description after having observed the crater care-

fully on eight separate occasions; he estimated its depth to be at least 1000 feet and its diameter something between 5½ and 7 miles. Up to this time, then, different observers' estimations of the size of Linné had varied widely, but, if we ignore Schröter's observation, no change of structure had been definitely established.

In October 1866 Schmidt re-observed Linné and noticed that its appearance had altered strikingly since he had last observed it twenty-three years previously: where before there had been a deep and distinct crater there was now a featureless white patch. In the following month he announced that the crater had disappeared. After several more months had elapsed he announced that a minute crater-pit, not more than a quarter of a mile in diameter, was just visible on the white patch that had replaced the vanished Linné. By 1868 this crater had increased in diameter to about one and a half miles. Today Linné appears to be a small crater about one mile in diameter.

It may be regarded as established that Linné is now smaller than it was during the period 1651-1866. Its disappearance and what looked like its replacement by a white cloud in the latter year may possibly be explained as the subsidence and collapse of the original deep crater, though the subsequent formation and gradual growth of the present crater is puzzling.

OTHER TYPES OF LUNAR SURFACE CHANGE

The floor of the crater Plato has also furnished some well-attested examples of lunar surface change. This crater floor is of a dark tint, smooth and featureless but for a number of minute crater-pits interconnected by a system of faint rays. Independent observers at different times have reported the disappearance of some of these pits, and it is safe to say that their visibility is variable. In addition to these unpredictable disappearances, the floor of Plato itself is subject to a periodic variation of brightness, the depth of tint being dependent on the time of lunar day (terrestrial month). This is impossible to explain by recourse to any 'topographical' theory of lunar change, and leads us on to the work of Pickering and his followers, which within the last half century has strongly suggested—although the suggestion has not been universally or even widely accepted—that some primitive form of vegetable life may still carry on a precarious existence on the moon's surface.

THE PARTLY BRIGHT AREAS

The first discovery produced by Pickering's intensive study of the moon was that of the new type of surface feature which he named the partly bright areas. These are small, light-colored areas which most usually occur on broken ground—crater floors and ramparts, and the upper slopes of mountain ranges are common sites. What gives these partly bright areas their outstanding interest is the fact that their brightness varies with the lunar day. Some twenty-four (terrestrial) hours after sunrise they begin to fade and decrease in size, and by the middle of the lunar afternoon they may have disappeared completely. Presumably they increase in size again during the long lunar night, for when they are next visible soon after the following sunrise their size and intensity is once more maximal. The peculiar nature of this variation—the size and brightness of the area being inversely proportional to the sun's altitude—suggested to Pickering that they might possibly be deposits of snow or, more probably, hoarfrost. As we have seen, other considerations indicate that the moon has long been without any trace of water; nevertheless, no more satisfactory explanation of these partly bright areas has yet been proposed.

THE VARIABLE SPOTS

The next feature to be discovered—also by Pickering—which hinted that the picture of a dead and waterless moon might need some revision was the variable spots. These spots first appear some hours after sunrise and increase in size and depth of color to a maximum some hours before sunset, when a rapid change in the opposite direction sets in; by the time the sun sets, and the terminator reaches the spot, its color is normal once again, and as a spot it no longer exists. Variable spots are not found within about 30° of the poles, and the nearer a spot is to the equator the more rapid is its cycle of changes. What are these spots, and what is the significance of their monthly changes? Pickering asked whether they might not be patches of some kind of lunar vegetation. This explanation, though once again at variance with earlier ideas concerning the nature of the moon's surface and of the conditions prevailing upon it, gives a satisfactory account of the phenomena that it sets out to explain.

But the revolutionary implications and disregard of theoretical considerations which characterize Pickering's theories have resulted in their somewhat unenthusiastic reception by the astronomical fraternity.

MECHANISM OF ECLIPSES

The moon, in revolving about the earth, traces out a great circle upon the star sphere. Similarly the sun describes in the course of a year the great circle known as the ecliptic. The two points where these circles intersect are called nodes: the ascending node where the moon crosses from the south to the north of the ecliptic, and the descending node where it passes back again from north to south. When the sun and moon are at opposite nodes simultaneously, the earth will lie directly between them, since the nodes are 180° apart; in this case a lunar eclipse will occur. Hence it is that eclipses of the moon can only occur at or

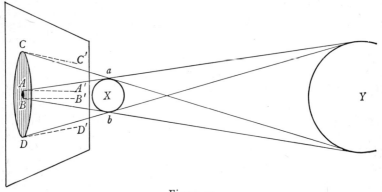

Figure 41.

near full moon. Thus there are two important differences between lunar eclipses and those of the sun: the former always occur at full moon, and it is the earth's shadow on the moon's surface that is observed; the latter occur at new moon, and this time it is the moon's shadow which crosses the earth's surface.

To say that the moon is in eclipse, therefore, means that it is passing through the earth's shadow. This circular shadow, as it sweeps across the moon's surface, is seen to consist of a dark central core, or umbra, surrounded by a less dense fringe called the penumbra. The formation of these two zones in the shadow is explained in Fig. 41, which shows a spherical body casting a shadow upon a flat surface; the illuminator is likewise a spherical body and not a point source. Actual experiment will demonstrate that the outer edge of the penumbra and the junction of the umbra and penumbra are not sharply defined, as in the diagram, but are hazy and indeterminate. A little thought, and the inspection of the figure, will show why the two shadow zones are formed. An observer stationed in the umbra AB will discover that the illuminating body is completely blotted from his vision by the eclipsing body; no light from the source can penetrate the cone $ABba$. An observer under the penumbra CD will not see a totally eclipsed illuminator, but a partially eclipsed one. The further he is from the umbra—i.e. the nearer to the outer edge of the penumbra—the smaller will be the fraction of the illuminating body that is observed to be eclipsed, and the lighter will be the tone of the shadow upon the screen.

Now suppose that the body X is in motion, so that its shadow moves across the screen. The umbra will trace out some such zone as $AA'BB'$, and the penumbra the zone $CC'DD'$. We have now reproduced the mechanism of eclipses. In the case of a lunar eclipse, Y is the sun, X the earth, and the screen the moon's surface (here represented, for simplicity, as a flat instead of a curved surface).

If the sun and moon reach, not opposite, but the same node simultaneously, then a central solar eclipse will occur. The fact that there is not a total solar eclipse at each new moon proves conclusively, without its being necessary to plot the paths of the sun and moon on a star map, that these two paths do not lie in the same plane. That is, that the planes containing the orbit of the moon and the apparent orbit of the sun (the terrestrial appearance of the earth's circumsolar orbit) are inclined to one another; since they both pass through the center of the earth, they must nevertheless intersect. The necessary result of this inclination of the ecliptic to the moon's path is that when either the sun or moon are not near a node there cannot be an eclipse.

Suppose that the sun and moon reach a node, not simultaneously, but in close succession. The body of the moon will then not completely cover that of the sun, and the result will be a partial solar eclipse (see Fig. 42). The farther the sun is from the node, the smaller will be the fraction of its disk which is obscured. Beyond a certain distance (which is easily calculable) there will, of course, be no eclipse at all.

At the same time, it must be noted that the simultaneous arrival of both bodies at the same node does not inevitably result in a total solar eclipse, though the eclipse must under these conditions always be central. For we have seen that planetary orbits are not circles but ellipses, one of whose foci is occupied by the center of the sun. Hence the distance of the moon from the earth and of the earth from the sun are subject to small variations which cause a variation in the apparent sizes of any two of the bodies concerned as seen from the third. Thus it is possible for the earth and the moon to assume positions in their respective orbits such that the angular diameter of the moon is slightly smaller than that of the sun. Under these circumstances, and when the centers of the sun and the moon are in the same line of sight, the sun will not be totally obscured: a narrow rim of photosphere will show round the moon's limb. Such eclipses are called annular, from the Latin *annulus,* a ring.

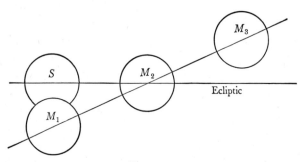

Figure 42.

The distances and sizes of the moon and sun are related in such a way that the shadow of the former on the earth's surface cannot exceed 167 miles in diameter; usually it is much less than this. Thus as the moon moves across the face of the sun its shadow traces out a comparatively narrow band across the earth's surface. An observer stationed more than about 84 miles from the center of the totality zone (assuming that its size is maximal) will see a narrow lune of sun round the moon's limb at the moment of the nearest approach to totality; he will, in fact, observe a partial eclipse. The further away he moves, the larger will be the observed solar lune. If he is situated more than about 2000 miles from the center of the totality zone he will observe no eclipse at all. These zones of course correspond exactly with the umbra and penumbra of lunar eclipses. The totality zone is the umbra of the moon's shadow; the zone from which the eclipse is observed as partial, is the penumbra. $AA'B'B$, in Fig. 41, is the totality zone, and the wider area covered by the penumbra (still a band-shaped zone, longer than it is wide) is the 4000-odd mile wide zone of the earth's surface from which the sun appears to be partially eclipsed, and which therefore receives some light direct from the sun.

LUNAR ECLIPSE PHENOMENA

When the sun and moon reach their respective nodes at the same time, the moon will be totally eclipsed, i.e. the whole disk will lie under the umbra. If they do not, the earth's shadow will sweep across a section of the lunar disk only. Under these circumstances, nothing but the penumbra may fall on the moon, but at total eclipses the shadow can be clearly seen to consist of a central dark umbra and a peripheral, lighter penumbra.

Since, in eclipses of the moon, it is the shadow upon the observed object that is seen, and not the eclipsing body itself as in the case of solar eclipses, a lunar eclipse is visible over the whole terrestrial hemisphere from which the moon is visible. We have seen that the lunar territory under the umbra receives no direct light from the sun. It might therefore be expected that it would be invisible. Actually, however, the totally eclipsed moon is only reduced in brightness, and usually rendered a deep red color: it is still visible, and—on account of its color—very strikingly so. The reason for this visibility is that the earth's atmosphere refracts the sun's rays, bending them into the shadow cone, just as a stick held partly under water appears to be bent. Thus all the light that illuminates the totally eclipsed moon has passed through the earth's atmosphere, and for this reason terrestrial meteorological conditions (especially the incidence of clouds) affect the appearance of a lunar eclipse. The redness of the refracted light is due to the preferential action of the atmosphere upon the radiation of mixed wave-lenghts of which sunlight is composed. The blue light is scattered, while the atmosphere has little effect on the red, which it transmits almost in its entirety. It is for the same reason, as has already been pointed out, that the day sky is blue, and that sunsets (when the sun's light has to pass through a maximum thickness of atmosphere) are red.

THE PLANETARY FAMILY

The order of the planets from the sun outward is Mercury, Venus, Earth, Mars, Jupiter, Saturn, Uranus, Neptune, and (most distant and most recently discovered of all) Pluto. We saw in Chapter III that the distances of the sun and moon can be discovered by the parallactic method, either directly or indirectly. Further, that the distances of the planets may be similarly determined; and, since the distance of the earth from the sun is known, we can arrive at the solar distances of those planets too remote for direct investigation, by the application of Kepler's third law. By a close observation of the motions and successive positions of each planet, it is also possible, with the assistance of the laws enunciated by Kepler and Newton, to reconstruct its complete orbit: to discover its eccentricity, the lengths of the major and minor axes (the planet's greatest and least distances from the sun), the period of revolution, and the velocity of the planet in any part of its orbit.

MERCURY: SOLAR DISTANCE

In this way it has been established that the mean distance of Mercury from the sun is 36 million miles, or about one third of the earth's. But the orbit is markedly eccentric—more so than that of any other major planet except Pluto—with the result that the solar distance varies considerably with different positions of the radius vector: it may be as great as 43 million miles or as little as 28 million. Thus Mercury's distance from the sun varies by about 42 per cent of its mean value, as compared with the earth's 3 per cent. This alone will cause appreciable temperature differences at the Mercurian surface at different times during its year.

MERCURY: OBSERVATION

But even 43 million miles is a relatively small distance, and it is this nearness of Mercury to the sun that causes the apparent proximity of the two bodies in the sky; we have seen that Mercury can never be further than about 28° from the sun. This restriction has important practical effects, for it means that whenever Mercury is visible to the naked eye it is near the horizon—certainly not more than about 20° from it—either the eastern horizon a short time before sunrise or the western horizon just after sunset. Now the least favorable way of observing a celestial object is to view it when it is near the horizon, for it is then being seen through a maximum thickness of atmosphere (see Fig. 43). The effect of the atmosphere upon telescopic 'seeing' is comparable with that of a thick, cloudy plate-glass window of uneven thickness and density, and studded with flaws, interposed between the observer and the object observed; a window, moreover, which is in constant and erratic motion. Fortunately, Mercury is a bright object, and it is this fact that allows the difficulty to be overcome. For when its position in the sky is known—as, through the application of Kepler's laws, it is known, and recorded in almanacs—it can be picked up telescopically during the daytime. Its altitude above the horizon is then greater than in the evening or early morning, and the effects of the atmosphere upon the 'seeing' are therefore lessened.

Those who aspire to see Mercury with the naked eye will do well to note the following facts. Elongations, when Mercury and the sun are, as seen from the earth, farthest apart, and when the interval between the rising (and setting) of the two bodies is greatest, are most favorable in the north hemisphere when they occur in spring or autumn, for then the ecliptic makes its largest angle with the horizon. Maximum elongations east in March or April (evening observation),

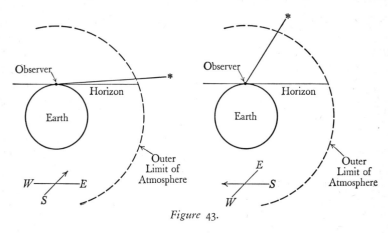

Figure 43.

or maximum elongation west when it occurs in September or October (morning observation), consequently provide the best conditions. Telescopic viewing will of course show that it is dichotomized at these times.

MERCURY: AXIAL ROTATION

Mercury's sidereal period is easily determined by inspection, allowance being made for the observer's motion, and is found to be a little less than eighty-eight days: this is the planet's 'year,' or period of circumsolar revolution. But its period of axial rotation is less easily determined, and is, indeed, not yet beyond doubt. The obvious directions to an observer wishing to determine a planet's rotation period are as follows. Observe the transit of some conspicuous surface marking across the planet's central meridian, note the time, observe the next transit, again note the time, and then subtract the first time from the second. But, unfortunately, Mercury exhibits no sharply defined markings that can be used for this purpose. Such markings as it has are so vague in outline that it requires telescopes of considerable aperture, employed when the planet is high above the horizon, to show them at all; even so, their ill-defined nature renders them quite unsuitable for the determination of the rotation period. Schröter believed that Mercury rotates on its axis in about twenty-four hours, and this view was generally accepted until 1889, when Schiaparelli suggested the much longer period of eighty-eight days, that in which Mercury completes one revolution of the sun. If this is so, Mercury always turns the same hemisphere toward the sun, just as the moon always turns the same face inward to the earth. This longer period is consonant with the negative results of the attempt made at Mt. Wilson to measure with a thermocouple the radiation from the dark side of Mercury, which also suggest that one hemisphere never receives direct heat from the sun.

How difficult it is to estimate the rotation period from observations of surface markings may be appreciated from the fact that the angular diameter of Mercury at elongation is the same as that of a twenty-five cent piece seen from a distance of about half a mile. This difficulty is aggravated by the persistent lack of sharply defined markings of any kind, the characteristic features being vague areas of a slightly darker tone than the general background of the planet's disk. Other observations which have been described at various times are a blunting of the cusps when the planet is in the crescent phase, irregularities in the outline of the terminator, and certain minute projections over the limb.

MERCURY: TEMPERATURE

Were it possible to isolate the problem of the rotation period from all others connected with the planet, this hiatus in our knowledge would not be of any great importance. But this cannot be done, for the problem is intimately bound up with the further problem of the temperature at the planet's surface. If one hemisphere is always turned toward the sun and the other never receives any solar light and heat whatever, the temperature difference between the two will be considerable. But if, on the other hand, Mercury rotates rapidly upon its axis, the difference of temperature between the sunlit side and the dark will be very much smaller. Radiometric measurements undertaken at Mt. Wilson Observatory indicate a mean temperature of about 340° C. for the center of the sunlit side. Owing to the great variations in Mercury's distance from the sun, to which attention has already been drawn, this will vary between a minimum of about 280° to a maximum in the neighborhood of 410°. As one travels from the sub-solar point* toward the edge of the illuminated hemisphere the altitude of the sun will decrease (since Mercury, like the earth, is a spherical body) and the temperature will drop. The temperature of the dark side seems to be very low indeed, and no radiation from it of measurable intensity can be detected with our present instruments. The extremely high temperature of the center of the sunlit side of Mercury (about equal to that of molten zinc and nearly twice that of molten tin) is of course due to the planet's relatively small solar distance, while the great difference between the temperatures of the sunlit and the dark hemispheres confirms the longer rotation period.

MERCURY: ATMOSPHERE

Though the lack of definite knowledge regarding the rotation of Mercury must also render our knowledge of its temperature regrettably inexact, one thing is certain. On account of its proximity to the sun and its high temperature (whatever the precise figure may be), Mercury cannot possibly have retained such atmosphere as it may once have possessed. The factor controlling the retention or loss of a planet's atmosphere is the difference between the velocity of its constituent molecules and the velocity at which any body could escape permanently from the planet's gravitational grasp. The first of these velocities is determined by the temperature of the atmosphere (since the hotter a gas is, the greater is the velocity of its component particles), and by the mass of the molecules concerned. The second depends upon the planet's mass (since a greater mass involves more powerful gravitational attraction upon the atmospheric particles, and correspondingly higher velocities are required in order to escape from that attraction), and upon its radius (since the atmosphere is farther away from the center of mass of a large planet than that of a smaller one).

We have already seen that the temperature of the sunlit side of Mercury is very high. If the planet has any atmosphere, convection currents would cause a circulation of air that would raise the temperature of all the atmosphere to a uniformly high value. Calculations show that the molecules of any atmosphere that Mercury may have will be moving with speeds considerably higher than, for example, those of the earth's atmosphere. Escape of molecules may therefore be expected unless the planet's gravitational pull is correspondingly greater than the earth's. But it has been found that this is not so, and the raising

*That is, the point on the surface at which the sun is directly overhead.

of the first threshold together with the lowering of the second make it quite certain that Mercury cannot have retained an atmosphere. As in the case of the moon, this conclusion is verified by the spectroscope, for the spectrum of Mercury bears no trace of absorptions other than telluric.

MERCURY: LINEAR DIMENSIONS

That Mercury's gravitational pull is less than that of the earth may be suspected as soon as its linear size is determined. This can easily be done—all that is required is the measurement of its angular diameter. This is found to vary from 5″ to 13″ according to the relative positions of Mercury and the earth in their respective orbits. Since the distance separating the two bodies is known, one has only to calculate what linear diameter would be required to give the observed apparent diameter at the distance in question. This linear diameter has been found to be about 3000 miles. Mercury is thus a much smaller body than the earth, only about half as big again as the moon. The surface gravity of a planet, i.e. the gravitational pull of the planet for a unit mass on its surface, may be shown to be directly proportional to the radius of the planet and to the density of the material of which the planet is constructed. Accordingly, if Mercury is made up of the same sort of material as is the earth, the surface gravity would be only three-eighths that on the surface of the earth. This would mean that a man weighing 200 pounds on the earth would only weigh 75 pounds on Mercury, although his mass would be the same. However, we cannot be certain of this value of the surface gravity until we have determined the mass of Mercury, since density is directly proportion to mass and inversely proportional to the volume of the object.

MERCURY: MASS

The most accurate method of determining a planet's mass is by a study of the motions and orbits of its satellites and the application of the laws of motion. But Mercury has no satellite, and we are thrown back upon the less accurate and more tedious method of perturbations. As Newton discovered, any two bodies attract one another with a force that is dependent upon certain properties and relations of those bodies. Hence Mercury's gravitational pull on Venus, for instance, will affect or per-turb Venus' orbital motion. A careful study of the nature and degree of this perturbation allows the mass of Mercury to be calculated by the application of Newton's laws, though the comparative proximity of both planets to the very much more massive sun largely deadens the perturbations, and the result is correspondingly inaccurate. As would be expected from its small size, however, the mass of Mercury is considerably less than that of the earth—only about 4 per cent.

MERCURY: TRANSIT PHENOMENA

Several other observations that confirm the conclusion that Mercury has no atmosphere must be noticed in passing. When one of the inner planets approaches the limb of the sun it is being lit from 'behind' by an extremely brilliant light. This light must pass through any atmosphere that the planet may possess, thus rendering it visible as a bright halo. Venus, which is known to possess a dense atmosphere, exhibits such a halo when passing into and out of transit, but nothing of the sort is to be seen surrounding the limb of Mercury under similar circumstances.

MERCURY: ALBEDO

The planet's albedo suggests the same conclusion. When a beam of light is directed upon an object a certain proportion only is reflected. Different types of surface reflect the incident light in different degrees, but no terrestrial object or substance is more highly reflective than newly fallen snow, which returns about 75 per cent of the incident light. This reflected fraction or percentage of the incident light is known as the albedo of the surface; the albedo of snow, for instance, is 75 per cent or 0.75. The albedo of clouds is also high—that of some terrestrial clouds is about 70 per cent. In the same way, those planets known to have atmospheres have high albedos; those of Venus and Jupiter are about 60 per cent and 50 per cent respectively. Not only do those bodies with dense atmospheres have high albedos, but the moon, with no appreciable atmosphere, has a low one—about 7 per cent only. And measurements of the albedo of Mercury show that it also is 7 per cent.

Thus in many respects Mercury and the moon may be regarded as similar bodies. Both are considerably smaller than the earth; both are without appreciable atmospheres; they are consequently subject to greater extremes of temperature than the earth; and their identical albedos would suggest that the nature of their surfaces is similar or identical.

VENUS: SOLAR DISTANCE, SIZE AND MASS

No difficulty is to be encountered in finding Venus, provided that it is not too near conjunction. It is more conspicuous than Mercury because it is larger and nearer to the earth; it is also brighter both because its albedo is a higher and because at elongations it is farther from the sun and therefore shines from a darker sky.

We have seen how Mercury's distance from the earth and from the sun, its linear size, and its mass may be determined; the methods of determination are the same in the case of Venus, and need not be again described. Suffice it to say that in many respects Venus is more like the earth, and less like the moon, than Mercury. Its diameter of about 7600 miles is only slightly less than that of the earth, and its mass is about four fifths of the earth's. Hence the value of g at the surface of Venus is only about 20 per cent less than that at the terrestrial surface. Provided, then, that the temperatures of the two bodies are not of a very different order, Venus may be expected to have an atmosphere.

VENUS: TEMPERATURE AND ATMOSPHERE

The questions of Venus's temperature and rotation period have received less certain answers than those of Mercury's. Its orbit lies within the earth's, though farther from the sun than that of Mercury, its mean solar distance being 67 million miles. The orbit is almost circular—less eccentric, in fact, than that of any other planet—and this value does not vary by more than one million miles throughout the course of the planet's year. It might be expected, therefore, that its temperature is somewhat higher than that of the earth though considerably lower than that of Mercury. Calculation, based upon its solar distance, would suggest a temperature of over 100° C., yet direct measurements record the very much lower figure of about —25° C. for both sunlit and dark sides. It is certain, however, that the relation between its temperature and its mass is such that it could have retained the molecules of all but perhaps the lightest gases.

Every line of independent research substantiates this result. Venus's albedo is high: between 60 per cent and 65 per cent. Although this is a little lower than the albedo of the brightest terrestrial clouds, it is higher than that of any known surface of rock or soil, and would suggest most strongly that we are not looking down on the solid surface of the planet but upon the upper layers of a dense vaporous atmosphere. That this atmosphere is both dense and deep is shown by two further observations. When describing the appearance of the totally eclipsed moon we found that a gaseous envelope is penetrated more deeply by red light than by blue; that is, by radiations of long wave-lengths than radiations of short. Yet photographs of Venus taken in infra-red light, the wave-length of which is even longer than that of visible red light, resemble closely the naked-eye appearance of the planet: they show a perfectly uniform and featureless surface. We must therefore conclude that even the infra-red radiations do not penetrate the fog blanket to the depth of the solid surface, and that the infra-red photographs merely depict a lower atmosphere level than that visible to the naked eye.

That it is not only dense but deep may be discovered from transit observations. The atmospheric halo that surrounds Venus when just outside the sun's limb has already been alluded to. Since the distances from the earth to all points on Venus's orbit are known, the measure-ment of the angular thickness of this halo will give us its linear thick-ness. In this way it has been established that the atmosphere of Venus cannot be less than 50 to 70 miles deep.

VENUS: SPECTROSCOPIC EVIDENCE

All these telescopic indications of the existence of a dense atmosphere are confirmed by the spectroscope. Even if the atmosphere is so dense that no light can penetrate as deep as the planet's surface, some of it will penetrate for a small distance, at least, before being scattered and reflected; absorption bands will accordingly be present in the spectrum.

A faint band in the infra-red region has been identified as that of carbon dioxide. Curiously enough, the absorptions of water are not found in the spectrum of Venus, despite the impenetrability of its atmosphere; neither are those of oxygen. It does not follow, however, that these gases do not occur in the atmosphere of Venus, but only that they do not occur in measurable quantities (about one thousandth of the concentration in the earth's atmosphere, in the case of oxygen) in the upper atmospheric regions which constitute the planet's visible surface. Sunlight only penetrates a comparatively short way into the fog blanket, and what the constitution of the lower levels may be we have no means of knowing. This being so, it is possible that light is thrown on the apparent absence of water in the atmosphere of Venus by the fact that nearly all the water vapor in the terrestrial atmosphere occurs within 7 miles of the earth's surface—that is to say, in the lowest atmospheric levels.

VENUS: AXIAL ROTATION

The fact that no surface markings are visible renders the estimation of the rotation period more difficult than that of Mercury. It is true that Venus's disk does bear some markings, but these are not of a type suited to the purpose of recording the period of the planet's rotation. They are vague, grayish areas, particularly noticeable near the terminator when Venus is in crescent phase, and are certainly atmospheric. Nevertheless, the older observers concluded that Venus rotates upon its axis in about the same period as the earth. Schiaparelli, however, favored a much longer period, and suggested 225 terrestrial days as the correct period. If this is so, the temperature difference between the sunlit and dark hemispheres must be considerable; yet bolometric measurements, although indicating a lower temperature than might be expected, show only a negligible difference of temperature between the two hemispheres, indicating that the dark side does radiate a measurable amount of heat. This appears to eliminate the very long period favored by Schiaparelli, and though nothing is yet certain, it is probable that the planet's day is longer than several terrestrial weeks but shorter than one terrestrial year.

The determination of the rotation period by means of the Doppler effect at opposite limbs is made difficult by the fact that when both limbs are visible (at superior conjunction) the angular diameter of the disk is too small for measurements to be made. Conversely, when the disk is large enough for accurate work to be undertaken, only one of the limbs is visible and therefore the size of the shift is reduced by half. Not too much weight can therefore be attached to such results as have been obtained, and the only conclusion that can be drawn from their negative character is that the rotation is not rapid, and is probably not completed in a period shorter than several weeks.

VENUS: PHASES

Venus, moving in an orbit nearer the sun than that of the earth, exhibits a full series of phases. When it is farthest from the earth, at superior conjunction, it will be fully illuminated; as it approaches and then reaches elongation, it will become first gibbous (i.e. of a shape intermediate between full and dichotomy) and then dichotomized; and as it proceeds from elongation to inferior conjunction it becomes an increasingly fine crescent, until at inferior conjunction it is invisible, having its illuminated hemisphere turned directly away from the earth. Now the distance separating Venus from the earth varies from about

26 million to 160 million miles, and this considerable difference is correlated with wide variations in its angular size. At superior conjunction the angular diameter is only 11″, while near inferior conjunction as a very fine sickle, the diameter is 64″. Hence the larger the fraction of the whole disk that is illuminated, the smaller is its angular diameter. For this reason Venus is not brightest when fully illuminated, but when a thick crescent, corresponding in phase to the five-day-old moon. At this time Venus is the most brilliant object in the sky (the sun and moon excepted); it is about fourteen times as bright as the brightest star, and is visible to the naked eye in broad daylight.

MARS: OBSERVATIONAL ADVANTAGES

Although Mars, the earth's neighbor on the side farthest from the sun, is smaller than Venus and never approaches as near the earth, yet we have a much more exact knowledge of its size and mass and of the physical conditions prevailing upon its surface. This is due to three factors in particular: the orbit of Mars lies outside that of the earth whereas that of Venus lies within it; Mars has two satellites; and Mars has a clear atmosphere which permits study of the actual surface of the planet. It will be remembered, in connection with the last point, that the surface of Venus is hidden from us and that of Mercury is seen with difficulty owing to the smallness of the disk and its unfavorable position for observation.

Figure 19 shows that when Venus is fully illuminated it is farthest from the earth and consequently subtends the smallest angle at the observer's eye; when it is near and comparatively large in angular measurement only a small fraction of the hemisphere that is turned toward the earth is illuminated. These circumstances represent a grave hindrance to telescopic study, a hindrance to which the study of the outer planets is not subject. It will be clear from Fig. 44 that the earth and Mars are nearest one another when the line joining them would, if produced, pass through the sun. When Mars is in such a position in respect of the earth it is said to be in opposition; it is then 180° removed from the sun and culminates at midnight. It is particularly to be noted that, unlike an inner planet, Mars is fully illuminated when nearest the earth and therefore subtending the greatest possible angle at the observer's eye: a concourse of circumstances that greatly aids satisfactory observation. Mars does not, of course, exhibit a complete cycle of phases as the inner planets do, but when in quadrature it is noticeably gibbous.

MARS: GEOCENTRIC POSITIONS AND LINEAR SIZE

There is another feature of Mars's orbit which is of the greatest practical importance and which must therefore be mentioned. The orbit is, like that of Mercury and unlike that of Venus, markedly eccentric. The planet's mean solar distance is 142 million miles, with a variation of some 13 million on either side. One result of this eccentricity will be seen from Fig. 44. If a number of radiating lines are drawn from the sun to the Martian orbit it will be found that the sections of these lines that lie between the orbits of Mars and the earth are of different lengths. That is, at some oppositions Mars is nearer the earth than at others.

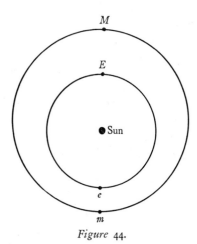

Figure 44.

When the two bodies are in the positions *m* and *e* respectively the opposition distance is minimal, and the opposition will be a particularly favorable one for observational purposes. The distance of Mars under these circumstances of favorable opposition is 35 million miles—9 million miles farther than Venus when at inferior conjunction. At least favorable oppositions the distance may be as great as 63 million miles, while at conjunction Mars recedes to an average distance of 235 million miles; it then has an angular diameter of only 3".5, and is an inconspicuous object in the morning or evening twilight.

But at favorable oppositions its angular diameter is 25", an angle subtended, at a distance of 35,000,000 miles, by a linear distance of 4200 miles. As regards size, Mars is thus intermediate between the earth and the moon.

MARS: MASS

Mars has two satellites, and this fact allows its mass and thence its surface gravity to be calculated with much greater facility and accuracy than is the case of moonless planets such as Mercury or Venus. On page 65 the Newtonian modification of Kepler's harmonic law is discussed briefly. Let us call M the mass of the earth, m the mass of the moon, A the mean distance of the moon from the earth, and P the sidereal period of the moon about the earth. Now using $M_p, m_s, a,$ and p for the corresponding quantities for the planet and its satellite we have

$$\frac{M_p + m_s}{M + m} = \frac{P^2 a^3}{p^2 A^3} \; .$$

From this the mass of the planet and its satellite may be computed in terms of the known masses of the earth and moon and the observed periods and distances. In case the planet has two or more moon's, as in the case of Mars, the effects of their masses can be eliminated and the mass of the planet determined with considerable accuracy.

This method is not only simpler but also more accurate than that dependent upon perturbations, and it is found that the mass of Mars is 11 per cent of the earth's; from this, and its known linear size, it follows that its surface gravity is only 38 per cent that of the earth's.

MARS: TEMPERATURE AND ATMOSPHERE

Mars is half as far again from the sun as the earth, and radiometric work has shown that its surface is correspondingly cooler. During the day the temperature in equatorial regions probably rises to $10°$ C., but during the night it falls to at least $-85°$ C., extremes which are consistent with a rarefied atmosphere. Considerations of this fact and of the known mass of the planet show that the velocity of escape is high enough for Mars to have retained an atmosphere, though one of lower density than that of the earth. A number of independent observations confirm this and establish quite definitely that a Martian atmosphere exists. Perhaps the most striking of these proofs is that provided by photographs of the planet taken in infra-red and ultra-violet light by means of color screens. Mars as depicted in the former is similar in appearance to the planet as photographed with ordinary light or as seen with the naked eye, all features known to be surface markings (they will be described shortly) being shown. But the ultra-violet photographs show a featureless blank. Clearly, the infra-red radiation has penetrated the atmosphere to the surface and thence been reflected to the camera in the terrestrial observatory. But the ultra-violet radiation of short wave-length is scattered in the upper reaches of the atmosphere, never reaching the surface; the ultra-violet photographs, in fact, are photographs of the planet's atmosphere. The particular significance of the photographs, however, lies in the fact that the images of the Martian disk are of different sizes in the two series, the ultra-violet and the infra-red: in the former they are measurably larger than in the latter. Obviously, then, since the former record the outer limits of the atmosphere and the latter the body of the planet itself, the difference between the sizes of the two sets of images represents twice the thickness of the Martian atmosphere. By careful measurement of this difference it has been estimated that the atmosphere of Mars is at least 60 miles in depth.

The albedo of Mars is higher than that of Mercury or the moon, though not so high as that of Venus—about 15 per cent. This is not incompatible with the assumption that Mars has a clear and, compared with the terrestrial, rather rare atmosphere; that it is clear is shown, too, by the fact that we can see the surface of the planet through it. Three other corroboratory facts should be noted. When the planet is in the gibbous phase a distinct twilight zone is observed; furthermore, surface details situated near the limb are fainter than those at the center of the disk, and than themselves when in the latter position. This, as has already been pointed out, can only be accounted for on the supposition that there is a rarefied atmosphere overlying them and that it is the greater thickness of this atmosphere through which the objects near the limb must be viewed that causes their partial obscuration. Finally, clouds have been observed floating above the Martian surface, especially near the limb where the sun is rising, and this would appear to put the matter beyond all doubt.

MARS: SPECTROSCOPIC EVIDENCE

The spectroscope, as usual, provides the final and conclusive piece of evidence. The bands of water vapor have been identified in the Martian spectrum, as also have those of oxygen. The atmosphere is nevertheless rare by terrestrial standards, and it has been estimated that at the Martian surface the concentration of these two gases cannot exceed about 5 per cent and 15 per cent respectively of that in the terrestrial atmosphere. More recent work has suggested that the latter figure may be too high, and that the incidence of oxygen is nearer 0.1 per cent of the earth's.

It is worthy of note, in passing, that the spectra of Mercury, Venus, and Mars are in complete contrast with one another: that of Mercury lacks all trace of atmospheric absorptions, that of Venus contains bands due to carbon dioxide but none of oxygen or water vapor, while that of Mars has unmistakable absorptions due to these two gases.

MARS: SURFACE FEATURES

A glance at Mars with quite a small telescope, when the planet is in favorable opposition, will reveal that the general color of the surface is orange and that a number of greenish markings are superimposed upon it. The old astronomers called these blue-green areas maria, or seas, and the name has persisted although it is now understood that they are not areas of water; for one thing, the sun is never reflected in them as it would be if they were liquid surfaces. In 1719 were seen for the first time the features to which the name polar caps was given. Mars rotates upon its axis in about $24\frac{1}{2}$ hours, and at each pole of this axis is situated an approximately circular white patch. The color and position of these patches suggested the obvious conclusion that they were composed of snow and ice, and were in every way analogous with our terrestrial polar icefields.

MARS: SEASONAL CHANGES

This guess was elevated from the realm of supposition when their changes of appearance were worked out in detail. Mars's axis of rotation is, like the earth's, inclined to the plane of its orbit,* and it is the varying position of this axis relative to the sun, as the planet moves round its orbit, that causes the change of seasons: when the northern hemisphere is inclined inward toward the center of the orbit it is summer in the northern hemisphere and winter in the southern, and vice versa. When the northern half of the axis is just beginning to tilt over toward the sun—when midwinter has just passed in the northern hemisphere—it will be noticed that two changes occur: the northern polar cap begins to shrink, while the southern, which has been small during the past summer, begins to grow larger. As the northern, 'summer' cap continues to shrink it is often seen to be surrounded by a dark band. For some time this band increases in width, its outer edge remaining approximately stationary while its inner edge remains contiguous with the retreating cap. At the same time the tint

*That is, to a Martian (as to a terrestrial) observer, the ecliptic is inclined to the celestial equator.

of the greenish areas of the northern hemisphere begins to deepen, the darkening being first noticed in the vicinity of the cap itself and thence spreading south toward the equator.

The generally accepted explanation of these annual changes is that with the coming of summer and the gradual rising of the temperature in the summer hemisphere, the polar cap begins to melt. The appearance of the dark band surrounding the diminishing cap would seem to indicate the existence of a temporary sea; on account of the prevailing low atmospheric pressure, however, it is unlikely that water in the liquid state could exist—the snow evaporating straight into water vapor without passing through the liquid stage. However this may be, the released water vapor disseminates throughout the atmosphere of the whole hemisphere, traveling southward. The darkening of the green areas is regarded as the germination and proliferation of some form of plant life under the stimulus of increased temperature and the liberated moisture. The polar caps provide another proof of the existence of a Martian atmosphere, for their changes are only explicable on the assumption of the alternate evaporation and precipitation of water into and from an overlying atmosphere. The conjecture, to be found in old textbooks of descriptive astronomy, that the caps may consist of solid carbon dioxide as now known to have been unfounded, since the temperature may be higher than the vaporizing point of this gas ($-80°$ C.) while the deposit is still in the ground.

MARS: THE 'CANALS'

At the favorable opposition of Mars which occurred in 1877 Schiaparelli announced the discovery of a new type of Martian surface feature, to which he gave the name *canali*. These appeared to him as faint dusky streaks, more or less straight, which traversed the orange areas of the planet's disk. The Italian word *canale* connotes 'channel' rather than 'canal,' and it is therefore unfortunate that the English-speaking world accepted the translation 'canal,' which the *Concise Oxford Dictionary* defines as 'an artificial watercourse for inland navigation'; no idea of artificiality is associated with the Italian *canale*. It is probably this circumstance, more than any other, that has convinced the popular mind of the existence of 'Martians,' for which there is no direct evidence whatsoever.

Two years later Schiaparelli confirmed his original observations. At neither of these oppositions was any other observer able to see the *canali* and, until the first independent observation was made in 1888, controversy raged in scientific circles regarding their objective reality. In 1893 Percival Lowell established an observatory in Flagstaff, Arizona, for the purpose of studying the surface features of Mars and also studying other planetary characteristics. Dr. Lowell was convinced of the reality of the canals on Mars and that they had been constructed by inhabitants of the planet for the purpose of irrigation. Many observers were able to see the canals, and maps of the surface of the planet, drawn by independent observers, agreed in their essential features. An equally well qualified group of observers was never able to see the canals, and controversy lasted throughout the early part of the present century. From the earliest days of their observation the canals have presented themselves to different observers in two main guises: as fine, straight, well-defined lines that might have been ruled across the planet's image with a sharp-pointed pencil; and as much thicker, blurred markings which lack both the definition and the geometrical appearance of the others.

Schiaparelli's original papers, together with the conventionalized method of drawing the Martian markings adopted by some American observers, undoubtedly exercised a potent influence at the time upon Martian observers generally: the danger of seeing what one expects to see (especially when the object is near the limit of vision) is very real. It is only in more recent years that the extreme linearity of the early observations of the *canali* has given way to the 'leopard-skin' conception of their true appearance. Briefly, what were seen and drawn by Schiaparelli, Lowell, and others as fine, geometrical lines are now recognized to be more truly represented as the demarcations of darker and lighter areas, or as series of more or less discontinuous markings. But to say that the *canali*, as originally described, were largely an optical illusion is far from saying that markings, which may have been misrepresented as linear *canali*, have no objective reality. Until photographs are taken with telescopes of large aperture and high resolving power, such as the new 200-inch, under excellent conditions of seeing, it seems futile to spend time debating the characteristics and purposes of surface features so close to the limit of modern telescopic equipment and visual observation alone.

MARS: SATELLITES

Mars has two satellites, discovered in 1877 at the same opposition that yielded the *canali* to Schiaparelli's sharp eyes. Their small linear size*

*Observations of their apparent brightness, combined with the assumption that their albedo is similar to that of Mars, suggest diameters of some 10 and 5 miles.

combined with their nearness to Mars itself renders them extremely difficult to observe, and accounts for their relatively recent discovery; while their *outré* behavior qualifies them for the title of most interesting and peculiar satellites in the solar system. Phobos is only 3,725 miles from the Martian surface, and since its orbit lies very close to the equatorial plane of the planet it never clears the horizon to latitudes above 70°. It revolves about its primary in 7h. 39m.; that is to say, the Martian month as determined by Phobos is only about one third as long as the day. Consequently, to an observer on the planet's surface it would appear to rise in the west and set in the east, passing from the new to the full phase in about four hours. Deimos, the second satellite, revolves at a distance of about 12,500 miles from the Martian surface in a period of 30h. 21m. This is so very slightly longer than the Martian day that it remains above the horizon for three days, during which time it passes through all its phases twice over.

BODE'S LAW

It was pointed out by Titius of Wittenberg as long ago as the eighteenth century that the distances of the planets from the sun stand in a curious mathematical relationship to one another. This relationship is usually expressed in the form known as Bode's law. The terms of the series

$$0 \quad 1 \quad 2 \quad 4 \quad 8 \quad 16 \ldots$$

are each multiplied by 3, giving

$$0 \quad 3 \quad 6 \quad 12 \quad 24 \quad 48 \ldots$$

If 4 is then added to each term, a fairly close correspondence is obtained between the terms of the series and the relative solar distances of the planets, taking that of the earth as 10:

Bode's Series	4	7	10	16	28
Solar Distances	3.9	7.2	10	15.2	?
Planet	Mercury	Venus	Earth	Mars	?

Bode's Series	52	100	196	388	772
Solar Distances	52	95.4	192	301	395
Planet	Jupiter	Saturn	Uranus	Neptune	Pluto

In the first place it is to be noticed that the correspondence deteriorates progressively in the case of the four outermost planets of the solar system. Secondly, there is no known planet occupying the gap which

Bode's series reveals between Mars and Jupiter at a distance from the sun equal to 2.8 times that of the earth.

THE ASTEROIDS

What can be the meaning of this gap? Its existence had been noted by Kepler, who suggested that it might be occupied by the orbit of a planet which was too small to be perceived. In 1800 von Zach calculated the orbit of this hypothetical planet and organized a band of twenty-four astronomers to undertake a systematic search of the zodiac in the hope of detecting it. Early in the following year Piazzi discovered a previously unknown planetary object, subsequently christened Ceres, and Gauss calculated its orbit and showed that it did indeed occupy Bode's gap. In quick succession, however, three more faint planets were discovered and named Pallas, Vesta, and Juno. This unexpected result of the work of the 'Celestial Police' suggested that the planet that originally occupied the Mars-Jupiter gap might have disintegrated into a number of fragments, of which Ceres, Pallas, Vesta, and Juno were the first four to be discovered. Nowadays, however, it is not conceived that the disruption of a single planet affords a likely explanation of the origin of the asteroids. It has been found that these bodies revolve about the sun in widely dissimilar orbits—both as regards eccentricity and inclination to the plane of the ecliptic: this does not suggest a common point of origin. In the second place there is no known reason why an already formed planet should disrupt in this fashion. What does appear more probable is that the asteroids represent material which has never condensed to form a single planetary body. The whole question is still wide open to conjecture, however.

The discovery of new asteroids proceeded apace from the early years of last century, and by the time that Wolf introduced the camera as an asteroid-hunting instrument in 1891 some 300 had been discovered. Wolf's technique accelerated the rate of discovery considerably, and today over 2000 are known, a small percentage of which are probably duplicated discoveries.

What the total number of asteroids is cannot possibly be laid down with any precision, although one calculation has suggested 50,000 as a possible rough figure. On the other hand, it is known that their aggregate mass cannot exceed about 1 per cent of the earth's, for if it did they would cause perceptible irregularities in the motion of Mars, whereas no such perturbations occur.

The asteroids are all small bodies, a fact which accounts for their having escaped discovery until less than 150 years ago. Only one, Vesta, is visible to the naked eye, and even it is very near the limit of naked-eye visibility. Some of the larger present measurable disk in large instruments, and Ceres, the largest, is known to have a diameter of about 480 miles. There is probably a continuous decrease in size from this figure, the smallest asteroids being indistinguishable from the largest meteors. None of the asteroids is sufficiently massive to have retained any trace of atmosphere, and they may be envisaged as completely barren lumps of rock, without air, water, or life in any form; probably the smaller ones are not spherical, like the major planets, but irregular in shape. This conjecture is borne out by the fact that the brightness of many of them varies in a regular manner which is suggestive of the axial rotation of asymmetrical and therefore unevenly reflective bodies.

The width of the zone occupied by the asteroids, bounded approximately by the orbits of Mars and Jupiter, is four times as great as the distance from the earth to the sun. Within this zone lie the orbits of the asteroids. But, as has already been mentioned, these are typically eccentric to a degree more reminiscent of cometary than planetary orbits. The eccentricity of some is so great that part of the orbit may lie beyond that of Jupiter or within that of Mars, the earth, or even of Venus. At the same time many of the orbits are steeply inclined to the plane of the ecliptic, the orbital inclination of Pallas being as great as 35°. They are thus not confined to the zodiac, as are all the major planets (except Pluto), the sun, and the moon.

In 1898 the asteroid Eros was discovered. A faint object, only about 17 miles in diameter, it was nevertheless of very great interest because at the time of discovery and for many years afterwards it was the nearest known planetary body to the earth, its minimum distance being 14 million miles. In 1932 Eros was dispossessed of this title by the discovery of an even smaller asteroid, Apollo, not more than a mile in diameter. Since that date the asteroids Adonis and Hermes have been discovered, both of which approach the earth even more closely than Apollo. Hermes, discovered in 1937, is at times less than one million miles from the earth; with a telescope, its movement against the starry background can actually be seen from moment to moment.

JUPITER: SOLAR DISTANCE AND LINEAR DIMENSIONS

The next planet outside Mars and the asteroid zone is Jupiter, the first of the so-called 'giant' planets. In almost every respect it is strikingly different from the planets we have already described, all of which in greater or small degree resemble the earth.

Jupiter's mean solar distance is 483 million miles, but owing to the eccentricity of its orbit it may be 23 million miles nearer or more distant than this. Its distance from the earth consequently varies from 367 million miles at the most favorable oppositions to nearly 600 million miles at conjunction. Yet at favorable oppositions, despite the great gap of nearly 370 million miles that separates Jupiter from the terrestrial observer, its angular diameter is 50″. Its corresponding mean diameter must be nearly 86,700 miles; that of the earth, it will be remembered, is less than 8000. The volume of Jupiter is therefore 1300 times that of the earth.

JUPITER: MASS AND DENSITY

Its mass can be determined with greater accuracy than that of any other planet, for not only has it eleven satellites, each of which allows a different and independent estimation to be made, but it is sufficiently massive and sufficiently far from the sun to cause easily measurable perturbations of Saturn. It has been found that the mass of Jupiter is 318 times that of the earth, or more than that of all the other eight planets together.

Enormous though this value is, it is not as great as one would expect from an inspection of the figure representing its volume. For since its volume is 1300 times that of the earth and its mass 318 times that of the earth, its density can only be one quarter of the earth's. The possible explanation of this surprisingly low density will be discussed later.

JUPITER: TELESCOPIC APPEARANCE, FORM, AND AXIAL ROTATION

Owing to the large size of its disk, the smallest telescopes will show the more obvious features of the Jovian system. Three in particular will be noticed at first glance: Jupiter is not a true sphere but is flattened very considerably at the poles, bulging a corresponding amount in equatorial regions; its disk is crossed, parallel to the equator, by a number of belts, alternately dark and light; four of its satellites move back and forth in the plane of the belts.*

The degree of Jupiter's polar flattening is greater than that of any other planet in the solar system with the exception of Saturn, and careful measurements of the angular subtention of its polar and equatorial diameteres have shown that there is a difference of nearly 6000

*The remainder of the satellites are not visible in small instruments.

miles between them. The polar diameter is 82,800 miles in length while that of the equatorial is 88,700 miles. It is known from laboratory experiments on the constitution and behavior of matter, and from mathematical deductions based upon such experiments, that when a non-rigid body rotates it will bulge equatorially, the polar regions being drawn down toward the equator. Up to a certain point the amount of the distortion from the spherical is proportional to the velocity of the rotation. The telescopic appearance of Jupiter would therefore lead one to expect a somewhat rapid axial rotation. When this is measured it is found that the expectation is justified. The belts and zones that stripe the Jovian disk contain many irregularities and individual features, any one of which may be used to determine the rotation period. If the reader were to observe an equatorial spot as centrally placed upon the disk at, say, 6 p.m. one evening, he would find that it is back again on the central meridian at ten minutes to four o'clock the following morning. But if he decided to check this determination by making a number of different observations and then taking the mean of the different values obtained, he would find himself in difficulties. Suppose that for his second estimation he chose a spot in high latitudes and, as before, observed it to be on the central meridian at 6 p.m. Then the next morning it would return to the center of the disk at five minutes to four. This discrepancy of five minutes in the two observations is much too large to be accounted for on the grounds of observational error, and he would quickly discover that the rotation period is actually different in different latitudes. Jupiter (or at any rate the visible portion of Jupiter) does not rotate as a solid body. The equatorial regions rotate once in about 9h. 50m., whereas the period in high latitude is about five minutes longer. Two points are to be noted: in the first place the rotation is, as we expected, extremely rapid—it imparts to an equatorial object a speed of nearly 27,000 miles per hour—and, in the second place (as we shall see), we have here a remarkable analogy between Jupiter and the sun.

JUPITER: SURFACE FEATURES

The second conspicuous feature of Jupiter as seen in a small telescope is the system of belts and zones with which its disk is crossed. These lie parallel to one another and to the equator, and since the axis of rotation is very nearly perpendicular to the plane of the orbit, while at the same time the orbits of Jupiter and the earth are only inclined to each other at a small angle, their edges appear as straight and not as curved lines.

In the same way a spot or other marking traces out a straight path across the planet's disk, and not the curved one it would pursue if the axis were inclined appreciably toward or away from the earth.

Though the minor detail of the belts is constantly changing, the larger divisions themselves remain tolerably stable, and changes in the relative positions, sizes, or general depth of color of the belts usually require several months at least for their consummation if a large area of the surface is involved. A telescope of quite moderate aperture shows that change of a minor order is going on the whole time. If the appearance of the disk is carefully recorded, preferably by drawing, and then re-observed about nineteen hours later, it will be seen that the finer detail of the belts, invisible in small instruments, is teeming with differences of shape, position, size, and, to a lesser degree, color. The equatorial region is in a particularly unstable state, and it is there that the most widespread and rapid changes in the configuration of the markings occur. Toward the poles the visible surface appears to be in a more stable condition and the belts much less susceptible to disturbance.

After the bright and dark belt-zone system the most important markings are the spots. These may be either dark or light and are sometimes very short-lived, though they normally persist for several months. New spots are being formed and old ones dying out continuously. Further alterations in the appearance of the markings are provided by the fact that the spots may have rotation periods slightly different from those of the substrata in which they lie. It is a significant fact and establishes another similarity between the sun and Jupiter, that the most rapid and frequent changes connected with the spots occur in two zones, in low latitudes on either side of the equator.

One other feature of the Jovian surface must be mentioned, for its size and semi-permanence place it in a class by itself. In 1878 a peculiar, oval-shaped marking was noticed in the south-temperate latitudes. It was pale pinkish in color and of abnormal size. The color darkened and the size increased until the spot was a great, dark-red patch, measuring about 30,000 miles by 7000. After being the most conspicuous object on the Jovian surface for a period of nearly thirty years it began to fade; in 1919 this fading accelerated, and by 1922 the Great Red Spot, as it had been named when in its prime, was only just visible. It experienced a slight and temporary revival in 1927 but is now rather inconspicuous. The cause of this gigantic and prolonged disturbance of the visible surface has been the subject of endless controversy from which

no acceptable conclusions have yet emerged. Like the smaller and more
ephemeral spots, its position relative to the substratum was not fixed—
i.e. its rotation period was not the same as that of other objects in the
same latitude. Furthermore, its velocity of rotation was not uniform,
but fluctuated in a regular and cyclic manner. The significance and
cause of this fluctuation are not known.

JUPITER: ATMOSPHERE

It will be clear from this short account of the appearance and behavior
of the visible surface of Jupiter that we are not looking at the planet's
solid surface but upon the upper reaches of a dense atmosphere. In no
other way can the continuous and, terrestrially speaking, gigantic and
cataclysmic upheavals, together with the dependence of rotational
velocity upon latitude, be explained. Again, we can hardly suppose
that a surface bearing so many points of similarity with that of the
sun can be solid; the state of constant turmoil, the birth and decay of
spots, often extremely rapid, the more rapid equatorial than polar
rotation, the restriction of greatest activity to two zones situated between the equator and each pole, are all characteristics shared by the
two bodies, and their significance cannot be ignored. The high albedo
(about 45 per cent) suggests that same conclusion, while the spectroscope knits all these loose strands together, as it were, to form a rigid
demonstration that the visible portions of Jupiter are gaseous.

JUPITER: SPECTROSCOPIC EVIDENCE

The spectra of the outer planets, unlike those of the inner, are all of
a type, certain characteristics growing merely more pronounced as we
move outward from Jupiter toward Pluto. The spectrum of Jupiter
consists of a continuous background due to reflected solar radiations,
and in addition a number of strong and broad absorptions; these occur
particularly in longer wave-lengths, the infra-red region being almost
completely absorbed. The strength of the bands indicates that the
atmosphere is dense, and their identification as the absorptions of
ammonia and methane is now complete; the former is estimated to
occur in quantities equivalent to a layer of 30 feet thick at atmospheric
pressure. Even if the other physical conditions were favorable to life
in any form resembling the terrestrial, such an atmosphere would
preclude the possibility of its occurrence on Jupiter: for neat smelling-
salts and marsh gas would be as lethal as cyanic acid.

JUPITER: INTERNAL STRUCTURE

An independent line of reasoning suggests that Jupiter's atmosphere is not only dense, but extremely deep. For the abnormally low density of the planet entails one of two alternatives: either the material of which it is composed is in some fundamental way different from that of the earth and of the other planets we have described, or else the solid body of Jupiter is small compared with the whole visible sphere; that is to say, the atmosphere accounts for a considerable fraction of the observed diameter. Since the planets are generally believed to be formed of solar material torn from the sun by the gravitational drag of a passing star in some remote epoch, it is believed that the densities of the solid planetary spheroids are not widely divergent (a belief supported by observation wherever this is possible), and consequently the latter alternative is favored.

It is on such considerations as these that the modern views regarding the physical nature of Jupiter are based. Though it was at one time widely believed that Jupiter might be entirely gaseous, it is now supposed that it consists of a small solid core* surrounded by a dense and exceedingly deep atmosphere. Jeffreys, from his mathematical studies of the densities, sizes, ellipticities, and temperatures of Jupiter and Saturn, concludes that the former probably consists of a small rocky core surrounded by a thick layer of ice, the whole enclosed by an atmosphere whose depth is about 9 per cent of the planet's radius. This atmosphere is probably chiefly composed of such gases as hydrogen, helium, nitrogen, oxygen, and methane and carries particulate clouds of some substance such as solid carbon dioxide, which occurs in our own atmosphere in the gaseous state.

JUPITER: TEMPERATURE

Jupiter's solar parallels, its probably largely gaseous constitution, and its great size led astronomers to suppose that it might have retained some heat of its own, that the core might still be molten or at least hot. But recent radiometric work has shown that its surface temperature is very low, certainly between —100° C. and —200° C., and probably not far off —140° C. This is the temperature that a body with no heat reserves would assume if placed at a distance from the sun equal to that of Jupiter. In other words, Jupiter radiates no more heat than it receives from the sun. These measurements also dispose of any idea that the cloud belts may consist of water vapor.

*Small, that is, relative to the visible atmospheric sphere.

JUPITER: SATELLITES

The last readily noticeable feature was the system of four satellites. On account of their high albedo and large linear size these are bright objects, and were it not for the proximity of the much more brilliant Jupiter they would be visible to the naked eye. Indeed, some observers possessed of abnormally acute long sight have claimed so to have seen them when at elongation. In the experience of the author, however, and probably in that of the majority of observers, field glasses will be required to show them. Two are slightly smaller than the moon, and two are larger than Mercury; with the doubtful exception of the satellite of Neptune, no other satellite in the solar system approaches them in size. Their orbits lie close to the equatorial plane of Jupiter, so that they appear to swing back and forth in front of and behind its disk. Their revolution periods vary from about one and three quarter days to just under seventeen days, and the outermost is rather more than one million miles from the planet. Since they were first seen by Galileo in 1610, seven more have been added with the increasing perfection of the telescope and the addition of the camera to the astronomer's equipment. These are all small bodies, and consequently, on account of their distance, very faint. The outermost moves in an orbit whose radius is 15 million miles and completes one revolution in about two terrestrial years; thus Jupiter has eleven different months, ranging in length from less than one terrestrial day to over two terrestrial years.

The three outermost satellites (XI., VIII., and IX.) exhibit the interesting phenomenon of retrograde motion. All of the planets in the solar system revolve about the sun in the same direction; the majority of the satellites likewise revolve about their planets in this same direction. Only a few of the satellites of the outer planets have motion in the opposite direction, or retrograde motion; those found to date being Jupiter XI., VIII., and IX., Saturn IX., Uranus I., II., III., and IV., and the only known satellite of Neptune.

Figure 45 (not to scale) shows the relative positions of the earth, the sun, Jupiter, and one of its satellites. It will be seen that a number of different things can happen to the satellite, as seen from the earth, during the course of its revolution about Jupiter. We shall assume that the satellite is moving in a counter-clockwise direction; when it reaches position 2 it will be directly between the earth e_1 and the limb of Jupiter. Moving to position 3 it will be seen to cross the planet's disk (it will be remembered that the planes of the orbits lie near the equatorial plane

of the planet) and pass off it when it reaches 3. Between 2 and 3, that
is, it will have been in transit. Just before it passes out of transit at
position 3 its shadow will fall upon Jupiter's limb; as the satellite
moves toward position 6 the shadow will cross the disk and leave it
when the satellite actually reaches 6.* Continuing around its orbit, it

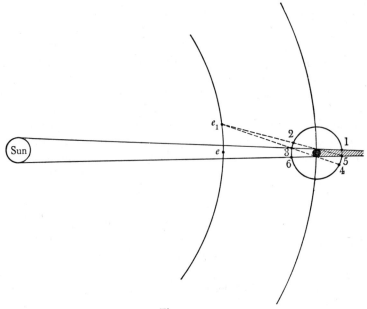

Figure 45.

comes to position 4, when it passes behind Jupiter, i.e. is occulted. But
before it can pass out of occultation at 5 it has entered the planet's
shadow and is therefore eclipsed, not passing out of eclipse and becoming visible once more until it has reached position 1. Like the relative
positions of the transiting satellite and its shadow, the order of occurrence of eclipses and occultations is clearly dependent upon the relative
positions of Jupiter and the earth. At opposition (to take the simplest
case) there can be no observable eclipses of the satellites, since Jupiter's
shadow falls directly behind it, as seen from the direction of the earth.

*The relative positions of the satellite and its shadow against the planet's disk
are obviously determined by the relative positions of Jupiter and the earth. At
opposition, for instance, when the earth is at e, the shadow will be invisible, since
directly behind the satellite.

DISCOVERY OF THE FINITE VELOCITY OF LIGHT

It has already been mentioned parenthetically that light is propagated with a velocity of approximately 186,000 miles per second. Though this value may now be derived with greater accuracy experimentally, it was first determined (and the finite velocity of light established) by the Danish astronomer, Ole Römer, as the result of observations of the eclipses of Jupiter's satellites. He found that predictions of the times at which eclipses would occur were marked by a curious rhythmic inaccuracy. Also that the extent of the discrepancy between the predicted and the observed could be correlated with the relative positions of Jupiter and the earth in their respective orbits, and specifically with their distances apart. When the planet was in opposition the eclipses would occur as predicted; as the earth moved away from Jupiter toward the other side of the sun their unpunctuality would increase; the maximum value of this lag—sixteen and a half minutes—would be attained at conjunction. Thenceforward, as the distance between Jupiter and the earth decreased once more, so would the difference between the predicted and the observed. Römer therefore made the brilliantly original suggestion that the extra sixteen and a half minutes was required by the solar light, reflected from the Jovian system to the earth, to travel the extra distance *AB* in Fig. 17. That is, light travels the diameter of the earth's orbit in sixteen and a half minutes. To accomplish this it must have a velocity in the neighborhood of 186,000 miles per second.

There is another point of historical interest about the Jovian satellite system. This system is a miniature replica of the solar system: Jupiter taking the place of the sun, and its satellites the place of the planets. Galileo's telescopic observation of the Jovian system was for this reason of particular importance as a factor in the astronomical renaissance and the supersession of the Ptolemaic by the heliocentric hypothesis.

SATURN: SOLAR DISTANCE AND LINEAR DIMENSIONS

Saturn is in many respects similar to Jupiter—and, in so far as this is so, unlike the 'terrestrial' planets—but in one respect, to be discussed later, it is to be sharply differentiated not only from Jupiter but from all the other members of the solar system.

Its mean solar distance is 886 million miles, and its distance from the earth consequently varies from 793 million miles to nearly 1000 million. Its angular diameter of 20″ at the former distance corresponds with a linear diameter of about 75,000 miles. It is thus slightly smaller than Jupiter, although its polar flattening is more pronounced, the polar diameter being only 67,000 miles. We should consequently expect to find that its axial rotation is more rapid than that of Jupiter.

SATURN: SURFACE FEATURES AND AXIAL ROTATION

Saturn's disk bears indistinct equatorial bands, very much fainter than those of Jupiter, and also occasional white spots. The faintness of Saturn's surface markings as compared with those of Jupiter cannot entirely be accounted for on the grounds of Saturn's greater distance, not only from the observer but also from the sun; they are intrinsically less boldly marked than Jupiter's. The observation of spots has allowed the rotation period to be measured, however, and it has been found to be ten and a quarter hours in equatorial regions. Owing to the rare occurrence of spots, particularly outside the equatorial zone, it has not been easy to determine accurately the rotation period in high latitudes. Such data as are available indicate that Saturn rotates more slowly near the poles than at the equator.

SATURN: INTERNAL STRUCTURE

Saturn thus rotates more slowly than Jupiter* despite its greater polar compression. This is somewhat puzzling, but it may indicate that the atmosphere of Saturn is deeper in proportion to the size of the planet than that of Jupiter: Jeffreys gives the depths of the atmospheric shells of Jupiter and Saturn as, respectively, 9 per cent and 23 per cent of their radii. This supposition does not conflict with the results of other lines of inquiry which will be mentioned later.

SATURN: MASS AND DENSITY

Light has been thrown on the problem of the size of the solid core of Saturn, as compared with that of the observed oblate spheroid, by a consideration of the properties dependent upon its mass. Fortunately, Saturn has a large family of satellites—nine certainly, and perhaps ten —so that its mass can be determined with accuracy. It has been found to be 95 times that of the earth. Since the volume of the visible spheroid (an uncertain proportion of which is atmosphere) is 735 times that of the earth, its density is even lower than that of Jupiter: less than one

---

*We have seen that the rotation of Jupiter would impart a velocity of some 27,000 m.p.h. to an object on its equator. The corresponding velocity in the case of Saturn is only about 22,000 m.p.h.

fifth of the earth's. Such a density has been likened to that of a lightly packed snowball. This again suggests that the core is smaller, relative to the size of the visible body, than that of Jupiter. Furthermore, mathematical investigation of the motions of the satellites suggests that the visible globe is strongly condensed centrally. It is interesting to note that of all the planets, Saturn is the only one which, were it placed in an ocean of cosmic dimensions, would float.

SATURN: SPECTROSCOPIC EVIDENCE AND ALBEDO

Moving progressively farther from the sun, we encounter also a progressive change in planetary spectra. The bands occurring in the spectrum of Jupiter occur also in those of the more distant planets, but their intensity increases continuously with increasing solar distance; a few new absorptions are also added. This suggests dense atmospheres and, as is known to be the case, decreasing temperature.

Saturn's high albedo (about 45 per cent), its Jupiter-like system of parallel belts, and the evidence of the spectroscope, all indicate that the visible surface is certainly gaseous. The extent of this atmosphere is, like the size of the solid core, a still unsolved problem.

SATURN: TEMPERATURE

In general, then, we may say that so far as is at present known the physical conditions prevailing upon Saturn are similar to those of Jupiter, only more so. This similarity extends to the planet's temperature. Radiometric measurements indicate a temperature certainly as low as —100° C. and probably as low as —150° C., but no lower. That this is somewhat higher than the figure obtained by calculation on the basis that Saturn has no source of heat other than the sun must be attributed to the uncertainty attaching to all such measurements. It is tolerably certain (and the temperature of Jupiter, which is not only a more massive and therefore more slowly cooling body, but is also half as near the sun as Saturn, confirms this) that any heat which Saturn may once have possessed has now been dissipated.

SATURN: RING SYSTEM

But the feature that differentiates Saturn from all the other planets and sets it in a class by itself is its unique ring system, well illustrated in Plate x. It consists of a flat ring, very thin compared with its breadth and diameter, lying in the plane of the planet's equator and separated from it by a wide gulf. This flat expanse is composed of two con-

centric and closely adjacent rings, separated by a narrow rift which
was discovered by Cassini in the second half of the seventeenth century
and which bears his name. Under favorable observing conditions it is
visible in quite small instruments as a fine black line running round
the whole expanse of the ring. That it is a real fissure in the surface
of the ring and not merely a surface marking is shown by the fact that
it is visible on both sides of the ring; furthermore, when it happens
that the ring system occults a star it can be seen shining through
Cassini's division with undiminished brightness. In the nineteenth
century Encke saw a very faint marking on the surface of the outer
ring, *A*, and concluded that it was another and smaller division. Owing
to its faintness, however, it is believed that it may be a thinning out
of the material of the ring rather than an actual gap; it is nevertheless
known as Encke's division. But the nineteenth century did add a third
ring to Saturn's system, though not by the subdivision of one of the
already known rings. The Crepe Ring, or ring C, is a faint and semi-
transparent extension of ring B inward toward the planet. It requires
fairly large apertures for its observation on account of the fact that it
is of such diaphanous texture, the planet being clearly visible through it.

The total width of the ring system from the outer edge of *A* to the
inner edge of *C* is more than 40,000 miles. This can be determined by
direct micrometrical measurement when the linear distance of Saturn
from the earth is known. In order to make even approximate estimates
of the rings' thickness and mass, other methods than direct measurement have to be employed. Unlike the equator of Jupiter, that of
Saturn is inclined at a considerable angle (27°) to the plane of the
orbit. Hence, as demonstrated in Fig. 46, the plane of the rings will

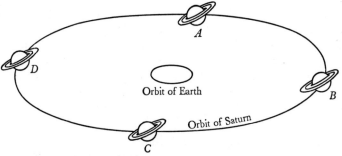

Figure 46. When Saturn is at *A* or *C* the rings are presented edge on to the
earth. When at *D* the southern, and when at *B* the northern, side of the rings is
visible from the earth.

pass through the earth twice in each complete revolution of Saturn about the sun; that is, in a period of about thirty years. At these times the rings will be viewed edge-on, and when this happens they disappear completely for several days; at most they are only just visible for a short distance on either side of the planet. This observation provides us with an upper limit for the thickness, for, if they were more than some ten to fifteen miles thick they would be visible from the earth when in the edge-on position. Compared with their breadth, therefore, their thickness is negligible: 10 miles as against 40,000, or less than 0.03 per cent. It may, of course, be very much less than this; all we can say is that it certainly is not more. The determination of the mass of the ring system is entirely mathematical and consists in the calculation of the maximum mass they could have without their gravitational pull affecting to a noticeable extent the motions of the satellites, for no such perturbations are to be observed. Here, too, we can do no more than assign an upper limit, greater than which their mass cannot be. The value obtained is one twenty-seven-thousandth that of the body of Saturn; this is equivalent to about 0.003 times the mass of the earth.

The nature of these gigantic and unique rings engaged the speculations of astronomers from the earliest days of telescopic observation. Nothing definite was established until Laplace, the French astronomer and mathematician, demonstrated mathematically that they could not be solid—that is, continuous planes like concentric rings of cardboard. He showed that such a structure would be unstable and that the gravitational pull of Saturn would disrupt it into a large number of fragments. Though this was only negative information, it was nevertheless a great advance, and paved the way for the further elucidation of the problem by Clerk Maxwell. Maxwell proved that not only could the rings not be continuous, but that they must be composed of innumerable discrete particles, each of which revolves about Saturn in its own orbit and may be regarded as a small, individual satellite.

The Doppler shift has been utilized to prove observationally the truth of Clerk Maxwell's theoretical account of the structure of the rings. The two possible explanations—in so far as Maxwell's allowed of any alternative—were that (i) each ring is a solid structure, or that (ii) it consists of a large number of individual particles, each revolving about the planet. If (i) represents the true picture of the ring, it is clear that the outer edge will revolve with a greater linear velocity than the inner, since it has farther to travel and the same time to do it in. But if the ring is composed of separate particles, each will move in accordance with the laws of Kepler. That is, the nearer a particle is to the planet, the higher will be its linear velocity. Thus the relative velocities of the inner and outer edges of the ring system will be the touchstone by which the rival hypotheses may be put to the test. These velocities can be measured by the amounts of the Doppler shifts of the Fraunhofer lines of the reflected solar spectrum when the spectroscope slit is adjusted to cut the outer and inner edges of the ring. Keeler, who first made this crucial observation, found that the radiations reflected from the inner edge of the principal ring were displaced to a greater extent than those from the outer, the displacements corresponding with velocities of 12½ and 10 m.p.s. respectively. Hence the ring cannot be a solid structure, but must consist of a large number of particles, each reacting individually to the gravitational pull of the planet.

ROCHE'S LIMIT, AND THE ORIGIN OF SATURN'S RINGS

After the nature of the rings, the most intriguing problem connected with them is probably that of their origin. Here again mathematics comes to the aid of the observer, and we are indebted to the theoretical work of Roche for some invaluable information concerning the interactions of planets and their satellites. When a satellite is far from the more massive body, the gravitational force exerted by the planet upon different parts of its substance is very nearly uniform. But the nearer it is to the planet, the more disparate will be the stresses within it, until, if the satellite were imagined continuously approaching the planet's surface, a point will be reached at which the conflicting stresses and strains will have become so acute that the satellite will be disrupted. Roche proved that in the case of a large planet and a small satellite, both of the same density, the satellite will be disintegrated when it passes a limit equal to 2.45 times the radius of the planet. Observation affords negative confirmation of this, for no satellite of any planet in the solar system lies within what is known as Roche's limit.

Now the significant fact about the Saturnian ring system is that the radius of the outer edge of ring *A* is 2.3 times the radius of Saturn itself. The obvious interpretation of this fact in the light of Roche's discovery is that at some past epoch one or more of Saturn's satellites have approached too near to the planet—passed Roche's limit—and have been torn to pieces; and that each individual fragment has continued to revolve about Saturn as one of the many components which together make up the rings. Three observational facts appear to lend support to this hypothesis: all the extant satellites revolve about Saturn in or close to the plane of the rings; both the rings and the inner remaining satellites are of abnormally high albedo, which may indicate similar composition and origin; and thirdly, the innermost satellites both of Saturn and of the other planets are in every case at distances from their primary which are well beyond Roche's limit. On the other hand, it is possible that the rings result from the reverse process. They may consist of matter which at some past epoch in the planet's history was ejected from the body of Saturn itself and which has not yet condensed into satellites. The whole question is still exceedingly obscure, but although no definite answer can be given it does seem probable that Roche's work holds the clue to the enigma.

SATURN: SATELLITES

Saturn's family of moons has nine members; a tenth was claimed by W. H. Pickering in 1905, but the discovery has never been confirmed. The largest, Titan, is larger than Mercury and the largest Jovian satellites. Their periods of revolution range from slightly less than one day to one and a half years; their distances from Saturn from 115,000 to 8 million miles. The main feature of interest about these bodies is that some, if not all, vary in brightness in a regular manner. This light variation is most marked in the case of Iapetus, and was even noticed by Cassini with the poor telescopic equipment of the seventeenth-century observer. The period of variation coincides with the period of the satellite's revolution about Saturn, and it is concluded from this that Iapetus (and others, which exhibit the same phenomenon) always turns the same hemisphere toward Saturn; in this it would resemble our own moon and, probably, the five inner satellites of Jupiter.

THE FURTHERMOST PLANETS

As regards size, mass, and other physical characteristics, Jupiter and Saturn are somewhat similar. The similarity between Uranus and Neptune, the next two planets in order from the sun, is even closer. Owing to their great solar distance (that of Uranus is twice Saturn's) they are faint and were not known to the ancients, although Uranus is just above the limit of naked-eyed visibility and can be found with the help of a star map when its approximate position has been determined from an almanac. They were discovered in the eighteenth and nineteenth centuries respectively, while the most distant of all, Pluto, was discovered in 1930.

URANUS: SOLAR DISTANCE AND LINEAR SIZE

Uranus's mean solar distance is 1,783 million miles; this is so great a distance compared with that of the earth from the sun that the planet's brightness and apparent size do not vary to any considerable extent during the course of the terrestrial year. Its mean angular diameter is slightly less than 4″ and corresponds with a linear diameter of about 31,000 miles. It was discovered accidentally by Herschel in 1781. That is to say, he was not engaged in a systematic search for a new planet outside Saturn, but merely noticed a strange object in the field of his telescope; it was at first taken to be a comet.

URANUS: AXIAL ROTATION

Its period of revolution about the sun is approximately 84 years, but its axial rotation is less easily determined. Telescopes of large aperture have shown faint equatorial belts similar to those of Saturn, but no surface marking is sufficiently well defined to be used for an accurate estimate of the rotation period. The polar flattening, however, suggests a fairly rapid rotation, and the period is believed certainly to lie within the limits of 8 and 12 hours. The most accurate estimate yet made is that of Campbell. Photometric* work has shown that Uranus is subject to a slight and recurrent variation of brightness, the period of which is about 10h. 50m. The most reasonable explanation of such a cyclic variation is that the planet is rotating on its axis in that period and that some areas of its surface reflect less of the incident solar light than others. Campbell's figure agrees well with that of about 10¾ hours derived spectroscopically by Lowell.

URANUS: MASS, DENSITY AND TEMPERATURE

The mass of Uranus can be derived from the motions of its four satellites and is found to be fifteen times that of the earth; this gives a density about equal to that of Jupiter. This fact, taken in conjunction with the high albedo (similar to that of both Jupiter and Saturn), the evidence of the spectroscope, and the similarity of such surface markings as are visible with those of Saturn, indicates that Uranus has a dense and probably extensive atmosphere. It receives less than 1/360 of the solar light and heat received by the earth, and its temperature of about —190° C. is slightly higher than would be expected were the sun the only source of heat. But the difference is too small and the practical

*A photometer is an instrument which measures small differences of brightness.

difficulties attendant upon the radiometric investigation of so distant a body, radiating so little heat, are too great for it to be stated categorically that Uranus has still some reserves of heat unspent. Its physical conditions, therefore, are of the same general type as those of Jupiter and Saturn.

URANUS: SATELLITES

Uranus possesses five satellites, the fifth having been discovered with the 82-inch reflector at the MacDonald Observatory early in 1948. The four satellites that had previously been known have periods ranging from 2½ to 13½ days and distances from the planet from about 120,000 to 365,000 miles. The most notable feature of the four-satellite system is its high inclination to the plane of the planet's orbit; this amounts to more than one right angle, with the consequence that the satellites do not move east and west across the telescopic field (as do those of Jupiter, for instance) but north and south. Very few data are available at present regarding the fifth satellite other than that it revolves about Uranus in approximately 30 hours and that its orbit is well within those of the four satellites previously known.

NEPTUNE: DISCOVERY

Neptune is so similar to Uranus that it may be regarded almost as its twin. In size it is slightly superior to Uranus, but because of its greater solar distance (nearly 2,800,000,000 miles) it is never visible to the naked eye. The story of its discovery is one of the best known and most interesting in the history of astronomy. Herschel's unexpected discovery of Uranus inevitably led astronomers to wonder whether there might not be other and still more remote members of the solar system. We have seen how the mass of a planet that has no satellites may be calculated by a consideration of its perturbing effects upon the orbits of neighboring planets. Each planet, were it the only member of the solar system other than the sun, would pursue an orbit which is exactly described by the laws of Kepler; furthermore, its motion in that orbit would be similarly calculable. If, however, there is another planet also revolving about the sun, its gravitation will distort the ideal motion of the first, as described by Kepler. Since the mass of the sun is much greater than that of any single planet, these perturbations will be small, just as an object held by a strong man can only be moved slightly by a small boy. Accurate observation and mathematical calculation based on the laws of Newton do, however, permit the astronomer to estimate not only the mass of the disturbing planet but also the direction of its action and therefore its approximate position.

About a hundred and fifty years ago it became increasingly clear that Uranus was not moving to schedule; that is, its observed motion and positions were deviating more and more from the calculated, even after a suitable allowance had been made for all the six planets then known. The only explanation of this disparity between the calculated and the observed was that some factor affecting the latter was not included in the former. That is, that there was a still more distant planet whose perturbing effect was not being taken into consideration. A detailed and extremely laborious mathematical examination of these perturbations led Adams and Leverrier to predict, almost simultaneously though independently, that the unknown planet was situated in such and such a region of the ecliptic. In 1846 Galle, at Berlin Observatory, discovered the new planet close to the predicted position. The discovery was a striking vindication of Newton's theory of universal gravitation.

NEPTUNE: PHYSICAL CHARACTERISTICS

On account of its great distance very little is known about Neptune, though its physical conditions are probably similar to those of Uranus (which it resembles closely in all ascertainable respects), allowance of course being made for the effects of its greater solar distance. Faint belt-like markings have been thought to have been seen upon it, but since the angular diameter of its disk is only about 2″.5, all such observations must be accepted with caution. Its linear diameter of rather more than 31,000 miles and its mass, approximately 17 times the earth's, are slightly greater than those of Uranus. Nothing definite is known of its temperature. Assuming that it has no internal heat and is entirely dependent upon the sun for such heat as it has, its temperature must be in the neighborhood of —200° C. Spectroscopic measures made at the Lick Observatory in 1928 indicate a rotation period of about 15 hours 50 minutes; this is in agreement with the evidence provided by a slight periodic variation of brightness observed many years ago by Maxwell Hall, from which a half-period of 8 hours was subsequently derived.

NEPTUNE: SATELLITE

Only one satellite is known, Triton. It completes its retrograde revolution about Neptune in a period of 5¾ days at a mean distance of some 220,000 miles. Its size has not been determined with certainty, but it may be even larger than the giants of Jupiter's satellite system.

PLUTO

Most distant of all the known planets is Pluto. Since it was discovered as recently as 1930, little is yet known of it. Its discovery was made as a result of a planned search based upon calculations of its approximate position upon the star sphere. In broad outline the history of the search and the final discovery was a repetition of that of Neptune. Since, however, Neptune had not completed one revolution of the sun since its discovery in 1846, certain elements of its orbit were not yet determined with great accuracy. Thus any apparent anomalies in its motion were not necessarily due to perturbations on the part of an ultra-Neptunion planet, but possibly to our inexact knowledge of its own motion. For this reason the mathematicians were thrown back upon the perturbations of Uranus for their data. Since the distance from Pluto to Uranus is many times greater than that from Neptune to Uranus, their predictions were less accurate than those of Adams and Leverrier, and Pluto escaped discovery for a correspondingly longer period. When it was identified on a photographic plate exposed in January 1930 it was 5° from the position predicted by Lowell.

Pluto's mean solar distance is approximately 3,673 million miles, or 39.5 times that of the earth. The orbit is abnormally eccentric for a planet, its solar distance varying by something under 2000 million miles, and at perihelion Pluto is actually nearer the sun than Neptune; the period of revolution is about 248 years.

Its temperature is undetermined, but probably lies in the neighborhood of —240° C. to —250° C.; an observer situated upon its surface would receive only 1/1600 as much light and heat as we receive on the earth. These figures follow from Pluto's known solar distance.

The angular diameter of the disk is less than 0″.4, which corresponds with a maximum linear diameter of about 4000 miles. Our present knowledge of its mass is even less definite, and all that can be said is that it is certainly less than that of the earth, and probably less than half this.

VIII. The Sun and *the* Stars

THE SUN: STELLAR STATUS AND SIZE

The sun is the central and most massive member of the solar system, and is gravitationally the ruler of that system. It is fundamentally unlike the planets; as we shall see, its spectrum alone proves that it is an incandescent body. In fact, it is a star, only differing from the myriad stars of the night sky in its comparative proximity. That it owes its greater conspicuousness to nothing but its nearness is shown by the fact that its absolute magnitude is only 4.85: if viewed from a distance of fifty light years it would only just be visible to the naked eye. At a distance of 32,000 light years (which may be roughly the distance to the center of the galaxy) its magnitude would be 20, and it would be invisible to the eye even with the aid of the Mt. Wilson 100-inch reflector although it would be within the photographic range of the instrument.

The calculation of the size of the sun is a simple matter, for we know both the size it appears to be (its angular diameter at mean distance is 31′ 59″) and also its linear distance. Thus, for a body to subtend an angle of 31′ 59″ at a point 93,000,000 miles distant from it, its linear diameter must be 864,000 miles. The volume of a spheroid of known diameter is also easily calculated, and it is found that nearly 1½ million earths would be required to build a body the size of the sun.

TELESCOPIC APPEARANCE

On turning a telescope (suitably adapted) upon the sun for the first time, the reader will probably be struck immediately by two things: the solar surface bears upon it one or more small black spots; and the center of the disk is noticeably brighter than the edges. The latter fact indicates that above the shining surface of the sun (known as the photosphere) there must be a cooler atmosphere. Figure 47 demon-

strates that it is possible to see to a greater radial depth at the center
of the disk than at the limb. And since the former is brighter than the
latter it follows that brightness increases with increasing radial depth;
from which, in turn, it follows that the temperature increases from the
outer atmospheric levels toward the solar center.

SPECTRUM

The solar spectrum (Plate VIIIa) consists of a continuous background
crossed by many thousands of fine absorption lines. These lines were

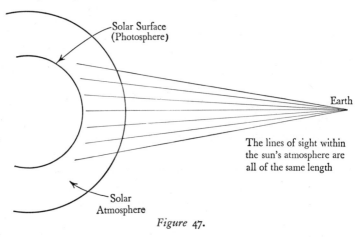

Figure 47.

first studied and mapped by Fraunhofer in 1817, fifteen years after
their discovery. The general type of the spectrum thus confirms the inference which we have already drawn from the telescopically observed
darkening of the limb: namely, that the photosphere is overlaid by a
relatively cool, gaseous atmosphere. It goes beyond this inference, however, in showing that the photospheric surface behaves spectroscopically
like an incandescent solid or dense gas under great pressure. Kirchhoff's
experiments and the theoretical work reviewed in Chapter VI demonstrate that it is the constituents of this atmosphere that impress the
Fraunhofer lines upon the continuous spectrum of the photosphere.

SURFACE TEMPERATURE AND THE SOLAR CONSTANT

That the photosphere is a radiating surface at a high temperature is
obvious without having to undertake any elaborate instrumental investigations. Precisely how hot, can be determined spectroscopically. In
Chapter VI the laws of radiation as worked out by Wien, Planck, and

Stefan, and Boltzmann were stated. Any one of these may be employed to derive the temperature of the photosphere, and it is a satisfactory confirmation of the validity of all of them that the results obtained are in close agreement with one another. Wien's law, based on a maximal intensity at a wave-length of $\lambda4750$, yields a temperature of 6070° K.; Planck's equation gives 6200° K.; and the Stefan-Boltzmann law, 5960° K.

It may be of interest to follow the application of the latter law as applied to this specific problem of the sun's surface temperature. It will be recalled that the equation is

$$E = BT^4$$

where E is the radiating body's rate of emission of energy,

T is its absolute temperature,
B is a constant.

The practical difficulty lies in the accurate determination of E. This is derived from the so-called solar constant, which is, in effect, the amount of solar heat received by a unit area of the earth's surface. It may be expressed in calories per square centimeter per minute, when its value is 1.94; or in ergs per square centimeter per second, when its value is 1.35×10^6.

But the sun is pouring out radiation in all directions, and not just upon our one square centimeter. In order, therefore, to discover the total amount of its radiation we must calculate the area of the sphere centered upon the sun whose radius equals the mean solar distance of the earth, and then multiply the number of square centimeters in this area by (if we are working in ergs) 1.35×10^6. If we write R for the mean distance from the sun to the earth in centimeters, the area we require is $4\pi R^2$. Writing k for the solar constant, the total radiation falling upon this sphere in one second=total radiation of the sun in one second=$4\pi R^2 k$. Writing r for the radius of the sun in centimeters, we have: radiation emitted by 1 square centimeter of the solar surface per second

$$= \frac{4\pi R^2 k}{4\pi r^2}$$

All the terms in this expression are known, and it can therefore be evaluated. The answer is 6.25×10^{10} ergs. This, then, is the term, E, which we require.

The value of the constant B has been found to be 5.735×10^{-5} ergs per square centimeter, and substituting the numerical values of B and E in the Stefan-Boltzmann equation, we get

$$T = 5740° \text{ K.}$$

A correction for the fact that the sun is not a black body (see p. 151), while the law strictly refers only to a perfect radiator, adjusts this figure to the 5960° K. already given.

THE SUNSPOT CYCLE

A great deal of information regarding the sunspots can be gained by telescopic observation alone, provided that it is continued over a long enough period. Moreover, a detailed study of the spots will yield valuable information regarding the sun itself. Early in the nineteenth century, Schwabe, a German amateur astronomer, turned his telescope on the sun for the first time and took note of the spots upon it. He continued his solar observations for nearly twenty years without interruption, except from cloudy days. Each day he made a note of the number of spots visible, and from this simple observation, and as the result of his great patience and perseverance, he discovered their most notable characteristic. Their numbers fluctuate in a fairly regular rhythm. At spot minimum no spots may be visible for days or even weeks on end. Gradually their occurrence becomes more frequent until at maximum there is rarely a day when several spots or groups of spots are not visible. The numbers then begin to fall off again until minimum is once more reached. This cycle from minimum to minimum, or from maximum to maximum, occupies rather more than eleven years; this is only the mean value, however, and periods four or even five years longer and shorter have been recorded. It must be remembered that the fluctuation only involves the number of spots, and not their individual size; large and small spots occur indifferently at all times throughout the cycle.

SOLAR ROTATION FROM SUNSPOTS

A few days' observation of the sun will reveal that the spots are moving slowly across the disk from east to west. New spots appear around the eastern limb and, having passed right across the disk (if they persist so long), disappear around the western. The time taken in passing from limb to limb is about a fortnight. It was this observed motion of the spots across the disk *en bloc* that led to the discovery that the sun, like the earth, is rotating on its axis. The earth is revolving round the sun in the same direction as the sun's rotation, and therefore the observed rotation as exemplified by the spots is not the true, or sidereal rotation period, but the synodic period. To obtain the former from the latter we must employ the equation with which we became familiar in Chapter II. If S is the observed, or synodic, rotation period of about 27 days as revealed by the spots; E, the earth's sidereal revolution period of 365 days; and P the sidereal rotation period of the sun; then

$$\frac{1}{P} = \frac{1}{S} + \frac{1}{E} .$$

If the equation is solved for the values above, it will be found that the sidereal rotation period is approximately 25 days.

But a curious anomaly makes it impossible to state simply that the sun rotates in such and such a period. For the derived figure depends upon the latitude of the spot upon whose motion the determination is based. A spot in high latitudes takes longer to travel from limb to limb than one nearer the equator. The sun, in fact, rotates in zones and not as a rigid body: the equatorial regions rotate more rapidly than the polar,* the two periods being about 24½ days and 34 days respectively. All that we can say briefly is that the sun's *mean* sidereal rotation period is approximately 25 days.

LATITUDE DISTRIBUTION OF SPOTS

The regular observer of the sun will sooner or later discover that spots do not occur in all latitudes with equal frequency. They are, in fact, confined to an equatorial band reaching to about 40° N. and S.† In slightly higher latitudes than these they are extremely rare and they are completely unknown in the vicinity of the poles themselves. But even the attainment of this conclusion will not have taught the observer the whole story of the distribution of the sunspots, for about twenty years after Schwabe published his discovery of the eleven-year cycle, Spoerer showed that the distribution of the spots in latitude varies with this cycle. At minimum there may be a few spots in high latitudes—usually about 35° N. and S. As the cycle proceeds, new spots are born in

*Since no spots occur in the polar regions, another method of determining the rotation period has to be employed, and will be described shortly. In the highest latitudes at which spots normally occur, the period is about 27½ days.

† More precisely, to two bands, one north and one south of the equator, for few spots occur between 5° N. and S.

progressively lower latitudes until, by the next minimum eleven years later, they are confined to the immediate vicinity of the equator. Shortly before the cycle comes to a close and these equatorial spots die out, the first few spots which herald the opening of the new cycle will have appeared in the higher latitudes again. The two zones occupied by these spots and their successors will in turn converge upon the equator, pass their maximum, and dwindle away in the equatorial regions at the next minimum.

Thus we can, by direct telescopic observation carried out over a period of years, establish three facts about sunspots:

i. Their numbers vary throughout a cycle whose duration is approximately eleven years.

ii. They are restricted almost entirely to two comparatively narrow zones, parallel to the equator and situated on either side of it, the latitude of which varies with the eleven-year cycle.

iii. The sun's rotation carries them across the visible hemisphere from east to west with velocities which vary with the solar latitude.

SPECTROSCOPIC DETERMINATION OF THE SOLAR ROTATION

The Doppler phenomenon allows the rotation of the sun in any latitude to be measured. Since estimates based on spot observations are restricted to the equatorial and temperate zones of the sun, this is of great value; without the spectroscope the determination of the rotation period in the spotless polar regions could never be undertaken. Figure 52 represents the sun as seen from a point in space directly above one of its poles. It will be seen that, owing to its axial rotation, one limb is approaching the earth, while the other is receding from it. The velocity of this line-of-sight motion can be measured by the extent of the displacement of the Fraunhofer lines; it amounts to about 1¼ m.p.s.— the east limb approaching the earth, and the west receding from it. Hence, since the linear size of the sun is known, the period of rotation in any latitude can be calculated. In this way it has been discovered, and could have been discovered in no other way, that the rotation period near the poles is ten days longer than in equatorial regions.

APPEARANCE, SIZE, AND STRUCTURE OF SPOTS

Thus far we have been considering only the motions and positions of the spots and for these purposes telescopes of low magnification or even naked-eye observations are sufficient. For study of the details of individual spots either a telescope equipped with a moderately high magnifying eyepiece or a photographic telescope of long focal length is desirable. With such instruments it will be noticed that an individual spot consists of two regions, an inner called the umbra, and an outer, less-dark region called the penumbra. These two main divisions of an individual spot consists of two regions, an inner called the umbra, and an outer, less-dark region called the penumbra. These two main divisions of an individual spot may be observed on Plates XI, XIII, and XIV. (On Plates XIII and XIV the left-hand picture should be studied.) Plate XI shows a highly magnified photograph of a large group of sun spots. The sizes of the individual members of this group may be estimated by comparison with the small circle in the lower left-hand corner of the plate which represents the size of the earth on the scale of the photograph.

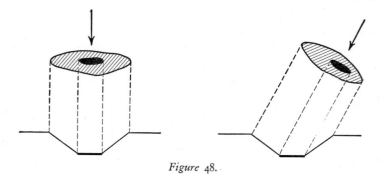

Figure 48.

In addition, one or several minute black spots, known as nuclei, may be visible within the umbra. It will often be noticed that the photosphere in the neighborhood of spots, and particularly of large spot groups, is brighter than elsewhere. Close scrutiny of individual spots sometimes reveals that filaments or bridges of this brighter material are thrown across the dark umbra from the surrounding photosphere.

In November 1769 A. Wilson, professor of mathematics at Glasgow, made a careful study of a large spot that had passed the center of the disk and was approaching the western limb. He noticed that the umbra was apparently displaced toward the center of the sun's disk. Two weeks later be re-observed the same spot after it had reappeared on the eastern limb and found the same displacement of the umbra relative to the penumbra, a displacement that decreased as the spot approached the center of the disk. He explained the displacement by assuming that the sunspots are actually depressions in the disk of the sun and that the effect is a foreshortening as illustrated in Figure 48. This so-called

Wilson effect has been a subject of dispute up to the present time. Many observations have been made during the past century and a half. One long series of observations indicates that the average large circular spot has an average depth of 450 miles. In some cases displacements away from the center of the disk have been reported. In 1939 Pettit made a long series of observations and found the displacement toward the center of the sun in the case of 26 spots observed near the limb of the sun. However, he explains the phenomenon as due to a large column of gas extending high up above the surface of the sun and surrounding the umbra of the spot.

Spots vary enormously among themselves as regards size, shape, motion (for spots usually have motions of their own, distinct from the motion imparted to them by the sun's rotation), and length of life. Some, typically the smaller, may be of only a transitory nature, while the larger ones may last through two, three, or, exceptionally, more rotations of the sun. In size the spots show great variety. The smallest that can be observed are about 500 miles in diameter,* while the largest, and even the more moderate ones, would engulf a body many times the size of the earth (see Plate XI). Indeed a spot must be 15,000 miles in diameter before it can be seen with the naked eye, and spots four times this size have been observed.

Sunspots are frequently found in clusters or groups. Such groups are illustrated in Plate XI and in the left-hand photographs on Plates XIII and XIV. It is customary to speak of the western member of the group as the leading spot, since it precedes the other members as they are carried across the disk of the sun by the solar rotation. The leading spot usually appears first with the following members developing a few days later. In a group which later becomes a large one, the leading spot and its immediate followers develop at about the same rate but with the distance in solar longitude between them increasing up to as much as ten degrees. At the time of maximum area of the group small unstable spots are frequently to be found between the leading spot and its large followers. As the life of the group progresses the principle following spot breaks up into smaller units and gradually fades out, with the leading member losing its collection of small spots and remaining as a single round spot which gradually fades out and disappears.

Lastly, it must be noted that spots appear to be centers of some form of electrical disturbance. Frequently the transit of a large spot or spot

---

*Since we have discovered the linear size of the sun it is a simple matter to discover the linear size of any object upon its surface.

group across the sun's central meridian is the herald of magnetic storms, heavy earth currents, and the occurrence of aurorae on this planet. It is significant that these terrestrial magnetic disturbances do not occur simultaneously with the solar disturbances believed to be their cause; the two are separated by a time lag of about twenty-four hours. This is most fortunate in its practical applications, for it permits the forecasting of magnetic storms by the observatories. The generally accepted explanation of these terrestrial counterparts of solar activity is that streams of electrified particles are ejected from the disturbed areas of the sun's surface and that these require some twenty-four hours to travel across the 93 million miles separating the earth and the sun. This supposition receives additional confirmation from the fact that very strong magnetic storms are frequently repeated after an interval of about twenty-seven days. Now this is the period of the sun's synodic rotation, and it seems legitimate to conclude that the stream of particles, having encountered the earth, is swept completely around the sun by the latter's rotation and after twenty-seven days encounters the earth once more. Interruption of short-wave radio, on the other hand, is simultaneous with the solar event and is probably caused by the emission of a flood of ultra-violet light.

In addition to specific correlations of this kind, there is a marked relation between the ebb and flow of the spot cycle and diurnal variations of the earth's magnetic field. At maxima the variations are large, and magnetic storms (which are nothing more than sudden and acute variations) common. At minima the extent of the diurnal variation is reduced by anything up to 50 per cent, while storms occur practically not at all.

TEMPERATURES AND SPECTRA OF SPOTS

We have seen that the temperature of the general photospheric surface is about 6000°. At such a temperature no compounds could remain undissociated. But the spectra of spots show the characteristic banded spectra of compounds, and in particular those of titanium oxide, calcium and magnesium hydride, and molecular carbon. Now the dissociation temperature of titanium oxide is in the neighborhood of 3000°, and spots are therefore shown to be considerably cooler than the surrounding photosphere—a conclusion suggested by their inferior brilliance. Temperature modifications of individual lines in spot spectra tell the same tale. These are of the general type described in Chapter VI: some lines are greatly strengthened while others, especially lines in the infra-red, are weakened; others, again, are unchanged or altogether absent.

Another common feature of spot spectra is the widening, doubling, or trebling of many of the lines, especially those situated in the longer wave-lengths. This is an example of the Zeeman effect and indicates, as laboratory experiments have proved, the existence of a strong magnetic field within the source; the spots, then, are centers of electrical disturbance. It is interesting to learn that Hale has detected the presence of spots by means of the Zeeman effect where no spots are visible to the naked eye. It might be suggested that the forces that normally lead to the formation of a spot are here operative but are not strong enough to create a visible disturbance of the photosphere.

PHOTOSPHERIC GRANULATION AND FACULAE

When the surface of the photosphere is examined under conditions of excellent seeing it will be noticed that its surface is mottled and granular. It appears to be made up of innumerable contiguous grains, only slightly brighter than the photosphere, which are commonly referred to as the rice grains. These granules are from 450 to 1300 miles in diameter, and Keenan estimates that at any given moment more than $2\frac{1}{2}$ million are visible over the whole disk. The exact cause and nature of this granulation of the solar surface are unknown, but it has been suggested that the granules are the crests of waves of unequally heated photospheric material.

Close examination of the brighter material that characterizes the vicinity of spots and spot groups show that it is not homogeneous or uniform in texture; rather, it consists of numerous irregular patches and worm-like filaments, which are some 15 per cent brighter than the photospheric background. These are named faculae, and at this point it will suffice to note two facts about them. Congregations of faculae tend to precede the formation of spots and to survive after they have vanished. Secondly, they appear to be more numerous near the edges of the solar disk than toward its center. The explanation of this, as we shall see later, is that they are clouds in the atmosphere, situated at considerable heights above the surface of the photosphere. Thus they are not diminished in brightness to the same extent as the photosphere in the peripheral region, while at the same time the reduced luminosity of the background renders them more easily visible.

THE FLASH SPECTRUM AND THE REVERSING LAYER

Both visual observation and the nature of the solar spectrum demonstrate that overlying the photosphere there is a cooler atmospheric layer. The question arises, is this atmosphere cool and therefore non-incandescent, or is it incandescent but nevertheless cooler than the photosphere? In either case its spectrum would consist of dark absorption lines. The question can only be answered if we have an opportunity to observe its spectrum when that of the photosphere (the continuous background) is blotted out. Then, if it were not radiating at all, the Fraunhofer spectrum would be invisible; whereas if it were incandescent, but less so than the photosphere, the Fraunhofer spectrum would be reversed, i.e. would consist of bright lines instead of dark.

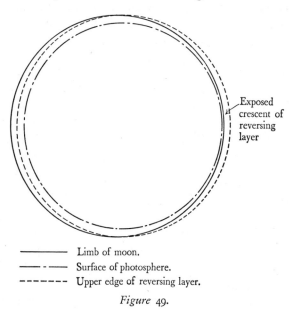

Exposed crescent of reversing layer

——————— Limb of moon.
——·——·—— Surface of photosphere.
— — — — — Upper edge of reversing layer.

Figure 49.

These conditions are provided at total eclipse. Figure 49 shows the solar disk, surrounded by the reversing layer, and the body of the moon at a moment just before totality. (To make the diagram clearer it is not drawn to scale, nor are the chromosphere or corona shown.) It will be seen that at this moment the photosphere is hidden by the body of the moon while a narrow lune of the reversing layer is still visible. At the moment of the final obscuration of the photosphere the Fraunhofer spectrum flashes forth as a set of bright lines; a second or two later, as the moon moves over the reversing layer also, they disappear. It is clear, therefore, that the reversing layer, though cooler than the photosphere, is nevertheless incandescent.

The matching of Fraunhofer lines with lines of spectra produced in the laboratory, the constitution of whose sources is known, has led to the identification of many terrestrial elements in the reversing layer of the solar atmosphere. This matching of solar and laboratory spectrograms is carried out as follows. The spectroscope slit is divided transversely into an upper and a lower half, either of which may be opened or shut independently of the other. The lower half of the slit is opened, the spectroscope is focused upon the sun, and the plate exposed. Then the upper half of the slit is opened, the lower half closed, and the spectroscope focused upon a source in the laboratory—incandescent iron vapor, let us say—care being taken not to move the plate. The plate is once again exposed, and developed. The spectrogram then consists of two spectra lying side by side, with equivalent wave-lengths directly above and below each other: one the spectrum of the sun, and the other that of vaporized iron. It can be seen at a glance whether any of the iron lines occur in the solar spectrum, and whether, therefore, iron occurs in the reversing layer. By taking a large number of such comparison spectrograms, changing the constitution of the laboratory source each time, it is possible to identify about 60 of the 92 terrestrial elements in the reversing layer. Some are represented by only a few lines, others by scores or hundreds; over 3000 lines of the iron spectrum have been mapped. Altogether, more than 23,000 individual lines figure in the most recent catalogue of the Fraunhofer spectrum. It is highly probable that the 30 apparently missing elements do in fact occur in the sun. Not only are all wave-lengths shorter than about $\lambda 3000$ absorbed by the ozone in the earth's upper atmosphere, but it must also be expected that the heavier elements in the sun would sink below the reversing layer where alone they are capable of producing absorption spectra.

When the flash spectrum is observed without a slit, each line is curved (being an image in monochromatic light of the still exposed segment of solar atmosphere) and as the moon's limb obscures successively higher and higher levels, so the lines of those elements that occur at different heights above the photosphere will drop out of the spectrum. Finally, only calcium, hydrogen, and helium remain before the spectrum disappears altogether. Knowing, as we do, both the sun's distance and the rate of the moon's motion across its disk, we can thus determine to what approximate heights above the photospheric surface the various elements extend. The reversing layer, the lowest of the atmospheric levels, stretches for from 100 to 200 miles above the photosphere; some of its constituents are confined to the lower levels while others occur throughout the whole stratum. As already explained, it is possible to deduce the density and pressure of a gaseous or vaporous source from its spectrum, and it has been found that the pressure in the reversing layer is no more than one ten-thousandth that in the earth's atmosphere.

THE CHROMOSPHERE

Without the aid of the spectroscope, the solar atmosphere can be studied only one rare occasions, and even then not in its entirety. By a cosmic fluke, the relative sizes of the sun and moon and their distances from the earth are just such that their apparent sizes as judged by a terrestrial observer are almost identical. It periodically happens that the moon passes directly between the earth and the sun; when this occurs the sun is said to be totally eclipsed, and at the instant of totality—which 'instant' may be as long as 7m. 40s., but is usually very much shorter— the solar disk is hidden by the body of the moon. Thus the glaring photosphere is obscured, while the less brilliant atmospheric levels are visible round the moon's limb. Two different zones can then be distinguished. The inner is blood-red, and appears as a narrow rim of flame to the moon's black disk. This atmospheric layer is the chromosphere, and it may be noticed that its outer edge bears small projections, which in fact are gigantic flames and clouds of incandescent gas. These prominences may be attached to the chromosphere at one or more points or may be entirely severed from it.

The spectrum of the chromosphere may also be observed during totality, and it has been established that it does not consist of a complete set of the Fraunhofer lines; furthermore, the lines are bright and not dark. The elements that by their absorption of certain wave-lengths of the photospheric light cause the Fraunhofer lines are therefore not situated in the chromosphere. Nor, as we shall see, are they situated in the corona, which is the outermost atmospheric region. This establishes that the reversing layer is situated immediately above the photosphere and below the chromosphere.

One feature of the chromospheric spectrum, which was unexpected at the time of its discovery, was that lines which are weakened in the spectra of spots are here strengthened. Since the solar atmosphere is cooler than the photosphere, just as the spots are, this was somewhat surprising. Later, however, the explanation was revealed by Saha, a physicist. Ionization, the line-modifying agency, is promoted not only by increased temperature but also by decreased pressure, and in the chromosphere the latter overrides the former. Thus line-modifications which were at first thought to indicate certain conditions of temperature are also in fact indicative of reduced pressure.

Until 1868 astronomers could only study the chromosphere during the short and isolated intervals of total eclipse; at all other times the glare of the more brilliant photosphere swamped it utterly. In that year, however, Janssen and Lockyer devised independently a spectroscopic method of observing the chromosphere at any time. Spectroscopic observation of the sun's atmosphere as the moon moves in front of it at total eclipse has proved that when not only the photosphere but also the reversing layer is obscured, there still remain some bright emission lines whose source must be looked for in the chromosphere. Now the effect of high dispersion upon a continuous spectrum is to weaken its intensity, the spectrum being lengthened and the same amount of light spread over a larger area. But the monochromatic lines of the chromosphere are not weakened by using a spectroscope of high dispersion; they are simply moved farther apart. Hence, if a spectroscope of high dispersion is adjusted upon the sun's limb and moved round it till one of the bright chromospheric lines appears, and the slit is then opened, the chromosphere in that region will be visible to the eye; for the intensity of the photospheric light in the sun's vicinity, which usually blots it out of visibility, is greatly reduced by the wide dispersion.

Since this discovery our knowledge of the chromosphere has increased rapidly. Its most remarkable feature is its instability. It is in a constant state of turmoil and upheaval, great flames and clouds of incandescent gas being ejected from its surface. These eruptions are known as prominences and can be clearly seen by the open-slit method with quite small telescopes. They may be roughly divided into two groups, quiescent and eruptive. The former are usually about 50,000 miles in height, and change neither their shape nor their position very rapidly. The eruptive prominences, on the other hand, are subject to very rapid changes: prominences have been observed to be ejected from the chromosphere with velocities approaching one million miles per hour to distances of more than half a million miles from the sun. By regular observation of the numbers and distribution of the prominences Evershed has been able to demonstrate that both are subject to cyclic variation whose period is about eleven years.

The thickness of the chromosphere is about ten times as great as that of the reversing layer, as can be estimated from observations with the slitless spectroscope at total eclipse. Its lower edge tails imperceptibly into the upper reaches of the reversing layer at a height of 100-200 miles above the photosphere, while the highest constituents such as ionized calcium occur exceptionally at heights as great as 8700 miles. Its chief constituents are calcium, hydrogen, and helium, and it is the red light of hydrogen that gives to the chromosphere its characteristic color. The quiescent prominences, which usually take the form of semi-detached portions of the upper reaches of the chromosphere, have the same spectrum and chemical composition as the regions from which they spring, but the eruptive prominences often contain certain substances, such as iron and tin, that are normally confined to the lower levels of the chromosphere.

THE CORONA

The outermost atmospheric shell is the corona. This appears as a pearly white radiance (the most beautiful of the various striking phenomena witnessed at total eclipses) surrounding the sun to a very much greater depth than the chromosphere (see Plate xii). Its outer edge is not concentric with the sun's limb, as is that of the chromosphere, though it may be approximately so. On the other hand, its figure may be much distorted from the circular by great beams or petal-like rays.

The study of the corona has been rendered excessively difficult by the fact that until 1931 it could only be seen for the short and isolated periods of total solar eclipse: serial or continuous observation has thus been impossible. That this deplorable state of affairs has been remedied is due solely to the historic work of Lyot, whose photographing of the corona without an eclipse has been one of the foremost observational achievements of this century. The difficulty of the observation, which had for so long proved insurmountable, sprang from three causes. In the first place, the enormous brilliance of the photosphere completely swamped the much gentler radiance of the corona: at a distance of 2′ from the solar limb, the brightness of the corona is about one million times less than that of the photosphere, and toward the outer regions it falls off even from this figure. In the second place, there was an instrumental defect to be overcome. A lens does not transmit 100 per cent of the light directed upon it, a certain proportion being scattered by the two faces and the edge of the lens, as well as by any bubbles in the glass, surface scratches or particles of dust. The resultant halo, when the sun is observed, is at least 200 times as bright as the corona. A third source of diffusion of the photospheric light is dust in the lower levels of the earth's atmosphere: this produces a halo which is at least 100 times brighter than the corona under normal conditions at sea level. Any one of these three sources of diffusion is thus capable of swamping utterly the much fainter glimmer of the solar corona, and all must be eliminated before it can be rendered visible.

Lyot managed to overcome the first two by constructing a type of telescope which he named the coronagraph; this consisted essentially of a system of diaphragms and screens. Also, only lenses of the finest quality were used. The third difficulty was overcome by erecting the coronagraph at the observatory on the summit of the Pic du Midi at a height of nearly 3000 meters above sea level.

Lyot's first coronagraph was built and put into commission in 1930, in which year also the first coronal spectrogram was obtained without an eclipse. In the following year came the first photograph of the corona itself.

Although the shape and outline of the corona are constantly changing, its general shape varies in a regular manner which is connected with the spot cycle of eleven years' duration. At spot maximum the depth of the corona is about equal all round the disk; it is at any rate not markedly deeper in one region than another, and certainly bears no particular relation to the solar equator and poles. But at minimum it consists of short tufts at the poles and long, more or less parallel-sided beams or rays at the equator.

Although the whole corona is extremely faint compared with the photosphere, its brightest regions may at times be intolerable to the naked eye. From the immediate vicinity of the chromosphere its brilliance decreases steadily; the inner regions are also yellower in tint than the outer. It is thus possible to make a rather vague distinction between the inner and outer corona, a distinction which is confirmed by the spectroscope. The spectrum of the inner corona consists of less than thirty bright lines, some of which have been known for upwards of seventy years, while others were only detected in 1937. That of the outer corona is quite distinct from this, consisting as it does of a faint replica of the ordinary Fraunhofer spectrum. This region is therefore understood to consist of non-incandescent particles which merely reflect and scatter the sun's light, superimposing little or no radiation of their own.

But what of the inner corona, with its emission lines? None of these has been matched with laboratory spectra, for the reason that the peculiar physical conditions prevailing in the corona (particularly its great rarefaction, favoring advanced states of ionization) cannot be reproduced experimentally. It was not until as recently as 1941 that Edlen of Upsala fathomed the secret of the inner coronal spectrum, and showed that nine tenths of the radiation from this structure depended upon 'forbidden' transitions in iron atoms more highly ionized than had previously been envisaged. In addition to iron, calcium and nickel were identified, and at the present time less than 3 per cent of the total coronal emission is still unaccounted for. It is instructive to reflect that without the theoretical background of ionization conditions and stationary states, discussed in Chapter vi, and relying solely upon laboratory work, this solution of the coronal spectrum would never have been achieved.

OTHER USES OF THE CORONAGRAPH

Following the publication of the photographs of the outer atmospheres of the sun obtained by Lyot with his coronagraph, the construction of other instruments of the same fundamental type was begun. It was found that not only could the corona itself be photographed with this instrument but also excellent images of the solar prominences could be obtained. Certain types of these prominences, known as spicules, were found to be associated with the type of disturbances on the sun associated with sunspots. Since sunspots in turn are associated with electromagnetic disturbances on the earth it was realized that photographs taken with the coronagraph could be used to forecast radio interference. Several coronagraphs were set up by the Germans during the Second World War for the sole purpose of forecasting radio conditions. A coronagraph of very high quality was established by the Harvard College Observatory at Climax, Colorado, and observations obtained by it were used by the armed services.

THE SPECTROHELIOGRAPH

During the last fifty years a vast new field of solar research has been opened up as a result of the invention of the spectroheliograph. This instrument was devised independently by Hale and Deslandres in 1889. If the slit of a spectroscope is brought to bear upon any region of the sun's disk, and the spectrum is observed to contain the lines of, for example, hydrogen, we know that a part at least of the region visible through the slit is composed of hydrogen. Now suppose that the eyepiece of the view telescope is replaced by a screen in which is cut a second fine slit. A narrow section of the spectrum will pass through this slit, the rest being caught on the screen. The position of the second slit is adjustable, so that any part of the spectrum can be made to fall upon it. If it is adjusted onto a hydrogen line, only the light from incandescent hydrogen will be able to pass to the photographic plate behind the second slit. The plate, when developed, will record the distribution of hydrogen throughout the area covered by the first slit, and nothing else. Now if the first slit is long enough to cover the whole solar disk, and is moved across it from limb to limb, the second slit being moved with it, a photograph of the sun in hydrogen light will be built up on the plate by a large number of adjoining strips, the images of the second slit. In this way the distribution of hydrogen, calcium, or whatever element is chosen, over the whole visible hemisphere of the sun can be photographed. Plate XIII shows a direct photograph of the surface of the sun (on the left) together with a spectroheliogram of the sun taken at the same time in the K-line of calcium. Plate XIV shows a direct photograph of the sun together with the corresponding spectroheliogram taken with the H_α line of hydrogen.

DISTRIBUTION OF SOLAR CALICUM

The solar calcium is distributed, as may be seen from an examination of Plate XIII, in clouds of various sizes. These clouds are larger than the faculae and are known as flocculi. It will be noticed from an examination of the direct photograph and the calcium spectroheliogram in Plate XIII that large flocculi, or clouds of superheated calcium vapor, occur in the regions where spots are to be found on the photosphere proper. In some cases the nucleus of the spot extends up through the bright cloud of calcium vapor. In most cases the calcium flocculi are bright, and hence hotter than the underlying photosphere, but occasionally they appear as dark objects at a lower temperature than the material below.

DISTRIBUTION OF SOLAR HYDROGEN

As is the case with calcium the hydrogen in the upper solar atmosphere is distributed in large clouds or flocculi. The characteristic difference between the hydrogen flocculi and those of calcium is that the majority of the hydrogen flocculi are dark. Furthermore, the calcium flocculi are usually compact, more or less rounded masses, while those of hydrogen are typically wisp-like. The bright hydrogen flocculi usually appear in the vicinity of sunspots, and close examination of spectroheliograms reveals a vortex structure, indicating a sort of cyclonic disturbance in the hydrogen gas above the sunspots.

We have already mentioned the fact that the larger sunspots frequently appear in groups with two main members separated by several degrees in solar longitude. Careful study of Zeeman effect indicates that the magnetic polarity of the leading and following spots of a large group are of opposite magnetic polarity. Examination of the vortex motions in the hydrogen flocculi above such a group of spots indicates that the direction of circulation of the hydrogen is opposite in the leading spot to that in the following. Furthermore, the types of magnetic polarity of the leading and following spots are such as could be accounted for if there were masses of free electrons associated with the glowing hydrogen vapor.

It has been found that when the hydrogen flocculi approach the limb they are often associated with prominences. This shows that, as might be expected from their relative darkness and therefore coolness, they are located in the upper reaches of the solar atmosphere; many of them, in fact, are nothing more than prominences seen in projection against the sun's disk. It is probable, indeed, that the prominences, calcium and hydrogen flocculi and faculae are all objects of a similar nature— i.e. clouds of gas or vapor—differing from one another only in respect of their height above the solar surface and, consequently, temperature.

It does not appear unreasonable to seek a connection between the darkness—and therefore the relative coolness—of the hydrogen flocculi and the fact that hydrogen is lighter than calcium vapor, for we might expect to find hydrogen at greater heights above the photosphere than calcium, and at this level it would certainly be the cooler of the two.

This inference has been verified by an interesting and very important refinement of spectroheliographic technique. Some of the lines of the solar spectrum, particularly those of calcium and hydrogen, are reversed, i.e. in the center of the absorption line there is a fine, bright emission line. In view of what has already been said of the formation of emission and absorption spectra, it will be recognized as probable that the dark line is caused by absorption in relatively low levels of the atmosphere, while the central bright reversal is caused by the same gas (since the wave-length is the same) at higher levels and in a state of greater incandescence. Thus, in adjusting the second slit first upon the edge of the line and then upon the bright central component, we are photographing different levels of the sun's atmosphere. In this way the vertical distribution of the solar calcium and hydrogen may be studied, and the supposition that the bright flocculi are at a lower level than the dark is substantiated.

THE STARS

Many facts about the stars can be learned from direct observation, and it will be convenient to open the following account of the nature of the stars with a description of these observables, considering in turn spectra, temperatures, colors, luminosities, masses, sizes, and densities.

SECCHI'S CLASSIFICATION OF SPECTRA

It has already been emphasized that the sun and the stars are fundamentally similar. This fact is a certain deduction from their spectra. Some seventy years ago, Secchi, a pioneer in astrophysics, showed that the vast majority of stellar spectra can be divided into four general groups. A characteristic spectrum of any one of these types is easily distinguishable from that of any other type, while at the same time being closely similar in most of its details to other spectra of its own type. Later work has refined and elaborated Secchi's classification of stars according to spectra, by the division of each of his types into a number of sub-types, and has enlarged its scope by adding several new ones.

THE HARVARD CLASSIFICATION

Today the accepted stellar classification is the Harvard or Draper Sequence, consisting of a dozen spectroscopic types, decimally subdivided. The advantage of a classification based on spectra is obvious, for the spectrum of a substance or of a star (a conglomeration of substances) is determined by its chemical and physical nature, and thus two stars with similar spectra are also similar in the most important and fundamental respects. In the same way, a classification of the animal kingdom according to skeletal structure is more fundamental, and therefore of greater value, than one depending upon some unsignificant characteristic such as, let us say, color of skin or hair.

The Draper classification is of the utmost importance in the understanding of modern stellar physics, and without some knowledge of it the general reader will miss much of the significance of the fact and theory of this great branch of astronomy. Over 99 per cent of all the stars whose spectra have been classified—a total of over a quarter of a million—fall into six of the twelve Harvard types. These are designated B, A, F, G, K, and M, and since stars of the remaining six types are of such infrequent occurrence we may profitably, with one exception, neglect them in this outline account.

Type B: All stars of this type are bluish-white in color, and their surface temperatures in the region of 20,000° K. The typical spectrum consists of a continuous background upon which are superimposed several prominent absorption lines; although ionized oxygen and nitrogen have been identified, these are primarily due to helium. For this reason, stars of type B are often called Helium stars. This name is, however, liable to lead to confusion, since the primary factor in the production of spectral differences among the stars is not constitution but temperature. For this reason, such names as 'Helium stars,' 'Calcium stars' and the like, should be taken as describing spectra and not the stars themselves.

Type A: These stars are of a yellower tint than those of type B, though the majority of them are still whitish; their surface temperatures are of the order of 10,000° K. The strong absorptions of helium have been replaced by those of hydrogen, and faint ionized metallic lines are present in some instances. Sirius is a typical example, and the members of this type are sometimes known as Sirian, or Hydrogen, stars.

Type F: Typically yellowish-white stars, with temperatures of about 7000° K., of which Procyon is an example. Just as the helium absorptions which characterized type B had faded in type A, so now the hydrogen lines of the latter are relatively inconspicuous. In their place the metallic lines which appeared faint in type A have risen to prominence; the lines of calcium are particularly prominent. F-type stars are known also as Calcium, or Procyon, stars.

Type G: Yellow stars, of which the sun is a typical example. The spectrum is characterized by the very great number of neutral metallic absorption lines that it contains. The hydrogen lines typical of type A are even fainter than they were in the Procyon stars, while the calcium absorptions in the violet are very strong. G-type stars are often referred to as Solar stars. The sun's temperature of rather less than 6000° K. is typical.

Type K: Deep yellow stars with temperatures of about 4000° K., of which Arcturus is an example. The hydrogen lines are once again fainter than in the preceding type, the absorptions due to ionized calcium now being at their maximum intensity. The characteristic feature of these spectra is the presence of absorptions due to carbon and certain of its compounds; in this respect they are reminiscent of spot spectra. Type K stars are known also as Arcturian, or Red-Solar, stars.

Type M: Red stars, with temperatures of 3000° K. or lower; Antares is an example. The fluted bands which first appeared in the last type are here much stronger, while the high temperature lines have disappeared.

The O-type stars must be mentioned at this stage, for although they are of little account numerically, yet their abnormally high luminosities have already drawn them into the discussion at several points. This great intrinsic brightness derives from their high temperatures, which range up to at least 50,000° K. At such a temperature, metallic lines would only occur in wave-lengths too short to penetrate the terrestrial atmosphere, and they are in fact absent from O-type spectra. Characteristic, however, are lines of ionized helium, doubly ionized oxygen and nitrogen, and trebly ionized oxygen.

PRELIMINARY DEDUCTIONS FROM THE HARVARD SEQUENCE

Perhaps the most remarkable thing about this sequence of types from B to M is the gradual transition both of the color and of the spectra of the stars throughout it. Blue-white merges into white, white into yellowish-white, into pure yellow, into orange, and finally into red. In the same way we find a progressive fading of certain absorptions and their replacement by new ones. Bands which characterize one type and are strongest in it have faded in the next type and are fainter still, or non-existent, in the next. The discussion of the significance of this feature of the Harvard Sequence must, however, be left till later.

In the meantime it should be noted that the discovery of the conditioning of the spectrum of a substance by its chemical composition and physical condition allows us to make two presuppositions regarding the stars that fall within these six classes of the sequence; that is to say, regarding 99 per cent of all stars. (i) We should expect the chemical composition, as well as such physical properties as temperature and mass, of all stars of the same type to be very similar, and (ii) since the spectra change gradually from type to type without any sharp breaks in the continuity of the sequence, we should expect the physical properties of the stars in adjacent types to be more nearly similar to one another than to those of stars belonging to more remote types. Arcturian and Antarian stars, for instance, resemble one another more closely than either resemble Solar stars or, even more, B-type stars. Both these presuppositions have been verified observationally.

STELLAR TEMPERATURES

We saw in Chapter VI that the temperature of a body which is too distant for direct investigation with a thermometer or thermocouple can be determined spectroscopically in two ways. (i) The brightness of the continuous background is not uniform in all regions of the spectrum; furthermore, the position of the zone of maximum intensity is dependent upon the temperature of the radiating source. The higher the temperature, the nearer to the violet, or short-wave, end of the spectrum does it occur; the lower the temperature, the nearer to the red end. (ii) Not only is polychromatic radiation affected in recognizable ways by temperature, but monochromatic radiation likewise. That is, the absorption lines in a spectrum, each caused by radiation of a single wave-length, are modified by the temperature of the source of the radiation. Comparison of the stellar spectrum with the flame, arc, and spark spectrograms obtained experimentally allow the temperature of the radiating surface layers of the star to be estimated.

By these and similar means it has been possible to verify our two suppositions in regard to temperature. It has been found that there is a steady temperature change along the sequence—the direction of the change being a drop from B toward M—and also that the temperatures of all stars of the same spectral type are of the same order; in other words, the spectral classification is also a temperature classification. The hottest B-type stars have temperatures of about 23,000° K., while that of the coolest M-type stars is about 2500°. The highest temperature of any star yet precisely investigated is that of Plaskett's star, about 28,000°, although stars of type O normally have temperatures in the neighborhood of 40,000° or more. At the other end of the scale there are certain stars of types which we have not mentioned, with temperatures as low as 2000°. These figures represent, with infrequent exceptions, the limits of observed stellar surface temperature. It is to be noted that stars whose temperatures are lower than about 2000° may well exist, for at such temperatures they would be non-incandescent and consequently we could not expect them to be visible.*

STELLAR COLORS

Since star colors are directly dependent upon temperature, it might be well to interpolate at this point a word on the connection between

---

* ε Aurigae, the coolest known star, has an estimated surface temperature of 1700°; the greater part of its radiation lies in the infra-red, i.e. is invisible.

color and spectroscopic type. Everyday experience demonstrates that as a lump of metal—an iron poker, for instance—is heated, it passes through the successive stages of non-incandescence, dull red heat, red heat, yellow heat, and finally white heat. If we had studied its spectrum throughout the changes we should have observed the brightest zone of the continuous background passing steadily from the red toward the violet end of the spectrum. This common knowledge might have led the reader to guess that the temperature is falling steadily along the sequence from B to M, for we have seen that the color change in this direction is the exact reverse of that just described for the poker. Since the temperature drop along the sequence is gradual, it follows that all tints of the color range from a blue-white heat to a dull red heat are represented. The following table shows the nature of this cor-relation between color and spectral type:

Type	Color	Percentage occurrence of stars bright enough to be visible to the naked eye
B	Bluish-white	16.6
A	Pure white	26.8
F	Yellowish-white	9.8
G	Yellow	11.2
K	Deep yellow or orange	26.0
M	Orange-red	9.6
⎰R	Even deeper red	Negligible
⎱N	Even deeper red	Negligible

The reader may be surprised to learn that stars of these conspicuous colors exist, for the majority of those visible to the naked eye appear to be of a nondescript white tint. This is due mainly to the fact that most of the reddish stars are faint, as can be seen from the third column in the above table. Antares is, indeed, the only conspicuous example of a really deeply tinted star. The colors of the majority of stars are various tints of yellow or white, but the difference between, for example, Sirius or Vega (pure white) and Arcturus (yellow) may be seen at a glance. Greenish and bluish stars also exist, but, with one exception, they resemble the deep red stars in being faint. The one exception mentioned is the star known as β Librae, a tolerably bright green star.

STELLAR LUMINOSITIES

The luminosity or real brightness (as distinct from the apparent brightness) of a star may be determined in several ways. Just as, having discovered the distance of the sun, we can calculate its linear diameter from its observed apparent diameter, so in an analogous way, having once discovered a star's distance, we can calculate its real brightness from its apparent brightness. The apparent brightness of a star clearly depends upon two factors: its distance from the earth and its real brightness. Without knowing one we cannot discover the other. The fact that two stars appear to be equally bright is no evidence of their really being so, for one may be twice or a hundred times as distant as the other. But once we know their distances a simple calculation will give us their real brightnesses. To facilitate this, the conception of absolute magnitudes was introduced, as explained in an earlier chapter.

Besides the absolute-magnitude scale, luminosity may be expressed by a figure which compares it with that of the sun. Thus a star whose luminosity is 10 is ten times as luminous as the sun, a star with a luminosity of 0.2, one fifth as luminous as the sun, and so on. It has been found that the range of luminosity is greater than that of almost any other stellar property. It varies from about 0.000002, the luminosity (discovered in 1944) of the companion of the star whose catalogue number is B. D.+4° 4048, to about 300,000, the maximum luminosity of a variable star named S Doradus.

VISUAL BINARIES

The basic observation in the determination of stellar mass is that of the binary star, of which something must now be said. A careful study of the night sky with the naked eye will soon reveal a number of pairs of stars, the two components of which appear to be very close to one another. Telescopic observation shows that they are comparatively common objects. We might at first be led to assume that in each such case the two stars really are near one another in space, as they certainly appear to be. But a moment's thought will show that this need not necessarily be so, for the sun and moon appear to be close together at solar eclipses although the moon is nearly four hundred times nearer the earth than the sun. Thus if two stars happen to lie close to the observer's line of vision—that is, in nearly the same direction from the earth—their angular separation will be small even if one is a hundred times more distant than the other. Angular proximity between two stars on the star sphere is not, therefore, sufficient evidence for their binary nature; the relationship may be purely optical.

There are, however, two ways in which a binary system may be distinguished from an optical double. First, by the detection of orbital motion about their common center of gravity in one or both of the components, and, secondly, by the detection of common proper motion of the two components. Even if no trace of orbital motion can be detected, we may be tolerably certain that the two stars form a binary system if they have a common proper motion. For the chances against two unrelated stars which happen to appear close together as seen from the earth having an identical proper motion, both as regards direction and speed, their real velocities being graded to their respective distances from the sun, are too enormous to permit us to appeal to coincidence.

STELLAR MASS FROM THE OBSERVATION OF BINARIES

The study of binaries has provided us with the fundamentals of our knowledge concerning stellar mass. If the distance of a binary system is known, its linear size may quickly be calculated from its angular size; furthermore, mere observation will give the period of the components' mutual revolution, providing this period is not too long for their orbital motions to be perceptible. With these two data—the linear separation of the two stars, and the period of their revolution about the system's center of gravity—it is possible to deduce the total mass of the system by means of Newton's revision of the harmonic law as enunciated by Kepler.
For

$$\frac{m_1 + m_2}{m_s + m_e} = \frac{A^3}{P^2}$$

where m_1, m_2 are the masses of the two stars,
      m_s is the mass of the sun,
      m_e is the mass of the earth, which, being negligible compared
        with the other quantities in the equation, may be disregarded,
      A is the separation of the two components in terms of the sun-
        earth distance, i.e. in astronomical units,
      P is their period in years.

If, furthermore, the motion of each star relative to the center of gravity can be determined, their individual masses may be calculated, just as the mass of the moon was calculated.

Such work as this has shown that the limits of stellar mass are more circumscribed than those of size or luminosity. The average total mass of a number of binary systems that have been investigated is 2.2 times that of the sun, the average mass of all these components only differing from that of the sun by 10 per cent. Stars even three times as massive as the sun are rare; so are stars less than one fifth as massive as the sun. Stars up to ten times as massive are very rare, while still more massive stars are quite exceptional.

SPECTROSCOPIC BINARIES

In addition to the more than 17,000 visual binaries known at the present time there are many binary stars in which the apparent angular separation between the two components is too small to be observed even with telescopes of the highest resolving power. The fact that such pairs do actually exist has been established by an interesting application of the spectroscope and the Doppler effect. Let us assume that we have two stars close enough together in space so that they are bound together by their mutual gravitational attraction. In order that the two stars shall not actually fall together both of them must be revolving about the common center of gravity of the pair. Unless the plane containing the orbital motions of the two stars is at right angles to the line of sight from the earth, each of the two stars will alternately be approaching and receding from the observer. For convenience in description, let us call one of these stars the primary and the other the secondary. When the primary is approaching the observer the secondary will be receding, and vice versa. We have already seen that when a source of light is approaching an observer the spectral lines are shifted toward the violet end of the spectrum and when it is receding the lines are shifted toward the red. If we assume that both the primary and the secondary are of equal brightness the spectral lines will be alternately double and single. This periodic doubling of the spectroscopic lines in a star was first announced in 1889 at the Harvard College Observatory after examination of a series of spectrograms taken of the star Mizar (ζ Ursae Majoris). If the brightness of one of the stars is more than three or four times that of the other, as is usually the case, the spectroscopic lines due to the fainter star will not be seen. In such a case the spectral lines of the brighter component will alternately and periodically shift from the red to the violet and back as the star approaches and recedes from the observer. These physical double stars, whose binary character can be determined only from the changes in their spectra, are known as spectroscopic binaries.

Except in the cases of eclipsing binaries (to be discussed below) it is impossible to determine the angle between the plane containing the two stars of a spectroscopic binary system and the line of sight. Accordingly, it is impossible to determine the complete orbit of the system even though the distance is known. The best that we can do is make a statistical assumption that the orbit plane is inclined at an angle of 45° to the line of sight. With this assumption and a knowledge of the distance of the pair we can make an estimate of the combined mass of the system, since the period is known. Results indicate that the masses of the spectroscopic binaries are of the same order of magnitude as those discussed above for the visual binaries.

The relative sizes of the shifts of the two sets of lines (where both are visible) give the relative line-of-sight velocities of the two stars, therefore also their relative distances from the center of gravity, and therefore their relative masses. If, for example, the shift of one set of lines is seven tenths as large as that of the other, then,

(*a*) line-of-sight velocity of star A : line-of-sight velocity of star B=7:10,

(*b*) linear distance of A from center of gravity : linear distance of B from center of gravity=7:10,

(*c*) mass of A : mass of B=7:10.

Only the relative masses of the two components of a spectroscopic binary can be deduced, since the orbit cannot be completely reconstructed owing to our ignorance of its inclination to the line of sight.

We shall see when we come to discuss eclipsing binaries, that in some cases the inclination of the orbit plane to the line-of-sight may be accurately determined. In such cases, since the line-of-sight velocities of the two are determined in linear units, the linear size of their orbits may be found. If any method is available for determining the angular separation of the two stars (as, for example, by an interferometer, see page 255) we can determine the distance of the system. The period of revolution of each star about the center of gravity is given by the time required for its spectrum to travel from greatest displacement toward the red to greatest displacement toward the violet, and thence back to the red again. From the period and the linear separation of the two stars, their combined mass can be calculated, as we saw a few pages back. And knowing both the combined mass and the relation in which each stands to the other (7:10 in the example), we arrive at the individual mass of each star.

FURTHER DATA FROM ECLIPSING BINARIES

It is interesting at this point to note how much information the ingenuity of the modern astronomer is capable of deriving from the study of these eclipsing binary systems. Knowing the components' distance and their combined apparent magnitude, the astronomer is in a position to calculate their luminosity, either in terms of the absolute magnitude scale or as compared with that af the sun, by means of the inverse-square law. The surface temperatures of the stars can be measured spectroscopically, and this, combined with their luminosity, takes us one step further—to the linear surface area which would be required to produce the observed brightness. From the surface area, the diameter is quickly calculated. And finally, from the linear sizes and masses, their densities can (as we shall see shortly) be derived.

Let us summarize the results of this chain of astronomical detective work: the following data have been derived for the spectroscopic binary which we have been considering:

Radial velocity of each component,
Orbital velocity of each component,
Combined and individual masses,
Linear separation at any moment,
Distance,
Absolute magnitude and temperature,
Linear diameters,
Densities.

Bearing in mind Kepler's third law, and the fact that the components of a spectroscopic binary are nearer to one another than the components of a visual binary, we should expect to find that the periods of spectroscopic binaries are shorter than those of the wider pairs which can be resolved visually. This has been found to be so: the shortest period of those binaries so far investigated is the two and a quarter hours of γ Ursae Minoris; the upper limit merges into the shortest periods of the visual binaries, there being a smooth transition of period from a few hours to several thousand years. At the lower end of this sequence are the spectroscopic binaries, and at the upper the widest visual pairs.

STELLAR SIZE

The luminosity of a star must depend upon two factors: the brightness of its incandescent surface, and the amount there is of it. Increase both, and the luminosity will increase; decrease both, and it will decrease; while an increase in one may just counterbalance a decrease in the other, the luminosity remaining unchanged. This relationship may be crudely expressed in the form

Surface brightness×Surface area=Luminosity.

We have already seen (Chapter VI) that the surface brightness of a black body varies as the fourth power of the temperature, for radiation in all wave-lengths. It follows, therefore, that if we know the temperature (or the color index, a function of temperature) as well as the absolute magnitude of a star, then its linear diameter is calculable.

This indirect method at arriving at stellar diameters has proved to be of the greatest value. For both stellar temperature and absolute magnitude are qualities about which a considerable mass of data has been accumulated.

Secondly, as just explained, stellar radii may be derived for a certain type of binary star—the eclipsing binary.

A third method is valuable in that it is especially applicable to the class of star known as white dwarfs, so that the impossibility of applying the interferometer (method 4, below) to these stars is mitigated. It is a deduction (beyond the scope of this book) from the general theory of relativity that the entire spectrum of a source will be displaced by an amount that varies with the value of the expression

$$\frac{m}{r}$$

where m is the mass of the source and r its radius. Before this method can be put into practice, therefore, the star's mass must be discovered. Although the method is theoretical and highly mathematical, it is interesting to note that in the case of the sun it yields a result which agrees very closely with the independently ascertained figure.

The final method of determining the linear diameter of a star requires two data: its angular diameter and its distance from the sun. If we know the values of both these, it requires only a simple calculation to discover how great its linear diameter must be in order to subtend an angle of x'' at a point y light years distant. Despite the enormous linear sizes of the stars (some have diameters running into hundreds of millions of miles) their distances are of such relative immensity that their angular diameters are minute. So minute, in fact, that not until the construction of the 200-inch telescope has it been possible to observe them as more than points of light.

Even the largest telescope can show a measurable disk for only the very largest and nearest stars. In order to determine the diameter of any appreciable number of stars, the mode of behavior of light known as interference must be utilized. If light from a source is split into two beams and then recombined, these two rays will, under certain circumstances, interfere with one another with the production of a characteristic effect. To avoid going into too detailed and technical an explanation of the phenomenon of interference, it will be enough to take a specific example. Suppose that the upper end of a telescope is covered with a screen in which two fine slits, some distance apart, are cut. Then light from a source in front of the telescope will be split into two beams, each passing through one of the slits, which are made to converge by the object glass to a focus in the plane of the eyepiece. The result of this combination of the two rays at the focus of the object glass is the formation of alternate dark and bright fringes to the image of the slits. These are known as interference fringes and their formation depends upon this particular property of wave systems.

Now the appearance of the fringes depends, for a given source, upon the distance separating the slits. Adjustment of the positions of the slits will reveal the fact that at a certain distance apart the fringes will disappear. It can be proved, and verified experimentally, that this distance is related in a certain known way to the diameter of the source of the radiation.

This is the principle of the interferometer constructed and used at Mt. Wilson. By its means the angular diameters of a dozen stars of known distance have been measured, and from these data their linear diameters derived. The diameters of these twelve stars range from 12 to 500 times that of the sun. The diameters of at least four are larger than that of the orbit of Mars. They are Mira (o Ceti), Betelgeux (α Orionis), Ras Algethi (α Herculis), and Antares (α Scorpii), and their linear diameters together with those of two other giants are given in the table below:

STAR	DIAMETER IN MILES	DIAMETER COMPARED WITH THAT OF THE SUN
o Ceti	4.3×10^8	500
α Orionis	3.9×10^8	450
α Herculis	3.5×10^8	400
α Scorpii	2.5×10^8	290
α Tauri	2.9×10^7	34
α Bootis	2.1×10^7	24

The star ε Aurigae is worthy of mention at this point. It is a variable, a star whose brightness fluctuates. As recently as 1937 Struve and others have shown that in reality it consists of a close pair of stars, in mutual revolution, and that the brighter is some 3000 times larger than the sun: if it were placed at the center of the solar system, where the sun now is, its surface would lie between the orbits of Saturn and Uranus! It is also an interesting object in that it is both the most rarefied and the coolest (1700° K.) star known.

These stars which we have just been discussing are of course situated at the upper end of the range of stellar size. A more balanced conception of average stellar size is obtained from eclipsing binaries. The mean diameter of twenty-eight stars of this type is a little less than three times that of the sun. This result is substantiated by the indirect methods, already described; these indicate that the average size of stars throughout the galaxy is even lower than that derived from studies of the eclipsing binaries.

The angular subtention of the smallest stars is too minute for measurement by the interferometer, and the first method—that depending upon surface temperature and luminosity—must be employed. The smallest stars of all belong to the class known as the white dwarfs, and are considerably smaller than the sun. The following table illustrates this lower limit of stellar size:

STAR	DIAMETER IN MILES	COMPARED WITH THE SUN	COMPARED WITH THE PLANETS
Sirius B	30,000	0.034	$3\frac{1}{2} \times$ earth
Procyon B	7,000	0.008	less than earth
o Ceti B	155,000	0.178	about that of Saturn

STELLAR DENSITIES

Once the mass and radius of a star are known, its mean density may be derived from the expression

$$\text{density} = \frac{\text{mass}}{\text{volume.}}$$

We have learned that whereas the masses of different stars are confined within rather narrow limits, their volumes vary gigantically: the smallest stars are comparable with the earth, while the diameters of the giants are in certain cases comparable with that of the solar system. It follows that stellar density must likewise vary within very wide limits. The mean density of such a giant as Antares is only about 0.03 per cent that of ordinary air; a supergiant like ε Aurigae would be even more rarefied—probably about 3×10^{-9} times water. At the other end of the scale, among the dwarfs, where volume has decreased out of all proportion to mass, densities of the order of 50,000 times that of water are encountered. How matter can be compressed sufficiently to yield such densities will be discussed later.

Having reviewed the methods and results of studying the observable stellar characteristics, reference must be made to two fundamental relationships which connect, respectively, spectral type and mass with luminosity.

THE SPECTRAL TYPE-LUMINOSITY RELATION (RUSSELL DIAGRAM)

In 1913 Russell first produced the diagram that represents one of the most fundamental forms in which astrophysical data may be arranged. He arranged the luminosities of those stars for which data were available, in order of spectroscopic type. As soon as this was done, it became apparent that these two observables—type and luminosity—were intimately connected one with another. The nature of this interdependence is most clearly brought out when it is presented in graphical form. If a blank is prepared, the axes representing spectral type and luminosity respectively (see Fig. 50), and the position of each star marked with a dot—thus one whose type is G and absolute magnitude $+5$, would be represented by a point at the intersection of the horizontal line from $+5$ and the vertical line from G—then the disposition of these dots is not random. On the contrary, they cluster about two zones or lines, the first crossing the diagram obliquely from the top left-hand toward the bottom right-hand corner, the second branching off about two thirds of the way up the first and thence running out toward the upper right-hand corner of the diagram.

Let us inquire more closely into the significance of this two-branched distribution. Stars at the top of the diagram are of high luminosity, irrespective of type, and those at the bottom of low; while from left to right (spectroscopic types B to M) the star becomes progressively redder, irrespective of luminosity. Treating first of all the main zone about which the points cluster—that crossing the diagram diagonally—we see that the redder a star is, the lower is its luminosity. Reading off approximate values from the axes, we may derive the following values:

TYPE	ABSOLUTE MAGNITUDE
B	−2.5
A	+0.5
F	+2.5
G	+4.5
K	+6.0
M	+10.0

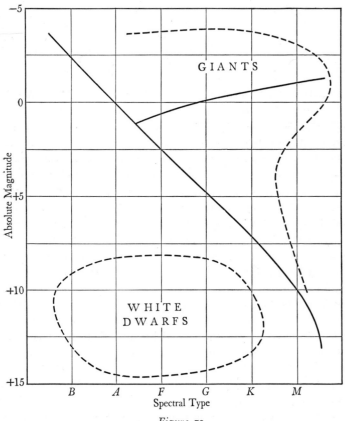

Figure 50.

This primary zone is known as the main sequence, and stars which lie on or close to it, as main sequence stars. About two thirds of the stars whose luminosities and spectral types have been accurately determined lie within 1 magnitude of the curve that the plotted points define.

The second branch of the diagram is particularly interesting. The plotted points of the Russell diagram are not in fact confined precisely to the two main branches, any more than the bullets of a good shot are confined exclusively to the bull's-eye, though they will be clearly concentrated upon this point. We have seen that in the case of the main sequence there is in fact an impressive concentration upon the curve defined by them. But in the second branch the crowding upon the central curve (marked, like the main sequence, by a continuous line in Fig. 50) is less clearly marked, and to a certain extent points occur over the whole area which is roughly indicated by the broken line, though progressively less frequently at greater distances from the central zone.

Let us consider what this distribution implies in terms of luminosity. All B-type stars are of much the same intrinsic brightness, the limiting absolute magnitudes being about -3 and $+1$. For each succeeding type, however, the range of luminosity increases; the extreme case is provided by the M-type stars, the vast majority of which (those belonging to the main sequence) have absolute magnitudes in the region of $+12$, though very much more luminous stars of the same type are infrequently encountered, up to absolute magnitudes of about -2. All the high luminosity stars are of course represented in the diagram by scattered points lying above the main sequence.

Thus, whereas red stars may be divided into two groups—those with high and those with low absolute magnitudes—this distinction becomes less and less clearly marked as we move back along the main sequence toward type B. Hertzsprung had drawn attention to the dichotomy among red stars as long ago as 1905, when he named the two groups 'giants' and 'dwarfs' respectively. But it was not until Russell investigated the relation between spectral type and luminosity, eight years later, that this division was also applicable, though in a decreasing degree, to the yellow and blue stars.

The terms 'giant' and 'dwarf' have subsequently come to be used in a rather different sense, Hertzsprung's 'dwarfs' now being known as main-sequence stars, the term 'dwarf' being kept for a special class of stars which we shall consider shortly, and the term 'giant' being generally applied to all stars of greater luminosity than main-sequence stars of the same type, i.e. to those stars lying well above the main sequence on the Russell diagram, in the area so labeled (Fig. 50). As can be seen from the figure, the main zone of the giants branches away from the main sequence roughly at right angles to the luminosity axis: in other words, the giants, unlike the main-sequence stars, are all of the same order of luminosity—several hundred times that of the sun. We shall learn presently that the term 'giant,' though originally based solely upon luminosity, is particularly appropriate in that these stars are also more massive than the stars originally termed 'dwarfs.'

WHITE DWARFS

The third occupied area of the Russell diagram lies well below, and separated from, the main sequence, where a few scattered points record the existence of the peculiar class of star known as white dwarfs.* In opposition to the giants, the luminosities of these stars are lower than those of main-sequence stars belonging to the same type. Only a handful of white dwarfs have so far been discovered: this, however, does not necessarily indicate that they are of rare occurrence, but rather reflects the fact that owing to their exceedingly low luminosities only those in the immediate vicinity of the sun are likely to be detected.

The following table demonstrates their low luminosities and the apparent faintness which goes with them; all five stars are nearer than about 80 light years:

STAR	ABSOLUTE MAGNITUDE	EQUIVALENT MAIN SEQUENCE ABSOLUTE MAGNITUDE	VISUAL MAGNITUDE
Sirius B	+11.3	+2.5	+8.4
Procyon B	16.0	(2.5)	13.5
o Ceti B	7.5	0.0	9.6
40 Eridani B	11.2	0.6	9.7
van Maanen's Star	14.3	2.5	12.3

The investigation of the nature of the white dwarf, Sirius B, illustrates well the Holmesian procedure which the astronomer follows in discovering the mass, luminosity, density, size, and other properties of

*Properly so called, in the modern terminology. The stars that used to be known as 'red dwarfs' are those lying at the bottom of the main sequence, i.e. main-sequence M-type stars.

a star. Sirius itself is a comparatively near neighbor, so that the parallactic method gives accurate results: its distance is 8.8 light years. Its spectral type is early A; thus it is a white star with a temperature (determined spectroscopically) of some 10,000°. Since we know its distance we can calculate the linear dimensionis of the orbit of its companion from its angular dimensions. Thus we can discover that Sirius B revolves about its primary in an orbit of about the same size as that of Uranus about the sun; its period is 49 years. Hence it may be deduced that the combined masses of the two stars is 3.5 times that of the sun. Thus:

$$k\left(m_1+m_2\right)=\frac{a^3}{P^2}$$

where k=a universal constant,
      a=the mean separation of the components,
      P=the period of revolution.

In the case of Sirius, observation gives P=49 years and a=$7''.55$. This angular separation at a distance of 8.8 light years is equivalent to a linear separation 20.4 times as great as that between the earth and the sun. Hence, substituting in the equation,

$$\frac{(20.4)^3}{49^2}=m_1+m_2$$

Or, $m_1+m_2=3.5.$

As we have seen, an investigation of the absolute orbits of the two components—i.e. their orbits about their common center of gravity—is necessary to reveal the individual mass of each component. That of Sirius B turns out to be one third as great as that of its primary; yet it is very much fainter, only emitting one ten-thousandth as much visible radiation as Sirius A. In other words, its mass is 85 per cent that of the sun while its luminosity is less than ⅓ per cent. The obvious conclusion to be drawn from this is that it is a very low temperature star, radiating much less intensely than either the sun or Sirius A. But it has been found that its spectrum is almost identical with that of Sirius A; that is, it is an A-type star, and must consequently have a considerably higher temperature than the sun. This being so, the only way to account for its faintness is to assume that it is very small. Calculation based on this assumption shows that it cannot have a diameter of more than about 25,000 miles. It is thus a body whose volume is about 27 times that of the earth, and diameter about 3 times that of the earth. Yet its mass is 250,000 times the earth's. From which it follows that its density is some 40,000 times as great as that of water: 1 cubic inch of the matter of Sirius B would weigh a ton. Even this fantastic figure is surpassed by some other white dwarfs: the type F dwarf known as van Maanen's star has an estimated density of several million times that of water, while the density of another, discovered by Kuiper, is estimated by him to be in the region of 40 million times that of water!

The position of the red dwarfs at the end of the main sequence appears to be secure, but the place of the B, A, and F white dwarfs in the stellar evolutionary process is unknown. All that can be said is that they resemble the red, main-sequence stars as regards size and mass, while differing from them in the matter of their higher temperatures and therefore whiter color.

THE MASS-LUMINOSITY RELATION

The second important relationship that has been found to exist between the observable stellar characteristics which we have already reviewed is that between mass and luminosity. Once a sufficient number of binaries had been studied, it was possible to treat their data statistically, and in 1924 Eddington pointed out that if the masses and luminosities of these stars were plotted against one another, the resultant pattern was a smooth curve. Hence we learn that the mass and the luminosity of a star are in some way interdependent. Roughly speaking, the relation between them is such that if the masses of two stars are in the ratio 2 : 1, their luminosities will be as 10 : 1. Mass and luminosity are directly proportional to one another: a star whose absolute magnitude is —2.5 will be about twelve times as massive as the sun; one whose absolute magnitude is +4.8 will be equally massive as the sun; and one whose absolute magnitude is +10 will have only about one third the sun's mass. This relation holds good irrespective of spectral type and of temperature: thus, for example, a star of absolute magnitude 0.0 will be about four times as massive as the sun, no matter whether it be a white, type-A star of the main sequence or a reddish, K-type giant.

Combining this new knowledge with the already ascertained relation between spectral type and luminosity illustrated in the Russell diagram, it is clear that stellar mass suffers a continuous decrease along the length of the main sequence from B to M, whereas among the giants it maintains, with luminosity, a tolerably steady value.

One notable exception to the mass-luminosity relation is the white dwarfs. These are uniformly too massive for their luminosities. As an instance of this, we have already seen that the mass of Sirius B is more than three quarters that of the sun, while its luminosity is less than three thousandths of the sun's.

Had the investigation of stellar mass been confined to binaries, only a comparatively small amount of data could have been accumulated. But it was nevertheless sufficient to open up, by disclosing the mass-luminosity relation, a very much wider field. Once the relationship has been expressed in graphical form, it is only necessary to drop a perpendicular from the appropriate point on the luminosity axis to the curve for the mass to be read off with a probable maximum error of 20 per cent in the case of any star, binary or otherwise, whose luminosity is already known. This welcome extension of the field of operations substantiates the conclusion drawn from work in the more restricted arena of binary stars: that the masses of the vast majority of stars are not startlingly different from one another, differing at most by a factor of 200.

SPECTROSCOPIC PARALLAX

From what we have just learned of the mass-luminosity relation we should expect that there might be found some distinctive spectroscopic differences between the highly luminous giants and the comparatively dim 'dwarfs' of the main sequence, particularly the lower end of the main sequence. For whereas the masses of the giants have been shown to be of the order of fifty times those of the dwarfs, we have already seen that their radii are some hundreds or even thousands of times as great. Hence the force of gravity at the surfaces of the highly rarefied giants will be, compared with the dwarfs and despite the giants' greater masses, infinitesimal. We have seen in Chapter VI that ionization is favored not only by an increase of temperature, but also by reduced pressure. It follows, therefore, that a more advanced state of ionization should be expected in the atmosphere of a giant than in that of a dwarf of the same spectroscopic type; and that this should be reflected in the spectra of the two stars.

Such has actually been found to be the case: briefly, as the luminosity of a star increases, certain lines in its spectrum increase in intensity, while others weaken. Adams and Kohlschütter in 1914 constructed curves relating luminosity (absolute magnitudes) with observed intensities of these crucial lines. Thenceforward these curves could be utilized to deduce the distance of any star bright enough to yield a spectrum that could be distinctly photographed: from the observed condition of the crucial lines its absolute magnitude could be read off the curve, and a comparison of this with its apparent magnitude led straight to its distance by means of the formula,

$$M = m + 5 + 5 \log p.$$

This, one of the most surprising and extraordinary developments of recent astrophysics, has proved a powerful weapon in the hands of the astronomer. Thousands of spectroscopic parallaxes have now been determined, many of which would never have been discovered had the only available method been that of trigonometrical parallax. Nevertheless, the resources of spectroscopic parallax have today been rather exhaustively explored, and the spotlight has shifted to other of the methods, of wider application, described in Chapter IV. Within its limits —and it cannot be profitably applied to the upper half of the main sequence—it is reliable; indeed, beyond a certain distance (some 65 light years) it is more accurate than the photographic method. For whereas the margin of inaccuracy in the latter method widens with increasing distance, the error in the spectroscopic is constant and independent of the smallness of the parallax, being a slight indefiniteness in the calibration of the curves themselves, which results in a uniform uncertainty of about 0.5 absolute magnitudes. This is equivalent to an error in the derived parallax of about 20 per cent. The percentage error to be expected has been arrived at by determining the spectroscopic parallaxes of stars, other than those employed in the calibration, whose trigonometrical parallaxes were already known; the correspondence between the two was found to be reasonably close.

THE SUN AS A STAR

Once we have arrived at some idea of the range of stellar sizes, luminosities, temperatures, and other characteristics, the conclusion is forced upon us that the sun is a very ordinary member of the stellar hierarchy: it cannot even boast the inverted distinction of being abnormally small, dim, or in any other respect undistinguished. The essence of the sun's stellar status is contained in the simple statement that it is a G-type star of the main sequence, i.e. it is situated about midway between the blue giants on the one hand and the red dwarfs on the other: all other features follow from that.

The sun's mediocrity can best be demonstrated by tabulating the

maximum and minimum normal values for the different stellar characteristics, adjusted in each case to bring the solar value to unity (the
figures are necessarily approximate):

CHARACTERISTIC	MAXIMUM	MINIMUM
	(*Sun*= 1)	
Temperature . . .	5	0.4
Luminosity . . .	50,000	0.000002
Mass	10	0.1
Linear diameter . .	500	0.01
Density	400,000	0.0000003

VARIABLE STARS

One further stellar characteristic must be mentioned—variability. A
very large number of stars vary in apparent brightness: this may be
intrinsic in the star—i.e. its luminosity is variable—or may be ex-
trinsic. In the latter case the star cannot truly be considered as variable;
such stars have already been mentioned in connection with the determination of stellar mass: they are the eclipsing binaries.

EXTRINSIC VARIABLES: ECLIPSING BINARIES

The types of variation exhibited by different variable stars are diverse,
but several general types may be distinguished. The simplest way to
study the behavior of a variable is to note its magnitude at a series of
intervals, spaced according to the period of variation from maximum
to maximum, and then construct a curve whose axes designate Time
and Magnitude. This curve will be a direct representation of the star's
changing brightness and the magnitude of the star at any instant during the period covered may be read off at will. Such a curve is known
as a light curve and Fig. 51 is an example. The data plotted is for the
star Algol (β Persei) obtained by Stebbins from photoelectric measurements. Even a cursory glance at the curve will yield a considerable
amount of information regarding the binary system involved. In the
first place, since the duration of minimum light is very short, the eclipse
must be partial; were the eclipse central (i.e. total or annular) the
magnitude at minimum would remain fairly constant for an appreciable
time before mounting toward maximum again. The appearance of the
shallow secondary minimum indicates that one of the two stars is
fainter than the other; and the fact that the light curve rises (i.e. the
apparent brightness of the system increases) as the secondary minimum

is approached indicates that the fainter component is illuminated by the light from the brighter star and is approaching full phase (as viewed from the earth) just before it passes behind the brighter star. Detailed mathematical analysis of the curve yields a large amount of information regarding such things as the inclination of the orbit plane to the line-of-sight, the relative sizes and brightnesses of the two members of the system, et cetera. The insert in Fig. 51 represents, in approximate relative scale, the orbit of such a system with the fainter star partially eclipsed by the brighter one. In many eclipsing binaries the two stars are so close to each other that tidal forces produce actual distortion

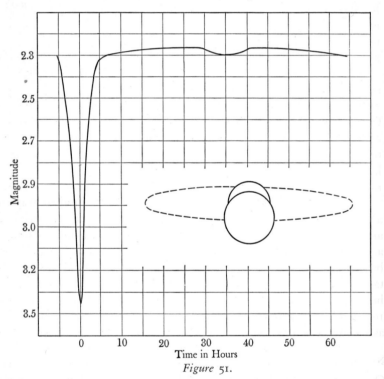

Figure 51.

of the members of the system from spheres to ellipsoids, and careful study of the light curve will indicate the amount of distortion of the individual components.

INTRINSIC VARIABLES: CEPHEIDS
Eclipsing variables—other than those that are distorted by tidal forces —cannot be regarded as true variables, for the actual light-output of

each star is constant. Such variations as are observed from the earth are due solely to the relative positions of the sun and the two stars in space. But there are certain types of variables whose light curves do not permit of interpretation along these lines. These stars are not binaries, but isolated stars, and the observed variation is intrinsic, involving not only apparent but also absolute magnitude. We must confine our attention to only one of the several groups into which such variables may be divided—the Cepheids.

Figure 32 shows the light curve of δ Cephei, the type star after which the Cepheids are named. It exemplifies three of the most characteristic features of this type of star: the variation is continuous, the rise to maximum is quicker than the fall, and the decline is not represented by a smooth curve. Why Cepheids should behave in this manner is not known, but the theory that they are pulsating stars is regarded as the most likely explanation. A star in such a condition would undoubtedly be variable, while other considerations indicate that its variation might well be of the Cepheid type. For example, the spectroscope shows that Cepheids have fluctuating radial velocities. These, however, are not of a type that could be accounted for on the grounds of the mutual revolution of two stars, for the maximum brightness is attained while the line-of-sight motion is toward the observer, and is minimum when the radial velocity is positive.

The period of a Cepheid may lie anywhere between a few hours and about fifty days; those whose periods are less than twelve hours are, as we have already learned, called cluster variables, although they are not entirely confined to the globular clusters. Their great intrinsic brightness is, from the practical viewpoint of discovering stellar distances, almost as important as the period-luminosity relation: a Cepheid of short period (say 24 hours) has at maximum a luminosity about 100 times greater than the sun: if the period is increased only so far as 10 days, the luminosity leaps to about 1000 times the sun's.

NOVAE

One further class of variable deserves mention. Occasionally it happens that, for no ascertained reason, a faint star suddenly blazes up, to shine with a brilliance that may outrival any other object in the night sky, only to die down again to its former insignificance. Such stars are called novae. The name dates from pre-telescopic days when novae really did appear to be new stars, for in almost every case they are too faint to be seen with the naked eye before the outburst. It is now known that we are concerned rather with the sudden brightening of an already existent star than with the birth of a new one, since the examination of photographs (where available, and of sufficiently low limiting magnitude) taken before the outburst invariably establishes the fact that a faint star existed in the exact position of the nova.

Little is known of the early history of novae, for the reason that they are not usually noticed until well on the way to maximum brightness. This rise to maximum is extremely rapid, the peak usually being reached within a day or two (at most, several weeks) of its discovery; during this interval its brightness may have increased a hundred thousandfold. Maximum having been reached, the brightness at once begins to decline, rapidly at first and then more and more slowly; the original magnitude is reached, in typical cases, several years later. This decline, many times more gradual than the meteoric leap to maximum, is usually varied by considerable oscillations of brightness.

It is therefore possible to summarize the history of a typical nova as follows. A sudden and spectacular rise to a prominence which may outshine all its neighbors and be the wonder of the night sky; Lundmark calculates that at maximum the average nova is 25,000 times more luminous than the sun. The glory is short-lived, however, and gradually the star slips back toward its former inconspicuous level; a few years later it is not even visible to the naked eye. Such a story as this might well be told as a cautionary tale to astrologically minded dictators.

Novae do not occur with equal frequency in all regions of the star sphere, but tend to congregate about the plane of the galaxy. Of thirty prominent novae whose positions and histories are accurately known,

16 lie within 10° of the galactic plane,
23 .. .. 20° .. ..
28 .. .. 30° .. ..
29 .. .. 40° .. ..
30 .. .. 50° .. ..

These figures show a sharp falling off of numbers in zones progressively farther from the plane of the Milky Way. Furthermore, novae tend to occur near the edges of the Milky Way rather than in its more central regions.

What can be the cause of the cataclysmic conflagration that the typical nova must represent? Four main lines of approach have been employed in an endeavor to answer this question. The first assumes the existence of binaries with very long periods, and also highly eccentric orbits and close periastron passage; that is, the two components pass extremely near to one another once in each period of revolution. It is argued that at periastron we may suppose great tides to be raised in each star, possibly with the formation of a third body; at any rate, it is assumed that tidal filaments would be wrenched from the bodies of the two stars. The weakness of this suggested explanation is that in order to produce anything like the appearance of a nova, the mutual approach of the two components at periastron would have to be very close indeed, and it is doubtful whether binary systems possessing at the same time highly eccentric orbits and a sufficiently close periastron passage do in fact exist.

A more general hypothesis on the same lines supposes that when any two stars—not necessarily the components of a binary system—approach closely or possibly collide, the resultant cataclysm would have all the appearances of a nova. While this contention may very well be true, it is difficult to believe that all novae are caused in this way. For, as we have seen, it is possible to arrive at some sort of idea of the density of stars in space; and this, combined with our knowledge of stellar motions, indicates that such stellar conjunctions must be too infrequent to cause all novae, bearing in mind their known rate of occurrence. (Though there may not be more than half a dozen bright novae in the course of a century, faint novae, discovered by the examination and comparison of photographic plates, are of comparatively frequent occurrence.) Furthermore, it is difficult to see how, after such an interaction between two stars, stable conditions could be restored in the space of a few years.

The third theory supposes that a star—dark or luminous—is carried into a region occupied by dark nebulous material, and that it causes a conflagration in much the same way that a meteor is heated to incandescence during its passage through the terrestrial atmosphere. This theory can claim to furnish an explanation of the preference shown by novae not only for the Milky Way (which is the zone both of the diffuse 'galactic' nebulae and also of the obscuring medium) but more specifically for the edges of the Milky Way. It also gives an explanation of some of the features of the complex spectroscopic history of the typical nova. It does not, however, explain all the observed spectroscopic changes and it is furthermore extremely unlikely that there exist any nebulae of sufficient density to cause the outburst.

It is the fourth hypothesis that is regarded with the greatest favor by astronomers today. This suggests that the nova is a—perhaps abnormal, perhaps common, perhaps inevitable—stage in the life-history of every star, and results from changes in its internal constitution and structure. A rapid expansion of the internal material of the star, amounting to an explosive outburst, is hypothesized. This may or may not be the result of a sudden temperature rise, but in any case the outer and visible regions of the star would be 'blown out' very rapidly without at first rising appreciably in temperature. This would explain certain of the spectral changes associated with the rise to maximum which indicate high negative line-of-sight velocities combined with little or no alteration of temperature as indicated by change of type. At maximum the star would begin to shrink again, while its temperature would rise steadily, perhaps as far as the 50,000° mark. This shrinkage associated with increasing temperature would continue until, some years after the initiation of the outburst, the star would be a white dwarf.

Stated briefly and baldly in this manner, the hypothesis may sound like pure romancing, an *ad hoc* fitting of the facts, without regard to probability or even possibility. Nevertheless, it does appear to follow from the mathematical investigation of the internal structure of stars that such a course of events may well be a stage—even a necessary stage—in the evolution of each individual star. The whole matter is still in an uncertain state, however, and few astronomers would be bold enough to state categorically that they know what causes a star to burst forth as a nova.

EXCURSION INTO SPECULATION

It was stated in the Preface that in this book would be found a systematic presentation of demonstrable and established facts, involving a minimum of controversial topics and such as require the reader to accept statements on trust. To the present point this claim has been faithfully substantiated, with only one or two lapses: as, for instance, the supposed origin of the lunar craters and ring plains.

The allied problems of stellar energy production and stellar evolution are still subjects for controversy and some speculation. Such great advances have been made in the fields of subatomic and nuclear physics within the last two decades that something should be said of them. The treatment will necessarily be summary, and it must be recognized that the results mentioned in these last sections are very far from final.

SOURCES OF SOLAR ENERGY

We saw earlier in this chapter that the sun pours forth energy at such a rate that 1.35×10^6 ergs per second of radiant energy cross every square centimeter of a sphere with radius equal to the average distance of the sun from the earth. This means that the total radiation from the sun each year is of the order of magnitude of 1.2×10^{41} ergs. By a number of independent methods geologists have gained the belief that the earth's crust solidified at least 3×10^9 years ago and that the radiation from the sun has been approximately constant throughout this period. From these figures we can see that during the lifetime of the earth in its present form the sun has radiated something of the order of magnitude of 4×10^{50} ergs or about 2×10^{17} ergs per gram of its mass.

Three theories have in the past been proposed to explain whence the sun gets this great reserve of energy:

(a) By simple burning. This is the obvious explanation: the sun is burning up its substance in the same way that, for example, a coal fire transforms its fuel into ash. But a coal sun would burn out in some 5000 years, and we know that it has in fact been 'burning' for at least 600,000 times 5000 years. Clearly, some other explanation must be sought.

(b) By contraction. When a gas is compressed, as every user of a bicycle pump knows, its temperature rises. If the sun were once a much larger, less dense, and cooler body than it now is—a giant, in fact—its own gravitation would have caused it to contract. Helmholtz, about the middle of last century, suggested that the heat of the sun had derived from gravitational contraction in this way. Yet this explanation, though an improvement on the combustion hypothesis, can only account for one thousandth of the 4×10^{50} ergs that represent the sun's actual radiation during the life of the earth in its present form.

(c) A third suggested source of the sun's remarkable source of energy has appeared during the twentieth century. In essence it is suggested that the sun's energy is subatomic: that is to say, it is derived from changes within the very nuclei of the atoms contained within its vast bulk.

NUCLEAR DISINTEGRATION

By 1919 the phenomenon of radioactivity, or the spontaneous transformation of the atomic nuclei of one element into those of another, was a commonplace and had been the subject of much investigation since its discovery by Becquerel twenty-three years previously. But in that year Rutherford changed the outlook of physics by approaching the medieval alchemists' ambition of *artificially* transmuting one element into another. Into a chamber containing ordinary air (which consists largely of nitrogen) he projected a stream of high-velocity α-particles—the nuclei, bereft of their orbital electrons, of the element helium. One of Rutherford's α-particles achieved a head-on collision with the nucleus of a nitrogen atom, and smashed it, with the resultant formation of two nuclei, one of oxygen and one of hydrogen. Since that epoch-making experiment, the new science of nuclear physics has progressed rapidly, and today many dozens of nuclear reactions have been promoted in the laboratory.

Two characteristics of such reactions are particularly to be noted:

(*a*) They are characterized by enormous liberations of energy, a typical nuclear disintegration releasing many thousand times more energy than even so violent a molecular reaction as the combustion of T.N.T. Whereas 1 gram of coal, on complete combustion, liberates only 3×10^{11} ergs, 1 gram of a mixture of lithium and hydrogen, entering into the nuclear reaction which produces helium, would liberate 2.2×10^{18} ergs of subatomic energy—10 million times as much!

(*b*) Nuclear reactions are extremely difficult to promote, since only rarely does a direct collision between a nucleus and a projectile—α-particle or proton—occur. And the stability of nuclei is such that nothing but head-on collisions with extremely powerful projectiles has any disruptive effect upon them. Hence the *total* energy liberated during an experimental bombardment is of microscopic proportions. Were it otherwise, the physicist, his laboratory, and half the county as well would be blown sky high.

THERMONUCLEAR REACTIONS

Whereas a sun composed of coal would go out in about 5000 years, a sun deriving its energy from nuclear reactions would have ample reserves to continue radiating for the thousands of millions of years which are required. But how is it that elements like nitrogen and carbon will enter into nuclear reactions in the sun, while they will not, except on the most niggardly scale, in the laboratory?

In 1929 this question was answered by Atkinson and Houtermans, with their theory of thermonuclear reactions. Eddington has shown that the sun's temperature reaches a figure of about 2×10^7 degrees at the center. Under such conditions, nuclear transformations would be greatly facilitated, for the individual nuclei (and free electrons) would themselves be traveling with velocities comparable with the projectiles of the physicist's laboratory—the component particles of a gas becoming more and more violently agitated as its temperature rises. Thus instead of there being, as in the laboratory, comparatively few projectiles with high enough kinetic energy to shatter nuclei, all the nuclei themselves become 'bullets' capable of disrupting one another. Nuclear reactions would then be possible which in the laboratory would require millions of years to complete. Such reactions are termed thermonuclear reactions.

Once started, thermonuclear reactions will generate enough heat to keep themselves going indefinitely, without the application of any further energy from an external source.

THE SOLAR REACTION

The theory having been established that conditions in the solar interior are such as would permit the nuclear transformations of the common, stable elements, and the further fact that these reactions would constitute a rich enough source of energy to provide the 2.4×10^{50} ergs which are required, it remains to identify the precise reaction or reactions that are responsible for the sun shining at the present moment. And here we are treading on very unsure ground.

The energy liberation of each individual reaction can easily be calculated for any given temperature, and this figure compared with the observed energy-production rate of the sun. In 1938 Bethe and Weizsäcker independently hit upon the reaction—or, more correctly, chain of reactions—that would produce the sun's 1.2×10^{41} ergs per year. Bethe concluded that the thermonuclear reactions proceeding within the sun are six in number, and form a closed chain whose first and last stages are the same. The cycle is thus repetitive, and will continue until the raw materials used up in the reactions are exhausted. Its net result is the building up of one helium nucleus from four hydrogen nuclei, energy being liberated in the process.

This energy does not, of course, appear from nowhere. According to relativity theory, mass and energy are equivalent terms, so that the 'destruction' of mass involves the liberation of the equivalent amount of energy. Now the mass of four hydrogen atoms is slightly greater than that of one helium atom. This lost mass reappears as energy, according to Einstein's equation linking mass and energy ($E=mc^2$).

Bethe concludes, therefore, that the sun is deriving its energy from the synthesis of helium nuclei out of hydrogen nuclei. Hydrogen is the 'fuel' and helium the 'ash' of the solar thermonuclear production of energy.

ENERGY PRODUCTION IN MAIN-SEQUENCE STARS

The question is at once suggested, do the other main-sequence stars derive their energy from the same reaction as is responsible for the sun's energy production?

Just as the physical conditions at the center of the sun can be calculated, so it is possible to discover the central pressure and temperature of any star whose mass, total radiation, and radius or surface temperature are known. It is also possible to calculate the energy production of the solar thermonuclear cycle at different temperatures, and it is found that the figures derived agree well with the observed luminosities of stars in the center and upper regions of the main sequence.

But among the low-temperature red dwarfs the solar reactions would be retarded or inhibited by the comparative thermal slowness of the protons. Here it is possible that the thermonuclear interaction occurs between protons themselves: three hydrogen nuclei combining in two stages to form a helium nucleus (α-particle) with the liberation of energy.

ENERGY PRODUCTION IN THE RED GIANTS

In the still cooler red giants, thermonuclear reactions would be virtually at a standstill. Gamow and Teller suggest that during the early stages of a star's existence it is a giant with large diameter and low density, and that gravitational contraction is the sole source of heat. Contraction would continue until the internal temperature had risen to a level at which the easiest and most rapid thermonuclear reactions are possible (about one million degrees). The generation of subatomic energy within the star would thereupon put an end to contraction, and a self-regulating, thermostatic mechanism would come into operation.

As soon as the supply of each element is exhausted—first those most easily induced to enter into thermonuclear reactions, and then those progressively more recalcitrant—gravitational contraction would set in again, and would continue until the central temperature were high enough to permit the reaction involving the next heavier element.

The temperature of a giant will therefore rise continuously from the onset of the first reaction. In other words, it will pass backward across the Russell diagram, traversing the Harvard sequence in reverse order;

eventually it will reach the main sequence, where, as we have seen, the temperature is high enough for the solar cycle to begin operation.

PASSAGE ALONG THE MAIN SEQUENCE

On reaching the main sequence, the star's short youth is over, and it is envisaged as entering upon its long period of maturity.

It would be natural to suppose that as its hydrogen supply is depleted, it will grow cooler and pass *down* the sequence toward the red-dwarf region. This, however, is not so, for the cloud of helium nuclei generated by the process is sufficiently opaque to radiation to prevent the internally produced radiation from escaping to the stellar surface whence it may be radiated away from the star. Thus the star's temperature and luminosity will increase with increasing rapidity, the star meanwhile passing *up* the main sequence.

The last hydrogen nuclei will ultimately be converted into helium, and the final contraction will begin. The star will shrink very rapidly, with a parallel falling off of luminosity, and since it has no further effective energy-producing reserves to offset this, it will fade out into darkness beyond the cooler end of the main sequence.

It must not be assumed from the foregoing account that all stars follow exactly the same stages in their evolutionary processes. The total mass of the original diffuse body of gas is in all probability the major governing factor. It may well be that a relatively small mass will pass backward through the Harvard sequence only as far as, for example, a G-type or F-type star and will then turn down along the main sequence. On the other hand, an infant star of relatively large mass may pass above the giant sequence and reach temperatures considerably above those to be expected for stars at the normal turning point to the main sequence. It should be pointed out that we actually find stars scattered throughout the Russell diagram.

Calculations, which are long and laborious, have been made for stars of different masses. In the case of a star of a mass approximately equal to that of the sun, the calculations lead to conditions for the sun at its present age which differ from those that we have observed by a factor of approximately 100. Such a discrepancy is not to be unexpected when we consider the numerous assumptions and uncertainties in the various hypotheses.

Any attempts made thus far to fit the white dwarfs into the sequence of stellar evolution have been unsatisfactory. Rapid advances are now being made in the researches of nuclear physics and it is futile to speculate about what the results will be.

IX. The Nebulae

ABSORBING MATERIAL WITHIN THE GALAXY

It will be recalled that the problem of plotting out the extent of the star system by assigning distances to such galactic objects as the open clusters was complicated by the hitherto unsuspected existence of a rarefied absorbing medium. This material pervades the galaxy and has the effect of stretching distance determinations that are based on apparent brightness. Two lines of approach led to this conclusion: first, Trumpler's work on the sizes and distances of the open clusters; and secondly, the marked avoidance of the galactic plane by the globular clusters and extragalactic nebulae. To remove the discrepancies following from the neglect of this factor, Trumpler was forced to assume an optical density of about 0.8 magnitudes per 3250 light years for the absorbing medium. He was further led to conclude that, although extending for considerable distances in the galactic plane, the medium's thickness measured at right angles to this plane was no more than a few hundred light years.

Not only did interstellar absorption cause the dimming of the light from distant objects, but it also implanted color-excesses upon the most remote sources of all, provided that these were within about 10° of the galactic plane. This not only indicated clearly that the absorbing layer was thin, but also that it was partly gaseous in composition. Different investigators of the characteristics of the interstellar absorption have reached curiously various conclusions. Seares, for example, deduces from his star counts that absorption of the type outlined by Trumpler cannot occur; a similar conclusion was reached by Elvey from different evidence; while Hubble and Humason have shown that the few extragalactic nebulae situated near the galactic plane exhibit little or no trace of general galactic absorption.

These divergent results may probably be reconciled on the assumption that although diffuse material concentrated in the galactic plane does effect absorption, yet it is far from homogeneous, probably being more accurately thought of as a patchy, flocculent structure, with areas of higher and lower density, than as a uniform medium.

GALACTIC NEBULAE

So far we have only considered indirect evidence for the existence of galactic absorbing material. There is, however, a great deal of direct, visual evidence also. The stars—isolated, in binary and multiple systems, and in clusters—and, perhaps, a few planets here and there, are not the sole constituents of the stellar system. There are, in addition, nebulae of various kinds. Nebula (Lat. cloud) was the name given to these objects by the early astronomers as being descriptive of their appearance, and the first class that we shall consider are in fact vast, structureless clouds of apparently glowing gas. Plates iv and v show two of these nebulae, the first being situated in the constellation Cygnus, the second being that which involves the stars of the Pleiades. These two photographs illustrate clearly some of the more characteristic features of the diffuse, irregular or galactic nebulae. They have no definite structure or shape; they are of vast proportions (long exposure photographs have shown that the nebula in the Sword of Orion, visible to the naked eye, extends over a great part of the constellation); and they are intimately associated with stars, which, as can be seen from Plate v, are not merely super-imposed upon the nebula or seen through it, but are actually involved in it. Thus the distances of many of the galactic nebulae may be determined from the distance of the stars embedded in them.

RADIATION FROM GALACTIC NEBULAE

At one time it was thought that these bright galactic nebulae shone by virtue of their own incandescence, and even that the involved stars might have been born from them by some process of condensation. Both beliefs have now been discarded; our ideas concerning the nature of the diffuse nebulae have undergone a complete revolution within the last fifty years. In 1912 it was discovered spectroscopically that the Pleiades nebula is not self-luminous, as had previously been believed, but shines by the reflected light of the involved stars; without these stars it would not be incandescent and would therefore be invisible. In one circumstance only it might be indirectly visible: were it projected against a rich part of the galaxy its presence would perhaps be deduced from the absence of stars in that region.

Later it was shown by Hubble that both the spectroscopic type and the visible size of any galactic nebula are determined by the temperature and luminosity of the involved stars; the higher the temperature and the greater the luminosity of the stars, the greater will be the illuminated expanse of nebulosity. Furthermore, no bright nebulae exist that do not contain stars of sufficient brightness to account for their visibility. Another observation that points to the same conclusion, that the more luminous stars are capable of rendering this type of nebula visible, is that faint stars are noticeably absent from those regions occupied by high-temperature stars and diffuse nebulae. This is believed to indicate that while the brighter stars are capable of illuminating the nebula, the fainter stars are either at too low a temperature to do so, or are situated at very much greater distances from the sun than the nebula; in either case the nebulous material would obscure them from the sight of the terrestrial observer.

GALACTIC NEBULAE AND INVOLVED STARS

The theory that the involved stars are born from galactic nebulae has suffered a complete reversal, and instead of believing that an inward movement of nebulous material toward a number of points resulted in the formation of stars at these points, modern astronomy favors the view that the radiation pressure of the high-temperature stars is scattering the nebulous material away from them in all directions. After what we have learned of the nature of electromagnetic radiation in Chapter VI, it should not come as a surprise to learn that radiation possesses momentum and therefore exerts a pressure upon any body, surface, or particle that either reflects or absorbs it. The force of repulsion depends upon the temperature of the source of the radiation; the higher the source temperature, the more violent the repellent force. It is the radiation pressure of the sun, acting upon the particles in the tail of a comet, which forces this tail always away from the head, with the result that when the comet is receding from the sun it proceeds tail foremost.

Two conflicting forces, therefore, are centered in the massive 'early type' stars which are found to be associated with diffuse nebulae: gravity, acting inward toward the stars' centers, and the repellent radiation pressure. The mechanism of radiation pressure being known, it is possible to calculate the relation between these two forces for stars of the types concerned, and it is found that in their immediate vicinity the radiation pressure outstrips the gravity many times. At the surface of the sun, which is a comparatively cool star, radiation pressure amounts to 65,000 tons per square mile; at the distance of the earth this is reduced to 2.6 pounds per square mile. Hence any nebulous material in the neighborhood of the involved stars would be swept away toward regions devoid of the hottest B-type and A-type stars. Internal motion has been detected in some of the diffuse nebulae spectroscopically, and so far as it goes (for these motions are not large) the evidence does not conflict with the conclusion arrived at through the theoretical consideration of radiation pressure. The spectroscope also shows that the diffuse nebulae are for the most part practically stationary after allowance has been made for the component of the velocity shift due to the sun's motion.

DISTANCES AND DISTRIBUTION OF THE GALACTIC NEBULAE

As already mentioned, their distances can be deduced in those cases where the distances of the involved stars are known. Some at least of the diffuse nebulae are near neighbors of the sun, the Pleiades nebulosity being only some 325 light years distant, and that in Orion about 600 light years; some of the fainter, on the other hand, are certainly very much more remote, and it must be supposed that they exist far out beyond the limits to which our telescopes can reach.

Their alternative name, galactic nebulae, derives from the fact that, like the open clusters, they occur most frequently in and near the galactic plane. The majority are to be found within 10° of the galactic plane itself. It will be remembered that this is the zone of avoidance of the globular clusters.

SPECTRA AND COMPOSITION OF THE GALACTIC NEBULAE

Characteristic lines in the spectra of the galactic nebulae were for many years not matched by any produced in the laboratory. It was therefore supposed that an unknown gas, which was named 'nebulium,' was present in the nebulae, and that it was through the excitation of the atoms of this gas that the unknown radiations were produced. But more recent knowledge of the structure of matter and of the table of elements has rendered this explanation highly improbable; it is now known that the lines of 'nebulium' do not indicate the presence of an unknown element, but rather that of familiar elements existing under unfamiliar physical conditions. Extremely low pressure—representing densities far below the minimum attainable in the laboratory—would be such a condition, and it is even possible to arrive at an idea of the mechanism whereby the 'forbidden' lines are produced.

Under normal conditions of pressure, the atoms of a gas suffer many thousands of collisions every second; even at the most extreme rarefaction the physicist can achieve, the average interval between interatomic collisions is only $1/1000$ of a second. In the gaseous nebulae, however, it is estimated that this interval is increased to from 10^4 to 10^7 seconds. Any transition that requires an appreciable time for its consummation, therefore, would be impossible at normal pressures and densities, since interference from another atom would always occur first; but under the conditions prevailing in the gaseous nebulae this would not necessarily be the case, and the atom would be left undisturbed for a long enough interval to complete the transition. These atomic states, from which transitions can only occur at long intervals, are called the metastable states, and Bowen has shown that they are at the back of the unknown radiations from galactic nebulae once thought to be due to 'nebulium.' In fact, they are caused by doubly ionized nitrogen and oxygen, and trebly ionized oxygen. Other familiar lines in the spectra of the diffuse nebulae were long ago identified as belonging to the spectra of hydrogen, helium, carbon, and neutral nitrogen and oxygen.

Spectroscopically, therefore, the diffuse nebulae fall into two classes: those with gaseous emission spectra consisting of bright lines only; and those, like the Pleiades nebulosity already mentioned, that have continuous spectra with superimposed dark lines, similar to those of the involved stars. This difference is attributed to the involved stars rather than to the nebulous material itself: for it is found that where the stars are of the hot early types (O and B), the gaseous spectrum is produced; where the stars are cooler than type B, continuous stellar-type spectra are produced. In the former case, the gaseous material is being excited to incandescence in a way perhaps similar to that productive of aurorae; whereas in the latter, the nebula is simply shining by the reflected light of the involved stars. This discovery in turn throws light upon the probable constitution of the nebulous material. For the emission spectra must depend upon the presence of isolated atoms, while the capacity of the cloud to reflect starlight argues the existence of larger particles than atoms. In other words, the diffuse nebulae are partly gaseous and partly dusty or meteoric—a conclusion in complete agreement with those of Trumpler which, it will be remembered, involved the existence of large particles (total absorption) and small particles (causing the observed color-excesses).

DARK NEBULAE

If the diffuse nebulae do not shine by virtue of their own unassisted incandescence, we might expect to find certain nebulae which, being situated near no high-temperature stars, are dark. Such nebulae, did they exist, would necessarily be confined (so far as human observation is concerned) to the galactic zone, since nowhere else is there provided a bright background against which they might be silhouetted. In 1919 Barnard published the first catalogue of 182 dark nebulae, one of which is illustrated in Plate xv. Their existence is an integral part of the theory that diffuse nebulae do not shine by their own light. The occurrence of dark nebulae had been known for over one hundred years, but until comparatively recent times they were regarded as starless holes running through the stellar system and aligned upon the earth. Once the frequency of their occurrence had been demonstrated by Barnard, the highly improbable nature of this explanation became clear, and the theory of obscuring clouds was substituted. Like the bright diffuse nebulae, they are not very distant, some being only a few hundred light years from the sun and none that are visible being more distant than, probably, about 1000 light years. (The distance can be gauged when, as often happens, they are associated with bright nebulosity and high-temperature stars.) This does not mean that they are necessarily restricted to the comparative vicinity of the sun—on the contrary, they are without a doubt distributed through the whole stellar system: but a dark nebulae situated at a much greater distance than 1000 light years would be difficult to detect since the obscuration of still more distant stars would be masked by the superposition upon it of nearer stars.

These diffuse nebulae, both bright and dark, are certainly of exceedingly low density, as shown by their limited powers of absorption despite enormous extent. Though more rarefied than even the most perfect vacuum that can be produced in terrestrial laboratories, they must nevertheless be regarded as localized areas of exceptional density in the general absorbing stratum which pervades the whole galactic plane.

INTERSTELLAR CALCIUM

Mention must be made of two other types of nebula encountered in the stellar system. The first of these is not a nebula in the usual sense of the term, for it is not visible (even by superposition upon a bright background) and appears to pervade the whole of galactic space: it is, indeed, something very like the absorbing medium that Trumpler was forced to hypothesize. Its existence went unsuspected until 1904, in which year Hartmann noticed that prominent calcium lines in the spectrum of the spectroscopic binary δ Orionis did not share the oscillations of the rest of the spectrum caused by the orbital motion of the brighter component about the center of gravity of the system. Similar stationary lines have since been detected in the spectra of hundreds of high-temperature white stars, and in some cases the lines of sodium, titanium, and potassium are also stationary. Slight displacements of the stationary lines toward the red or violet are accounted for by the sun's motion, and when this effect is eliminated it is found that the residual displacement is in the majority of cases negligible. The most plausible explanation is that between the star and the observer there is a certain amount of calcium, sodium, potassium, titanium, and possibly other elements as well, in the form of an extremely tenuous interstellar cloud, and that it is absorption by this matter which implants the stationary lines upon the spectra of certain stars. It is estimated that the density of this interstellar matter is of the order of magnitude of 25,000,000 particles per cubic yard. Its extreme tenuity can be appreciated when we realize that a cubic yard of air at atmosphere pressure contains a billion billion times as many particles as does this interstellar gas. However, tenuous as this matter may be, there is a tremendous depth between us and a distant spectroscopic binary and a large number of atoms would be available for producing the absorption lines.

The spectra of all binaries do not contain these stationary lines. In general, two conditions must be fulfilled: the star must be distant, and it must be of an early spectral type, usually O or B. The first condition is readily understandable, for a great thickness of such rarefied matter would be necessary for an absorption of detectable strength to be caused. Their apparent preference for the spectra of the early-type stars is presumably due to the fact that even were they present in the spectra of stars of later type than about B5, they would be obscured by the heavy lines that normally occur in these.

PLANETARY NEBULAE

The third type of intragalactic nebula is the planetary. Plate XVI shows that these objects are quite unlike the diffuse nebulae. They are small, round, well-defined, and might almost be mistaken for planets when seen with small telescopes. They are comparatively rare objects, fewer than 200 being known, and are all invisible to the naked eye; this is due both to their faintness and to the smallness of their disks, the majority of which are not more than a few seconds of arc in diameter. Their apparent smallness is, however, the result of distance rather than of linear insignificance, for van Maanen has shown that the diameters of over twenty planetaries are not less than several thousand times that of Pluto's orbit.

In small instruments even those planetaries with the largest angular diameters show no detail; they appear as faint, round disks of pale greenish or bluish light. But instruments of larger aperture reveal the existence of a faint central star in many of them. The spectroscope shows that they resemble the galactic nebulae in two important respects, however dissimilar the two cases of object may appear at first glance. The planetaries are gaseous, and they shine by reflection (or at least by excitation) of the central star; this is typically of the high temperature O-type. That they are not the flat disks they appear to be, but are spherical, is indicated by two observational facts; in no instance is any foreshortening of the disk observed, and it is proved by the Doppler effect that at least some of them are rotating axially.

The spectroscope has been instrumental in providing almost all our knowledge of the planetary nebulae. The spectrum is of the type that we saw in Chapter vi to be typical of glowing gases; the bright lines of hydogen are invariably present, those of helium usually, and those of nitrogen frequently. The temperature modifications of those lines show without a doubt that the temperature of the central star cannot in the majority of cases be much below 50,000°. Yet the luminosity of these stars (which can be deduced as soon as the distance is known) proves to be low. Considering their temperature therefore they must be very small.

The spectroscope has also revealed that the planetaries differ from the diffuse galactic nebulae in the matter of velocity. It will be remembered that the spectra of the latter showed, at most, small velocity shifts. The radial velocities of the planetary nebulae, on the other hand, are abnormally high; in extreme cases they may reach 125 m.p.s., the average being in the neighborhood of 20 m.p.s.

The planetaries follow the same distributional pattern as novae, open clusters, and galactic nebulae. That is, they crowd about the galactic plane and are only rarely encountered at any considerable distance from it. That is, at any rate, true of the apparently fainter planetaries, which from their faintness are assumed to be the more distant; the brighter and angularly larger are found outside the galactic region, but if we conclude that their relative size and brightness indicate nearness to the earth, then their real divergence from the galactic plane will naturally appear to be greater than it is. That the faint planetaries are in general more distant than the brighter is also indicated by the fact that they occur most commonly in that region of the galaxy with which we are by this time becoming somewhat familiar—the Sagittarius region where lies the galactic center.

EXTRAGALACTIC NEBULAE: SUMMARY OF DISTRIBUTION

Whereas in Chapter v we treated the extragalactic nebulae rather as anonymous counters in the game of probing the universe to the very limit of human inquisitiveness, we are now better qualified to inquire more closely into their nature. First, however, let us briefly summarize what we have already learned of their spatial distribution:

i. The extragalactic nebulae visible with present equipment occupy a volume of space stretching from less than 100,000 light years to 5×10^8 light years distant.

ii. It is estimated that within this region there are some 10^8 nebulae.

iii. Throughout the whole of the observable region, the large-scale distribution of the nebulae is uniform.

iv. Their small-scale distribution is, however, irregular, consisting of single nebulae, small groups, and great clusters. The nearest of these clusters, that situated in Virgo, is about 7×10^6 light years distant.

v. No falling off of numbers toward the outer edge of the observable region can be detected, indicating that we have not yet fathomed the system of extragalactic nebulae.

vi. The red-shifts in nebular spectra, if interpreted as velocity shifts, indicate that the more distant a nebula, the greater its velocity of recession.

It is expected that observations with 200-inch reflector will extend the limit of observable space to 10^9 light years.

CLASSIFICATION OF THE EXTRAGALACTIC NEBULAE

The extragalactic nebulae are for the most part extremely faint objects, and only one, that in Andromeda, can be detected easily with the naked eye; on clear moonless nights it appears as a faint misty spot resembling a nebulous star. When studied with telescopic cameras the extragalactic nebulae are found to present a number of closely allied forms, and a classification based upon the systematic differences displayed by the several hundred brightest nebulae has been evolved; for only these few are angularly large enough for anything of their structure to be made out, the vast majority of the white nebulae showing on photographic plates as formless specks, hardly distinguishable from faint and ill-defined stars. Among the more conspicuous extragalactic objects, however, two main classes are distinguishable, the second of which may be further subdivided:

1. Irregular,
2. Regular: (a) globular, or to a greater or lesser exent elliptical;
          (b) spiral: (i) normal,
                   (ii) barred.

IRREGULAR NEBULAE

Irregular nebulae need hardly detain us, since they comprise only about 2 per cent of the total. The Magellanic Clouds (see Plate vi) are prominent because near examples of this type of system, and about half of all known irregular extragalactic nebulae are generally similar to them: they show no traces of rotational or other symmetry, and are largely resolvable into stars, star clusters, and clouds, and irregular nebulosity of the galactic type. Without doubt they are stellar systems.

ELLIPTICAL NEBULAE

Members of Class 2 (a) are to be observed in a graded variety of forms, but all differ from the irregular nebulae in three important respects: their rotational symmetry, their lack of resolution, and the existence of a bright nucleus. This variety of form is due to a combination of two factors; different inclinations to the line of sight and real differences in shape. Visually they vary from round disks to elongated, cigar-shaped, or spindle-shaped forms (Plate xvii) whose axes are related to one another as about 3:1. Nebulae exhibiting every gradation of flattening between these limiting forms are known.

Now if these nebulae were truly discoidal (as two plates, rim to rim) these varying appearances would result merely from different inclinations of their major axes to the line of sight: if viewed edge-on they would appear cigar-shaped; if directly from the prolongation of the minor axis, round; and intermediately, elliptical with a greater or lesser degree of flattening. But a sufficiently large number of these nebulae are known to treat them statistically, and by this means it has been found that more of the circular nebulae occur than the law of averages would warrant. Some of the round nebulae must, therefore, not be discoidal and viewed from a point on the projection of the minor axis, but truly spherical; thus they would appear spherical from whatever direction they might be viewed. Once this was established, it was realized that many of the intermediate types might be ellipsoidal (viewed edge-on) rather than discoidal (viewed from a point between the projections of their median plane and minor axis). Thus we have a transition from a spherical nebula through increased polar flattening to a discoidal nebula which may appear either cigar-shaped or circular, according to the angle of vision.

SPIRAL NEBULAE

The spiral nebulae resemble the elliptical in being 'flat'; that is, their diameters are very much greater than their thickness. Normal spirals consist of a central, discoidal nucleus, from diametrically opposed points on whose periphery project two arms. These arms leave the body of the nebula approximately tangentially, and the nebula, when seen from a point on the projection of its minor axis, is reminiscent of a pyrotechnic pinwheel (Plate xviii). That it is a flat structure may be seen in those cases where the nebula is viewed edge-on (Plate xix). In some spirals the two arms appear to have bifurcated with the formation of a four-arm spiral.

About one spiral in three is not of this normal type, but falls into the category of 'barred' spirals. Plate xx shows examples, and it can be seen that the arms, instead of issuing direct from the nucleus as in normal spirals, issue from the outer ends of a bar of matter in which the nucleus is centrally placed.

Just as a sequence of forms—from spherical, through increased polar flattening, to the critical 3:1 figure—is observed among the elliptical nebulae, so a formal sequence, which in all probability also represents a temporal sequence, is exhibited by the spiral nebulae, both normal and barred. Treating the sequence as temporal—i.e. as one through which each nebula passes in the course of its existence—we may describe the successive changes as follows. At the beginning of the sequence the nebula is hardly distinguishable from a 'late' elliptical nebula. The arms are inconspicuous and small compared with the main body or nucleus of the nebula. A steady outward transference of matter from the nucleus to the arms results in the latter becoming increasingly more massive at the expense of the former. Simultaneously the arms uncoil. About halfway along the sequence the homogeneous texture of the nebulous matter begins to break down: condensations start to form, at first sparsely, in the outermost regions of the arms; these increase in number and spread inward to the nucleus, which by this stage will have shrunk to a mere shadow of its former state. In the final stage the nebula consists entirely of widely opened arms (the nucleus having disappeared), which in turn consist of clouds and clusterings of faint star-like points, interspersed with unresolved material which may either be nebulous or may consist of stars too faint and too numerous to be individually visible. Another feature of late spirals which is reminiscent of our own galaxy is the common occurrence of patches and blotches of dark obscuring material, presumably analogous with our dark nebulae. Obscuring matter is also to be observed among early spirals of the normal type; here it takes the form of a peripheral band encircling the nebula in its median plane; this formation is consequently only visible in the case of nebulae that are oriented edge-on to the observer (Plate xix).

THE EXTRAGALACTIC SEQUENCE AS A PROCESS

During the course of the modifications of the early globular type whose end point is the late spiral, the brightness of the nebula does not alter to any material extent. Its size, on the other hand, does. How this interesting fact has been established will be explained at a later stage. As the nebula passes along the sequence its diameter grows steadily from (taking average and only approximate figures) about 6000 light years to 30,000 light years; this extension in the median plane is of course the necessary concomitant of the reduction of the axis perpendicular to it as flattening proceeds.

The most striking feature of the extragalactic objects, when classified in this way, is the uniform nature of the changes to which they are subjected throughout the sequence: starting as undifferentiated globular masses, they are progressively flattened; when a certain critical stage in this process is reached a new factor emerges, and the formation of arms begins; more and more matter is transferred from the body of the nebula to its arms, which at a second crucial point begin to break up into star-like condensations. The largely resolved, wide-open spirals are then only differentiated from the irregular nebulae by the traces of rotational symmetry that still remain. It is impossible not to conclude that we are dealing with different members of a single family, all of which conform to a basic pattern which is modified systematically from the beginning to the end of a limited sequence.

THE ROTATION OF GASEOUS MASSES

Added significance is attached to this conclusion by Jeans' theoretical investigation of the behavior of a rotating gaseous mass, and the bearing of this work upon the question of the size and nature of the extragalactic nebulae. It is supposed that the mass is far enough from other bodies to be gravitationally insulated. It will then assume a spherical form which rotation will flatten at the poles. Under stress of its own gravitation it will shrink, and with increasing shrinkage its rotation will increase in accordance with the law of the conservation of angular momentum. This in turn will cause an increasing flattening of the poles and bulging of the equatorial regions. When a certain stage in the accelerating rotation is reached, the mass will become unstable; in the same way a flywheel that is allowed to rotate too rapidly will shatter into fragments. Jeans has shown in another connection that a liquid mass on reaching this critical stage of instability will split in two. The gaseous mass, however, behaves differently. It will now be discoidal with a comparatively sharp periphery. As the rotational velocity increases, matter will be ejected from two diametrically opposed points on the circumference. This matter will issue as jets and will be of low density, since the heaviest constituents would have gravitated to the center of the mass, leaving the less dense in the upper levels. With always increasing shrinkage and rotation, more and more of the substance of the nucleus will be forced into the arms; these will gradually assume a spiral configuration as a result of rotation. Thus, starting with a perfectly spherical body of gas, we reach a stage when it is transformed into a discoidal nucleus of decreasing mass and spiral arms of increasing mass. The more rarefied matter in these arms will tend to condense into separate agglomerations until they have been transformed into discontinuous systems of knots, clusters, and single condensations. Thus the more condensed the arms the smaller will be the nucleus, since both processes start and run concurrently. Eventually the nucleus will have been completely sapped, the arms will have become entirely condensed, and the original gaseous mass will have been transmogrified into a heterogeneous spiral system of isolated masses.

THE OBSERVED AND THEORETICAL SEQUENCES COMPARED

The various stages in this process are strikingly reminiscent of the different types of extragalactic nebula that are to be observed. In order of time, on the analogy of the theoretical sequence, we have the spherical nebulae, slightly flattened nebulae, and discoidal nebulae; all these are, so far as telescopic resolution is concerned, uncondensed. Next we have nebulae with large discoidal nuclei and homogeneous arms, followed by all stages of the transference of matter from the nuclei to the arms; along this sequence it is noticed that progressive condensation of the arms, with the formation of star-like points and clusterings, is occurring. Even in details the correspondence between the theoretical and observed sequences is exact; for instance, the rotation of the nebulae, the outward movement of matter from the nuclei along the arms, the inversely related size of the nucleus and degree of condensation in the arms have all been established observationally.

Whether the problem is approached from the observational or theoretical direction, therefore, it is tolerably certain that the fundamental difference between the various types of extragalactic nebula is one of age.

SPECTROSCOPIC EVIDENCE

The spectroscopic observation of the extragalactic nebulae is rendered difficult by their faintness, which forbids the use of the high-dispersion prisms required to produce a spectrum long enough for detailed study. Not only are the spectra necessarily short, but spectroscopic examination is confined to the brighter central regions of the brighter nebulae. The majority of these yield spectra of a stellar type—a continuous background upon which are superimposed numerous fine absorption lines—and most commonly of type G, that of the sun. A minority of spiral nuclei have spectra of quite a different type: the bright-line emission spectra, similar to those of the planetaries and some diffuse nebulae, which are indicative of incandescent gases under low pressures. Owing to the practical difficulties just mentioned, quantitative analysis of extragalactic spectra has not progressed far, but calcium, iron, and hydrogen have been identified in a number of nebulae. So far as the evidence goes, therefore, the spectroscope indicates that even the apparently undifferentiated nuclei of the majority of spirals are not gaseous masses but star clouds. The first step toward the direct photographic resolution of a spiral nucleus (M. 31) was made by Baade in 1944, an observational achievement of first importance.

THE NATURE OF THE RED-SHIFTS

We have seen how the discovery of the red-shifts provided astronomers with an additional distance criterion—or, rather, with a welcome confirmation of results obtained by the use of other criteria. The red-shifts are an objective phenomenon, and the linearity of the relation between distance and spectral displacement is unimpeachable. So long, in fact, as the displacements are merely accepted as spectral shifts to the red, and no questions asked, all is plain sailing. Inevitably, however, the nature and cause of the shifts became the subject of speculation. When first detected and measured, they were unquestioningly accepted as velocity shifts of the normal, familiar type. But as Humason pressed on his investigations among more and more remote nebulae the immense velocities* encountered threw the gravest suspicion on the validity of the theory seeking to explain the red-shifts in terms of the Doppler phenomenon. It is verging on the incredible that such velocities as have already been measured are real, yet what alternative explanation is there of the observed shifts? The question is of the most fundamental importance, for upon it depends the nature of our whole world picture and a great deal of theoretical cosmology. The question is still unanswered, although some preliminary clearing of the ground has been achieved.

At present no agency other than recession is known that could produce the red-shifts. If, therefore, they are not velocity shifts, they are a reflection of some physical principle of which we are ignorant. Although this alternative is of altogether too problematical a nature for unquestioning acceptance, the phenomena force us to explore its possibilities. We saw in an earlier chapter that the energy and corresponding wave-length of a quantum were related in the manner.

$$E_\lambda = C$$

where E is the energy, λ the wave-length, and C a constant. If the wave-length is increased—i.e. the spectrum is shifted toward the red —the energy of the radiation is correspondingly decreased. This loss of energy attendant upon a red-shift may be envisaged as occurring primarily in one of two ways. Either the wave-length is increased, as it would be were the source in motion away from the observer, which would result in the familiar Doppler or velocity shift; or else the energy itself might be reduced in transit from the source to the observer. If such a decrease of energy could be effected, the spectrum would be shifted toward the red, and the natural deduction would be that the source had a positive radial motion. It is at this point that we have to

*It must be borne in mind that these velocities are purely geocentric, i.e. relative to the terrestrial observer.

fall back upon the mysterious 'unknown' as an explanation, for we are ignorant of any mechanism whatever that could effect the leakage of energy during transit without causing parallel effects which would easily be observable, but which are in fact absent from nebular spectra.

Nor is it possible to differentiate between a red-shift due to a lengthening of the wave-length by movement of the source and a shift due to leakage of the energy carried by the quanta as they traverse inter-nebular space. For while it is true that a source in rapid recession would appear fainter than an equally luminous stationary source at the same distance, we utilize apparent luminosities as the only distance criterion capable of reaching to the most distant nebulae where these effects are of considerable proportions. Until, therefore, a distance criterion independent of apparent luminosity can be developed, no certain answer can be given to the crucial question: Do the red-shifts really represent recession?

For all these reasons the shifts are commonly referred to, outside the popular press, where sensation is rated more highly than truth, either as red-shifts or as apparent velocity shifts; and where they are called velocity shifts, without qualification, it is with the unspoken proviso that this is a convenient and obvious term until more specific contrary evidence is forthcoming.

LINEAR SIZES OF THE EXTRAGALACTIC NEBULAE

It has already been stressed that although luminosity remains sufficiently constant all along the sequence from globular to irregular nebulae to be used as a criterion of distance, this is not true of linear diameter; for if a spherical object is subjected to a process of flattening, it must expand in a direction at right angles to the axis of flattening: thus a rubber ball, compressed between two plates, will expand laterally between them. In the same way it might be expected that the extragalactic nebulae will exhibit linear diameters which are a function of their degree of flattening. This is in fact the case. As soon as distances, and therefore linear diameters, of a representative collection of each type of nebula had accumulated, it became apparent that the globular nebulae had the smallest diameters and late spirals the largest, intermediate types having diameters appropriate to their positions between these two extreme types. The ascertained data regarding the linear diameters (in light years) of the extragalactic nebulae may be summarized as follows:

	Globular	Late elliptical	Early barred spiral	Late normal spiral	(Irregular)
Diam. (L.Y.)	6,000	16,000	18,000	31,000	(21,000)

These figures are only approximate and, if anything, are on the low side: the true figures may well be twice, or even three times, as great. The reason for this is that the longer the photographic plate is exposed, the larger grows the image of the nebula, showing that the outer regions are not only faint but extensive. These figures refer to what is rather vaguely known as the 'main body'—that part of the nebula which is visible on any well-exposed plate.

MASSES OF THE EXTRAGALACTIC NEBULAE

Similarly approximate figures may be derived for the masses of the nebulae. One method was developed by Öpik and depends upon a single datum: the shift in a nebula's spectrum at a given distance from the nucleus, due to rotation. If a nebula is viewed edge-on, and is in rotation, one side will be approaching the observer, and the other receding from him (see Fig. 52). Hence one edge of the nebula will show a Doppler shift indicating recession, the other a shift indicating approach. The nebulae exhibit such unmistakable signs of rotational symmetry that even were such shifts not measurable, we should still be perfectly justified in postulating their rotation about their minor axes. But the spectroscope proves this to be a fact by revealing the

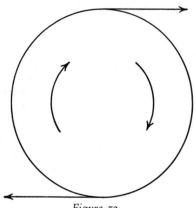

Figure 52.

existence of these rotational shifts. Clearly the size of the shift, varying with the line of sight velocity, will depend upon how far out from the nucleus the spectroscope slit is adjusted. Knowing, in the case of a nebula whose distance has been determined, the linear diameter of the mass between the two positions of the slit, and also the velocity of rotation at a pre-selected distance from the axis, the laws of motion allow the calculation of the total mass within this limit. Since the outer regions of any extragalactic nebula are too faint for investigation, it follows that this method will yield results short of the true figures for the whole nebular mass. The masses of four of the brighter nebulae derived in this way as respectively (in terms of the sun) 1,000,000,000; 9,000,000,000; 30,000,000,000; and 35,000,000,000.

MEAN DENSITY OF MATTER IN THE UNIVERSE

Knowing the volume of the observable region, the approximate number of nebulae in the region, and the average nebular mass, it is a simple matter to calculate the average density of matter in that region of space which we know. The result emphasizes the extreme emptiness of the universe: for if all the matter in the observable region were distributed uniformly through it, the density of the resultant medium would be between 10^{-28} and 10^{-30} grams per cubic centimeter, equivalent to one grain of sand distributed throughout a volume equal to that of the earth.

THE GALAXY AND THE EXTRAGALACTIC NEBULAE COMPARED

The idea has for many years been entertained by speculative thinkers that the galaxy might itself be a late-type spiral. Our knowledge both of the extragalactic nebulae and of the galaxy has now reached a stage at which it is possible to give serious consideration to this hypothesis. In view of the facts that have already been set out in the preceding pages, let us compare the extragalactic nebulae, more especially the late spirals, with the galaxy, paying particular attention to the following characteristics of each: (i) rotation, (ii) mass, (iii) size, and (iv) content.

At the outset it might be said that perhaps the most attractive general feature of the hypothesis is that it introduces uniformity into the large-scale organization of the observable region of the universe. On the one hand we have some hundred million extragalactic nebulae, all closely related, and one other object of a different type, a unique system which also happens to be our home—a conception uncommonly like an aftertaste of Aristotelian geocentricity. And on the other, we have an universe stocked exclusively with nebular-stellar systems, all built to the same fundamental pattern.

I. ROTATION

The discovery and subsequent measurement of the axial rotation of extragalactic nebulae naturally raised the question, Is the galaxy likewise rotating about its minor axis? If the reader goes out of doors on a starlit night and, gazing up into the firmament, considers this question for himself, he will probably be forced to admit that, if the matter rested in his hands alone, we must for ever be ignorant of the answer. Yet the problem has been tackled and solved. We not only know that the galaxy *is* rotating, but we know approximately how long the sun requires to complete one galactic revolution, the direction of the galactic center, and the direction of the sun's orbital motion at the present time.

The fact of stellar motion was already a commonplace in the eighteenth century, when the elder Herschel set himself to discover the direction and velocity of the sun's motion relative to its stellar neighbors. We have already learned in Chapter IV that later studies of the proper motions and radial velocities of large numbers of stars situated in all regions of the star sphere have permitted the location of the solar apex and antapex, as well as its velocity toward the former and away from the latter relative to the stars chosen for the investigation. But what information does this discovery, itself a masterpiece of observation and deduction, provide about the supposed rotation of the galaxy? Unfortunately, none. For all the stars chosen as 'street lamps' were comparatively bright and near and therefore members of the Local Star Cloud. This was the result neither of chance nor mistake: bright and near stars were deliberately chosen so that their spectra should be clearly visible and accurately measureable for velocity shifts, and also because a near star may be expected to have a larger proper motion than a remote one. Hence, although the derived velocity of 12 m.p.s. towards a point near Vega is likely to be accurate, it refers only to the motion of the sun within the framework of the Local Star Cloud, and not to the motion of the sun within the framework of the galaxy. The problem of what the Local Star Cloud itself is doing—whether or not it is rotating about the galactic center—is not touched. The only way in which information concerning this rotation can be obtained is to use stars outside the Local Star Cloud, i.e. faint and distant stars.

If the Local Star Cloud, and with it the sun, is revolving about the galactic center, non-cluster stars between the sun and the center will be revolving more rapidly than stars situated between the sun and the edge of the galaxy.* Let us consider the case of the eight stars repre-

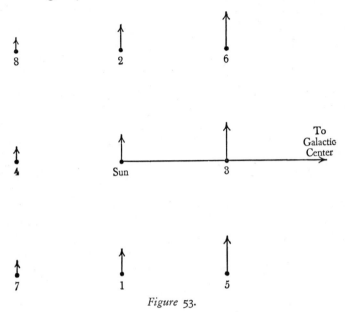

Figure 53.

sented in Fig. 53. It is assumed that they are all galactic stars lying well outside the Local Star Cloud; also, for the sake of simplicity, that they have no random motions, their only motion being that imparted to them by virtue of the galactic rotation. In the case of each star the length of the arrow is proportional to the distance that it will be carried by galactic rotation in a given period of time. If a terrestrial observer now studies the motions of these stars, making the necessary allowance for the motion of the earth about the sun, he will get the following results. Stars 1 and 2 will possess no measurable proper or radial motions—they are stationary, relative to the sun. Star 3 also will possess no radial motion, but will, owing to its greater space motion, appear to drift forward. Similarly star 4 will drift backward, while showing no line-of-sight

*This follows from Kepler's harmonic law, and assumes that there is a concentration of mass at the galactic center. Subsequent work on stellar motions has indicated the correctness of this assumption: the galaxy does not rotate 'solid,' like a flywheel.

motion. Stars 5 and 6, on the other hand, will not only show a forward drift but will also have, respectively, negative and positive radial motions. In the same way, stars 7 and 8 will combine a backward drift with radial motion.

The clearly defined differences in the observed motions of stars lying in different directions, assuming the galaxy to be rotating, are sufficient to provide the basis of a crucial investigation. If stars do in fact exhibit motions of this character, notably of drifting in two preferential directions, then we not only know that they are due to galactic rotation, but may also distinguish the direction of the galactic center. Independent analyses of the proper and radial motions of different groups of remote stars by a number of observers have shown conclusively that such is the case; furthermore, they mutually agree in placing the galactic center in the direction already indicated by Shapley as the result of his work on the spatial distribution of the globular clusters—toward Sagittarius. That this result is materially correct cannot be doubted: independent analyses of the motions of the bright O-type and B-type stars, of Cepheids, and of planetary nebulae up to distances of 60,000 light years all yield the same result.

The galactic center is located among the star clouds of Sagittarius at an approximate distance of 30,000 light years.

The sun, together with its near neighbors, is at present moving toward the constellation of Cygnus. The velocity imparted to them by the galactic rotation is in the neighborhood of 170 m.p.s. From these two facts it follows that the sun completes one revolution of its galactic orbit in about 220,000,000 years.

II. MASS

Once these facts were established, it was further possible to gain a rough idea for the mass of the galaxy by means of the Kepler-Newton laws of motion. The average mass of a star being known, simple division gives the number of stars in the galaxy. Approximations being involved in each of the steps to this result, it is not to be wondered at that the results obtained should be discordant within fairly wide limits. They range from about 3×10^{10}, the more probable estimate of Seares, to 2.7×10^{11}, that of Eddington; the estimates of other workers mostly fall between these limits. Considering the nature of the data, it is a matter for surprise that the agreement is so close. It seems probable, therefore, that the stars in our system are to be numbered in ten-thousands of millions, and perhaps in hundreds of thousands of millions.

The first two stages of our comparison of the galaxy with the late-type spirals are complete. Like the extragalactic nebulae, the galaxy is in rotation. Though only established in recent times, this conclusion has been suspected ever since the characteristic ellipsoidal form of the galaxy was demonstrated by Herschel at the end of the eighteenth century. And secondly, the galaxy and the only spirals concerning which we have data are comparably massive. The figures in each case are of necessity only approximate, but the correspondence is suggestive and probably significant.

III. SIZE

The Cepheid determinations of twenty years ago established beyond cavil that the apparently largest and also the brightest—and therefore, as a safe bet, the nearest—spiral was extragalactic. But this conclusion was not without its attendant difficulties; and though all these have now been resolved, one of them is worth a brief glance. Not only had speculation long toyed with the idea that these objects might be extragalactic, but had constantly added the rider 'and stellar systems like our own', or, as they were often termed, 'comparable galaxies.' The first spirals to be plotted on a linear scale of distance all turned out to be considerably smaller than the galaxy: astronomers have never forgotten the salutary lesson that Kepler and Copernicus taught the believers in the unique status of the home of *homo sapiens,* and any theory that sets our earth or our galaxy on a plane above the normal scheme of things is viewed with suspicion, and will only gain provisional acceptance as a last resort to save the phenomena. Yet if the spirals were as near as they were thought to be, and the galaxy as large as was thought, then certainly the galaxy was a giant among them. The distance determinations were accordingly suspect. This slur on the early distance determinations was, however, removed by two subsequent developments. First, it transpired that the estimations of galactic diameter were too large: its supposed diameter of 300,000 light years has been reduced, as a result of new knowledge about galactic absorption, to something nearer 100,000 light years. And at the same time the spirals have been shown to be larger than originally suspected. That the brightness of a spiral such as M.31 falls off gradually toward its perimeter has been demonstrated by the fact that the longer a plate is exposed, the larger the area of nebula that is recorded. But the degree to which this extension could be carried was not realized until extremely delicate photometric investigation with a photoelectric cell proved that the nebula is at least twice as large as is visually apparent. The combination of these revised estimates of the size of the galaxy on the one hand, and of the spirals on the other, has gone far toward removing the original discrepancy and has reduced the star system to a scale comparable with that of the late-type extragalactic nebulae. Though there is still considerable uncertainty regarding the precise size of the galaxy, the investigation has proceeded far enough to justify the confident statement that the spiral nebulae are indeed 'comparable galaxies.'

IV. CONTENT

Having established these preliminary agreements between galaxy and spirals as regards rotation, size, and mass, we can now proceed to a comparison of their respective contents, so far as these are known. And here some of the most impressive evidence for the identity of the two is to be found.

Stellar resolution in a considerable number of the nearer nebulae has been confined to the late-type spirals. A number of interesting facts concerning the stellar and other identifications are worth collecting together.

i. The luminosities (absolute magnitudes) of the brightest galactic stars and the brightest stars in the spirals are of the same order: so far as the evidence goes, galactic and nebular stars are built on the same pattern.

ii. Variables of precisely the same types as galactic variables are found in great profusion in the resolvable nebulae.

iii. Novae, which also occur in great numbers in the spirals, are similar to galactic novae in appearance and behavior.

iv. Patches of bright diffuse nebulosity are of common occurrence in the spirals, as in the galaxy.

v. Dark nebulae likewise occur abundantly in both. Among spirals, it is most noticeable in the edge-on nebulae, where it appears as a peripheral band.

vi. Vast star clouds and even open clusters of the galactic type occur in the late spirals: in addition, the spectroscope indicates that in many cases the visually unresolvable nebular nuclei consist of star clouds, which, seen from a smaller distance, would no doubt resemble the clouds of our Milky Way.

vii. The peculiar distribution of the globular clusters has already been described: though certainly to be classed as galactic objects, they are for the most part situated outside the galaxy as defined by the stars, galactic nebulae, and open clusters (see Fig. 35). In 1932 Hubble announced the discovery of 140 objects similarly situated with regard to the great Andromeda spiral. These are conjectured to be globular clusters, though the identification has not yet been definitely established. If they are, the discovery will provide still another, and very striking, detailed similarity between the galaxy and a representative extragalactic object.

viii. Finally, there is the close correspondence between the observed shapes of the spirals and the conjectured shape of the galaxy. Both the galaxy and a spiral are circular in plan and highly flattened in the direction of the axis of rotation. In each case the flattening is the result of this rotation.

THE GALAXY AS A LATE-TYPE SPIRAL

All this constitutes an impressive mass of evidence that the spirals and the galaxy are identical types of object: that, in other words, our own stellar system is a late-type spiral. Reviewing this evidence, it becomes abundantly clear that the galaxy and the extragalactic nebulae are truly 'comparable galaxies'; that they differ from one another primarily as regards age, or degree of development along the sequence of observed forms; and it is highly probable that the galaxy is a late spiral. That it is not an early spiral is indicated by the prevalence of star clouds and, generally, the high degree of resolution reached. That it is not an irregular nebula, despite this advanced stellar resolution, is established by the evidence for rapid rotation, which must involve rotational symmetry—a characteristic which the irregular nebulae notably lack.

We may, then, envisage the galaxy as a lenticular, heterogeneous congeries of stars and other matter, probably between 50,000 and 100,000 light years in diameter. Its major axis is from seven to ten times as great as its minor axis, this highly flattened form deriving from its rapid rotation. The galactic center lies among or beyond the star clouds in the Sagittarius region of the Milky Way, and at a distance of about one quarter of the galactic diameter.

In addition to stars and star clouds, the system contains a vast amount of undifferentiated matter, partly gaseous and partly meteoric. Not only does irregular nebulosity, capable of the complete obscuration of radiation passing through it, abound in the median plane, but the whole system is permeated by an even more tenuous absorbing medium which is probably of a gaseous nature. An analogy may possibly be drawn between the peripheral absorbing matter seen in edge-on spirals, and that which is responsible for the great rift which splits the Milky Way into two streams between the constellations of Cygnus and Centaurus. The obscuring matter is concentrated toward the galactic center and probably masks this center from the terrestrial observer.

It is probable that the remains of spiral arms unwinding from the central regions would still be visible to an extragalactic observer. Not only do the studies of the extragalactic nebulae show the existence of such arms to be most probable, but Oort's complex and painstaking analyses of stellar distribution and comparative star density may be interpreted as revealing their actual existence. It is within them that the star clouds (including that containing the Local Star Cloud) would be chiefly located, the regions between the arms being characterized by considerably lower star densities.

Trumpler's three-dimensional model of the open cluster system also reveals traces of spiral structure. In particular, the clusters in Auriga, Cassiopeia, and Perseus appear to delineate a spiral arm, and Trumpler believes that the galaxy is, as viewed from the north galactic pole, a right-hand spiral.

This is as far as we can go with existing equipment. All the more fundamental problems connected with the large-scale structure and organization of the universe must probably await observations with the 200-inch giant of Palomar for solution. The future will always hold in store greater and more magnificent conceptions than the past; and, despite the awe-inspiring achievements already realized, it is to the future that we must turn our eyes.

APPENDIX

AN INTRODUCTION TO SPHERICAL ASTRONOMY AND SYSTEMS OF TIME MEASUREMENT

SPHERICAL SPACE

The concept of the sphere as the perfect solid has been familiar to philosophers and scientists for at least three millenniums. In all of the ancient systems of astronomy we find the sky referred to as a spherical dome spreading above the earth. In the early years of the fourth century B.C. the concept of the earth itself as a sphere was introduced, and by the latter part of the third century actual observations had been made for the determination of dimensions of this spherical earth. Hipparchus invented trigonometry during the second century B.C. and applied it to calculations of distances and directions in a space confined to the surface of a sphere. In all of the ancient systems the earth was considered fixed at the center of a sphere carrying the stars. This sphere revolved about the earth once each day, with the moon, sun, Mercury, and the other planets all moving in spheres between the outer star sphere and the spherical earth. This system was completely described by Ptolemy during the second century of the Christian era and remained virtually unchallenged until the sixteenth century.

In spite of the fact that we now know that the earth is not spherical, that the planets do not move in spheres, and that the stars are not attached to any sphere that revolves about the earth, nevertheless for a great many problems in spherical astronomy the ancient concept is still employed in a modified form. For all except the refined problems of geodetic surveying the earth may be considered a sphere. In all except the complicated problems of modern cosmography we may consider the stars at attached to a celestial sphere centered on the earth, with the moon, sun, and other members of the solar system projected out to the surface of this sphere. The general problems of this projecting of relatively close objects out to the star sphere are discussed under the general topic of parallax in Chapter III. In the discussion of problems of spherical astronomy it is more convenient to speak of the star sphere as revolving about a fixed earth than it is to speak every time of the apparent revolution of the star sphere due to the real rotation of the earth on its axis.

CO-ORDINATE SYSTEMS IN SPHERICAL SPACE

The method of locating the position of a point in a plane relative to some fixed point in the plane by the so-called rectangular Cartesian system is known to most people. For example, in a well-ordered classroom a teacher may locate any student in the room by counting rows from the front of the room toward the back and seat numbers to the right or left of the aisle immediately in front of the desk. For example, John Doe in fifth row third seat right. To be more explicit we draw two perpendicular lines through the reference point and measure co-ordinates of X as plus or minus distance from this origin of co-ordinates along one line and co-ordinates of Y as so many units of distance plus or minus along the perpendicular.

In spherical space (that is, space confined to the surface of a sphere) we encounter difficulties with the so-called rectangular Cartesian co-ordinates: There are no 'straight' lines, and there are no familiar units of distance. Any plane passed through the center of a sphere will cut out on the surface a circle known as a great circle. Lines drawn from the center of the sphere to two points on the surface will subtend a definite angle at the center of the sphere. In astronomy we use three systems for measuring angles:

1. The familiar degree, minute, and second system in which 60′ = one degree and 60″ = one minute. Accordingly, one circumference is 360°, or 21600′, or 1296000″ of arc.

2. The hour, minute, and second system in which one circumference = 24 hours, 1440 minutes, or 86400 seconds of time.

3. The radian system in which 2 π radians = one circumference. Hence, one radian = 57.°29578 = 3.ʰ81972.

The length of the arc of the great circle between the two points in spherical space may be given in either one of the three systems of angle units mentioned above, the numerical value being equal to the plane angle subtended at the center of the sphere between the radii to the two points. This distance cannot be expressed in linear units (i.e. feet, yards, miles, meters, et cetera) unless the radius of the sphere is known in those units.

To set up a system of spherical co-ordinates we first pass a line through the center of the sphere (C in Fig. 54) that will intersect the surface of the sphere in the points P and P'. We next pass a plane through the center of the sphere that is perpendicular to the line just described. This plane will cut out on the surface of the sphere the great circle $QDVQ'$. The line PCP' is known as the fundamental line, the plane is known as the fundamental plane, and the great circle $QDVQ'$ is known as the fundamental circle of the spherical co-ordinate system. We next select a point D on the fundamental circle (or a direction CD in the fundamental plane). The fundamental line, plane, and

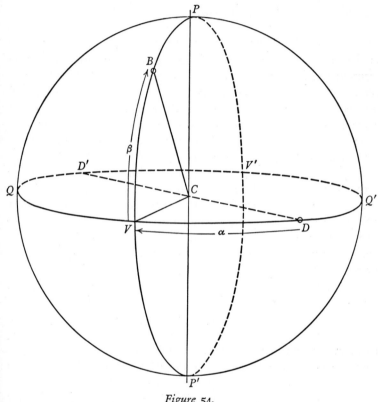

Figure 54.

point or direction define what is known as the reference frame in spherical space, just as the origin and the two perpendicular lines (axes) define the reference frame for rectangular Cartesian co-ordinates in plane space. To locate the position of a point B in the spherical space relative to the reference frame just established we pass a plane through B that contains the fundamental line. This plane cuts out on the spherical space the great circle $PBVP'V'$. From elementary conditions of solid geometry this plane must be perpendicular to the fundamental plane and the great circle must be perpendicular to the fundamental circle at points V and V'.

The first co-ordinate of B is measured from D along the fundamental circle to V and the second is measured along the great circle containing B from V to B. In Fig. 54 these spherical co-ordinates are designated by α and β respectively. It will be noted that they are numerically equal to the plane angles DCV and VCB.

SPHERICAL CO-ORDINATES ON THE EARTH

As early as the second century of the Christian era cartographers had discussed the spherical co-ordinates of latitude and longitude on the earth. The terms probably arose from the fact that the then-known civilized world extended around the Mediterranean Sea, which is long in the east-west direction and wide in the north-south. In terms of our definitions of general spherical co-ordinates we define those on the earth in the following manner:

1. The fundamental line is that passing through the center of the earth and the north and south poles of rotation.

2. The fundamental circle, known as the terrestrial equator, is cut out by the equatorial plane passing through the center of the earth perpendicular to the axis of rotation.

3. Planes passing through the earth that contain the axis of rotation cut out on the surface of the earth great circles known as terrestrial meridians. The fundamental point in the terrestrial system of spherical co-ordinates is the point of intersection of the meridian through Greenwich, England, and the equator.

To define the position of a place on the spherical earth we pass a meridian through that place and measure the co-ordinate of longitude from the point of intersection of the meridian through Greenwich either east or west along the equator to the point of intersection of the local meridian through the place and the equator. The co-ordinate of latitude is measured along the local meridian north or south from the equator to the place in question. Longitude may be expressed either in hours, minutes, and seconds of time, or in degrees, minutes, and seconds of arc east or west from Greenwich. Latitude is always expressed in degrees, minutes, and seconds north or south of the equator.

Navigators frequently find it convenient to express distances on the surface of the earth in linear rather than angular units. For this purpose the nautical mile is defined as one minute of arc on a great circle of a sphere whose area is equal to the area of the theoretical geoid (a sphere slightly flattened at the poles). Using the values for the dimensions of the earth accepted at the present time the nautical mile is found to be equivalent to 6080.27 feet. Within an error of 2/10 of 1 per cent this is equivalent to 15/13 of the statute mile of 5280 feet.

HORIZONTAL SYSTEM OF SPHERICAL CO-ORDINATES ON THE CELESTIAL SPHERE

The celestial sphere is defined as a sphere of infinite radius with the earth at the center. On such a sphere all distances must be expressed in angular units. In the horizontal system of spherical co-ordinates the fundamental line (see Fig. 54) is the direction of the plumb line for any observer on the surface of the earth. This line intersects the celestial sphere in the observer's zenith and nadir. The plane perpendicular to this line, or the fundamental plane, is the plane of the observer's astronomical horizon. The fundamental direction is the direction of true north on the horizon. All great circles on the celestial sphere that contain the direction of the plumb line, and hence pass through the observer's zenith and nadir, are known as vertical circles. To define the position of an object on the celestial sphere in this horizontal system of co-ordinates we pass a vertical circle through the object. The co-ordinate of bearing is measured from the fundamental direction (i.e. true north) on the astronomical horizon toward the east through 360° to the point of intersection of the vertical circle through the object and the horizon. The co-ordinate of altitude is measured from the plane of the horizon along the vertical circle to the object. For many centuries the word azimuth was used to indicate the direction of the point of intersection of the vertical circle through the object and the horizon. The astronomical definition of azimuth is the angular distance from the south point of the horizon to the west through 360°. This means that azimuth, in the strict sense of the term, is equal to the bearing as defined above minus 180°.

This system of co-ordinates is more or less familiar to everyone. If you should look out of the window and notice a strange object in the sky which you could not identify you might well call your neighbor on the telephone. Since he cannot see you, you could not point to the object and say, 'It is right up there,' but you could say, 'The object is in the southwest and up about a third of the way from the horizon.' To express these co-ordinates scientifically you would say, 'The object has a bearing of 225° and altitude of 30°.' If the object were in the east, you would say, 'Its bearing is 90°'; if in the northwest, 'Its bearing is 315°.'

Since the fundamental line in the horizontal system of co-ordinates is the direction of the plumb line through the observer, it should be evident that at any particular instant the horizontal co-ordinates of an object on the celestial sphere will be different for every individual on the surface of the earth. If two observers are separated by a distance of one nautical mile, the positions of their respective zeniths will differ by one minute of arc. As a matter of fact, all of the astronomical methods for determining the position of an observer on the surface of the earth may be reduced to the one fundamental problem of determining the location of the zenith on the celestial sphere.

The most casual observer of the heavens has noticed that the horizontal co-ordinates of practically all celestial objects are continually changing from minute to minute. These diurnal motions are described in Chapter 1. Because of these variations of horizontal co-ordinates with change of position of the observer and also with the passage of time, they cannot be used conveniently for compiling a general catalogue of positions of stars for the entire heavens.

EQUATORIAL SYSTEM OF SPHERICAL CO-ORDINATES ON THE CELESTIAL SPHERE

In Chapter 1 we saw that the changes in the horizontal co-ordinates of an object are due to the rotation of the earth. To compensate for this motion we set up on the celestial sphere a reference frame directly correlated with the direction of rotation of the earth.

The fundamental line in this equatorial system of celestial co-ordinates is the axis of rotation of the earth extended to meet the celestial sphere in its north and south poles of rotation. The fundamental plane, perpendicular to this line, is congruent with the equatorial plane of the earth and cuts the celestial sphere in the great circle known as the celestial equator. Planes passed through the celestial sphere that contain the axis of rotation cut out on the surface of the sphere great circles known as hour circles. That particular hour circle that passes through the observer's zenith and nadir is also a vertical circle and is known as the local celestial meridian of the observer.

In selecting the fundamental direction for the reference frame in this system of co-ordinates either one of two points may be used:

(1) that point of intersection of the local meridian with the equator which is above the horizon (upper culmination of the celestial equator);

(2) that point of intersection of the ecliptic with the equator which is known as the vernal equinox.

To define the position of an object on the celestial sphere by the equatorial system of co-ordinates we pass an hour circle through the object.

1. The first co-ordinate is measured from upper culmination in the direction of rotation of the celestial sphere through 360° or 24 hours to the point of intersection of the hour circle through the object with the equator. The second co-ordinate is measured along the hour circle from the equator north (+) or south (—) to the object. The two co-ordinates are known as hour angle and declination respectively.

2. The first co-ordinate is measured from the vernal equinox along the equator in the direction contrary to that of the rotation of the celestial sphere through 360° or 24 hours to the point of intersection of the hour circle through the object and the equator. This is known as right ascension. The other co-ordinate of declination is as defined under 1.

As the celestial sphere rotates, the co-ordinates of declination and right ascension remain fixed, since the rotation of the sphere is parallel to the equator and the vernal equinox is a point on the equator. However, the co-ordinate of hour angle continually increases from zero with the object on the meridian at upper culmination around through 24 hours or 360° back to culmination again.

Catalogues are published for the stars that are 'fixed' on the celestial sphere, giving the right ascensions and declinations for some particular epoch such as 1950.0. Due to precession and nutation, the position of the vernal equinox on the equator changes slightly with time, and small corrections have to be applied to the catalogue positions to get the actual positions of the stars on dates other than that of the epoch of the catalogue. Slight corrections to catalogue positions must also be applied to allow for proper motions when these are known. Ephemerides and almanacs are published each year giving the right ascensions and declinations of the various members of the solar system for each date.

OTHER SYSTEMS OF SPHERICAL CO-ORDINATES ON THE CELESTIAL SPHERE

A number of other reference frames for spherical co-ordinates are used in certain particular fields of astronomy. Among these may be listed:

1. A system using the ecliptic as the fundamental plane, and the vernal equinox as the fundamental point on the ecliptic. In this system celestial latitude and longitude are defined. These are used by workers in the field of celestial mechanics.

TABLE OF SYSTEMS OF SPHERICAL CO-ORDINATES DISCUSSED IN THE TEXT

Figure 54	*Terrestrial*	*Horizontal*	*Equatorial*	
Line *PCP'*	Axis of rotation of earth	Plumb line at station	Axis of rotation of the celestial sphere	
Plane *QDVQ'*	Plane of equator	Plane of horizon	Plane of celestial equator	
Circle *QVQ'V'*	Terrestrial equator	Astronomic horizon	Celestial equator	
D	Meridian of Greenwich, England	True north point of horizon	Upper culmination of equator	Vernal Equinox
VBP	Local Terrestrial meridian	Vertical circle	Hour circle	Hour circle
α	Longitude Long. or λ West $\lambda=+\lambda$ East $\lambda=-\lambda$	Bearing	Local hour angle *LHA*	Right ascension *RA* or α
β	Latitude Lat. or φ north $\varphi=+\varphi$ south $\varphi=-\varphi$	Altitude *h*	Declination dec. or δ north $\delta=+\delta$ south $\delta=-\delta$	Declination dec. or δ north $\delta=+\delta$ south $\delta=-\delta$

The symbols shown below the various terms above are standard in astronomy and in navigation. These symbols are those used in the text.

2. The galactic system, which uses the plane of the galaxy as the fundamental plane. The fundamental point on the 'galactic equator' is one of the points of intersection of the celestial equator with this great circle. This system of co-ordinates, in which galactic latitude and longitude are defined, is used by workers in the field of general cosmography.

TRANSFORMATION OF CO-ORDINATES

In order that the horizontal co-ordinates of an object may be determined when the equatorial co-ordinates are given or the equatorial coordinates determined when the horizontal are given, both systems of co-ordinates must be represented on the celestial sphere. In Chapter 1 we saw that the altitude of the pole of rotation of the celestial sphere is equal to the latitude of the observer. Figure 55 is a representation of the celestial sphere for an observer in latitude 42° North. The plane of the paper is the plane of the observer's celestial meridian shown as the circle *NPZSP'*. The zenith, *Z*, is shown at the top and the horizon is shown as the circle *NESW*. *P* represents the north pole of rotation

and is on the meridian at an altitude above the north point of the horizon by an amount equal to the terrestrial latitude of an observer in
north latitude (in this case 42° N.). The celestial equator is shown by
the circle *LEUW*. The direction of the arrow indicates the direction
of rotation of the celestial sphere. On the diagram we have shown a
celestial object at *O* and through it we have passed the vertical circle
ZOB and the hour circle *POH*. The horizontal co-ordinates of *O* are

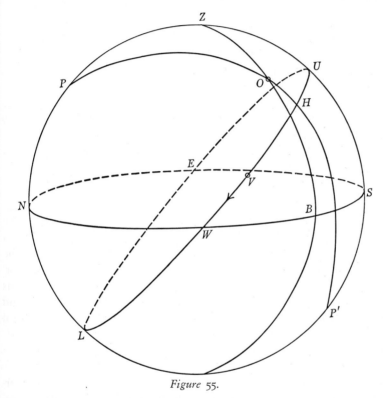

Figure 55.

represented by the altitude, *BO*, and the bearing, *NESB*. (In the figure
the altitude is approximately 52° and the bearing approximately
218°). The equatorial co-ordinates of *O* are shown as hour angle *UH*
and declination *HO*. (In this case the hour angle is approximately
1^h 30^m and the declination approximately 10° N.) The right ascension
of the object cannot be determined unless we know the hour angle of
the vernal equinox. If we assume the vernal equinox to be at the point
represented by the point *V* at hour angle of 05^h 10^m, then the right

ascension of the object would be *VH*, or about three hours and forty minutes.

The spherical triangle *PZO* is known as the astronomical triangle. The sides of this angle may be seen to be equal to:

$$PZ = 90 - \varphi \quad (\varphi = \text{latitude})$$
$$ZO = 90 - h \quad (h = \text{altitude})$$
$$PO = 90 - \delta \quad (\delta = \text{declination})$$

The apex angles of this triangle are:

$$ZPO = t \quad (t = \text{hour angle})$$
$$PZO = 360 - B \quad (B = \text{bearing})$$
$$ZOP = q \quad (q = \text{parallactic angle})$$

If we know any three parts of this triangle the others may be determined by the methods of spherical trigonometry. The various problems in that branch of astronomy known as spherical astronomy—and the majority of the problems in celestial navigation—are concerned with the trigonometric solutions of this astronomical triangle.

For those who are not familiar with trigonometric methods or those who are interested only in approximate results, very satisfactory solutions may be made by graphical methods. The first step is to draw a circle that will represent the observer's celestial meridian. Place on that circle the zenith and draw in the celestial horizon; then place on the meridian the pole of rotation, at an angle above the horizon equal to the latitude of the observer, and draw in the plane of the celestial equator. Since the equator is 90° from the pole, by definition, the altitude of the point of upper culmination will be equal to 90– latitude. The point of intersection of the horizon nearest to the elevated pole will be the north or south point of the horizon, depending upon whether the observer is in north or south latitude. The east and west points of the horizon may be established by remembering that objects rise in the east and set in the west and, therefore, once the direction of rotation of the sphere is indicated, as by the arrow in Fig. 55, the east and west points are determined.

In order that an object may be located on the diagram it is necessary to know either the horizontal or the equatorial co-ordinates. If the horizontal co-ordinates are given, the bearing is estimated around the horizon from the north point toward the east through 360° and a point marked on the horizon. In Fig. 55 the bearing is given as 218° and the point on the horizon will be 38° along from the south point (180°)

toward the west point (270°). Through this point the vertical circle is drawn through the zenith and the nadir. The object is then located by estimating the altitude up from the horizon along this vertical circle (52° in the case discussed in Fig. 55) and the point O is marked. To represent the equatorial co-ordinates of the object, the hour circle (POP') is drawn through the object and the poles of rotation. The hour angle, UH, is estimated along the equator from its point of upper culmination to the intersection of the hour circle through the object ($1^h 30^m$ in Fig. 55). The declination, HO, is estimated along the hour circle from the equator to the object ($+10°$ in Fig. 55). The declination will be either north or south ($+$or$-$) depending upon whether the object is between the equator and the north or south pole of the celestial sphere.

These estimations of angular distances along the various circles, which are projections of great circles on the sphere onto the plane of the paper, require considerable practice before proficiency is attained. More accurate results can be obtained by drawing the circles on the surface of a sphere, and the most accurate results are obtained by trigonometric solution of the astronomical triangle, PZO. However, with sufficient practice, results accurate to within 10° in each of the unknown co-ordinates can be obtained. A set of sample problems will be found at the end of this appendix. If the object is east of the meridian, that is, with bearing less than 180° or hour angle greater than 12 hours, it may be more convenient to bring the east point of the horizon to the front side of the diagram. This can be done by simply considering the sphere to rotate in the opposite direction from that indicated in Fig. 55, that is, by pointing the arrow on the equator in the opposite direction.

Small circles drawn through the object parallel to the equator will represent the diurnal path of the object and the points of intersection of this circle with the horizon (i.e. where the altitude is zero) will give the bearing of the points of rising and setting. The altitude of the point of intersection of the diurnal circle with the equator (i.e. the point of upper culmination of the object) may be proved, by simple geometry, to be equal to 90—the latitude of the observer. Navigators and surveyors measure the meridian altitude of an object of known declination for the purpose of determining their latitude.

PHYSICAL TIME AND ITS MEASUREMENT

In the physical sciences time is regarded as a measured duration. Two intervals of time are equal, by definition, when an object moving in equilibrium passes through equal distances in the two intervals. The moving object may be considered as the clock and for many millenniums mankind, either consciously or unconsciously, has used the rotating earth as the fundamental clock. To be in equilibrium an object cannot be acted upon by any external forces, or if such forces do exist they must completely cancel each other. A moment's consideration will show that the earth is acted upon by a great variety of external gravitational forces, and timekeeping devices developed within the present century have begun to detect slight irregularities in the rotation period of the earth. However, for timekeeping within an accuracy of a few seconds per century the rotating earth, or the apparently rotating celestial sphere, may be considered as satisfying the definition of the fundamental clock.

To determine the distance moved by the fundamental clock there must be some fixed point outside the object relative to which the movement can be measured. Up to the present time no such fixed point has been found outside of the earth. The systems of timekeeping developed through the ages have used various objects that we now realize are not fixed points on the celestial sphere. At the present time three such objects are employed: the real sun, the mean sun, and the vernal equinox.

APPARENT TIME

The earliest systems of timekeeping of which we have any records used the true sun as the reference point. The Babylonians and early Greeks divided the day, from sunrise to sunset, into twelve equal parts and the night into twelve equal parts. This meant that the day hours were longer than those of the night during the summer season, while in the winter season the reverse was true. Our own method of dividing the day comes from the Egyptians and Romans, who divided the whole day into twenty-four equal parts numbered in two groups of twelve. The various peoples began their day at different times. For the Babylonians the day began at sunrise, for the Jews and Greeks at sunset, and for the Egyptians and Romans at midnight. In every case the twenty-four-hour day was equal in length to the time required for the sun to pass from culmination with the meridian back to the same culmination again. Due to the fact that the apparent motion of the true sun along the ecliptic is not uniform, the length of the solar day varies with different seasons of the year. For the ancient peoples this presented but little difficulty. During the interval while the sun was above the horizon the hours could be marked by the position of a shadow cast by an obelisk or a gnomon. The crude timekeeping instruments for marking the hours of darkness or cloudy days were so inaccurate that the variations in length of the day introduced but little confusion. In these modern days true solar time is seldom used by the general public except for the ornamental sun dials that are found on various buildings and in many parks and gardens.

For many problems in surveying and in navigation, apparent time is still used and the apparent solar time at any instant is defined as the hour angle of the true sun. From the definition of hour angle we find that the apparent solar time is $00^h00^m00^s$ with the sun above the horizon and on the meridian. For civil purposes it is more convenient to have the day begin with the sun below the horizon and on the meridian (i.e. at midnight). For this reason it has become the standard practice to use apparent civil time, which is the hour angle of the true sun $+12^h$ rather than true solar time. This means that when the true sun is on the observer's meridian and above the horizon the apparent civil time (frequently called apparent time) is $12^h00^m00^s$.

MEAN AND CIVIL TIME

With the improvements in the design of mechanical clocks the variations in length of the true solar days became intolerable. These variations in length are due to the fact that the true sun is moving in the ecliptic with variable speed, while the celestial sphere is rotating parallel to the celestial equator. To compensate for these motions a mean sun is defined as a fictitious object that moves along the equator with uniformly increasing right ascension, completing its revolution in one year or 365.2422 M.S.D. Mean solar time is defined as the hour angle of the mean sun. In order that the zero hour, or beginning of a day, may occur during the hours of darkness in most of the inhabited regions of the earth, civil time is generally used and this is defined as mean time $+12^h$. Since the mean sun is a fictitious object it cannot be observed, and mean time can never be found by direct observation. Apparent time, which can be directly observed, is converted to mean time by use of the equation of time. The equation of time is defined as apparent time minus mean time. The following table indicates the

values of the equation of time for the first day of each month of the
year 1950:

	a.m.		a.m.
1 January	$- 3^m 14^s$	1 July	$- 3^m 31^s$
1 February	$-13 \quad 25$	1 August	$- 6 \quad 16$
1 March	$-12 \quad 38$	1 September	$- 0 \quad 15$
1 April	$- 4 \quad 12$	1 October	$+10 \quad 01$
1 May	$+ 2 \quad 50$	1 November	$+16 \quad 18$
1 June	$+ 2 \quad 27$	1 December	$+11 \quad 16$

These values remain constant from year to year to within a few seconds.

In many countries the archaic custom of dividing the day into two
twelve-hour periods is still in use. The day begins at zero hours mean
time and then continues until twelve o'clock noon. From this point the
counting is repeated from one hour to twelve hours midnight. On this
system the morning, or a.m., hours are actually civil time while the
afternoon, or p.m., hours are mean time or true hour angle of the mean
sun. The mean solar day, that is the interval from midnight to midnight, is equal in length to the average of the lengths of all the apparent
solar days during a year.

SIDEREAL TIME

Sidereal time is used by astronomers for the purpose of determining
the hour angles of celestial objects when their right ascensions are
known. This sidereal time is defined as the hour angle of the vernal
equinox. In Fig. 55 the vernal equinox is assumed to be at V and its
hour angle, UV, is 5 hours and 10 minutes. This means that the sidereal
time at the instant for which the diagram is drawn is $05^h 10^m$. The
hour angle, HA, of the object represented in Fig. 55 is $01^h 30^m$. Since
we have already defined right ascension as the angle measured
along the equator from the vernal equinox in a direction contrary to
the direction of rotation of the celestial sphere to the point where the
hour circle through the object intersects the equator, it should be immediately evident that the right ascension of O must be $05^h 10^m$ minus
$01^h 30^m$ or $03^h 40^m$. Conversely, if the sidereal time θ is given and the
right ascension of any object, α, is known, then the hour angle of the
object, t, can be immediately determined from the relation $\theta - \alpha = t$.

Since the vernal equinox is defined as a point of intersection of the
equator and the ecliptic it has no objective reality and hence sidereal
time cannot be directly observed. However, a brief consideration of the

relationship between sidereal time, hour angle, and right ascension will show that when an object is on the meridian at upper culmination its hour angle is zero, by definition, and the sidereal time at that instant will be equal to the right ascension of the object. In the almanacs published by all of the major governments of the world the 'clock stars' are listed at great length. The right ascensions of these clock stars are accurately known and, by means of an instrument known as a meridian transit, the exact instant, or sidereal time, of the passage of these stars across the meridian can be determined by observation. Observations of the transits of these clock stars are made at the U.S. Naval Observatory and at the government observatories of many other nations; these accurate determinations of sidereal time form the fundamental basis for the timekeeping systems of the world.

SIDEREAL AND MEAN TIME

From the definition already given for the mean sun it should be evident that there is one more 'sidereal day' in a year than there are mean solar days. This means that a clock keeping sidereal time will gain on a clock keeping mean time by one day in a year or approximately four minutes per day ($3^m 55^s.746$ M.S.T.). Looking at it from another point of view, we may say that the right ascension of the mean sun is increasing at the rate of approximately four minutes per day. Mean time has been defined as the hour angle of the mean sun and hence the sidereal time at any instant is equal to the mean time plus the right ascension of the mean sun ($\theta = MT + \alpha$ MS). An accurate value of the right ascension of the mean sun may be determined for any instant of mean time by interpolation from an almanac. While this interpolation must be carried out for all problems where great accuracy is desired, nevertheless values of sufficient approximation to locate the position of the vernal equinox on a diagram of the celestial sphere similar to that in Fig. 54 may be obtained by assuming that the sun moves ahead four minutes per day. The determination of sidereal time by this method is comparable in accuracy to that of determining civil time at any instant by a mechanical clock whose minute hand advances by jumps of one minute.

If we assume that every month is thirty days in length this would give a motion to the mean sun of two hours per month. The right ascension of the mean sun is zero when it passes through the vernal equinox, which takes place on 21 March approximately. Accordingly, we should say that the right ascension of the mean sun on 21 June is six hours, on 21 September it is twelve hours, and on 21 December it is eighteen hours. If we wish to find an approximate value of the right ascension of the mean sun on any particular date, we find the number of months that have elapsed from 21 March to that 21st day of the month closest to the given date and multiply this number by 2. This will give the number of hours of right ascension. Then find the number of days before or after the 21st of the selected month, multiply this number by 4 and subtract or add the number of minutes thus determined from the hours. For example, to find the right ascension of the mean sun on 15 August: 21 August is the closest integral month date and this is the fifth month from 21 March. Hence, $5^{mo} \times 2^h = 10^h$. The date for which we are determining the right ascension is 15 August or six days before the 21st. Therefore, we must subtract $6 \times 4^m = 24^m$ from the 10^h. This gives the value $\alpha MS = 09h. 36m.$ on 15 August; a value that differs from that given in the U.S. Nautical Almanac for 1950 by about five minutes. Since five minutes of time is equivalent to $1° 15'$ of arc, the error of determination of the right ascension of the mean sun is considerably less than the errors of estimation of angle on diagrams similar to Fig. 54.

TIME, TERRESTRIAL LONGITUDE, AND STANDARD TIME

In all of the definitions of time given thus far we have used the hour angle as measured from the observer's local celestial meridian. Since any celestial meridian is the projection of a terrestrial meridian onto the celestial sphere, the times at any particular instant for observers on different meridians of longitude will not agree. The angular difference, measured along the equator, between any two meridians is equivalent to the difference of terrestrial longitude and, hence, is equivalent to the difference in time. Since the fundamental meridian for defining terrestrial longitude is the meridian of Greenwich, England, it should be evident that the difference between any local time and the corresponding Greenwich time at the same instant is equal to the longitude of the observer. Because of this, many writers define longitude as the difference between local time and Greenwich time and express this longitude in units of time measurement. Expressed in symbolic form this definition becomes $\lambda = GXT - LXT$, in which the X refers to the symbol for any sort of time, either solar, apparent, mean, civil, or sidereal. In even more general terms longitude may be defined as the difference between the Greenwich hour angle of a given object and the local hour angle of the same object at the same instant

GHA—LHA$=\lambda$). As mentioned above (p. 310) west longitude is called plus ($+\lambda$ is west and $-\lambda$ is east).

Before the days of rapid transportation, individual localities used their own local times. Usually the municipal clock indicated the local civil time on the twelve hours a.m. and p.m. system. By 1870 the railroad operators had found the confusion of local times to be intolerable and each railroad adopted as 'railroad time' the local civil time of its main office. While this simplified matters for the railroads it merely served to increase the confusion for the traveling public. In 1884 an international conference was held and the present systems of zone time and standard time were agreed upon.

For zone time the fundamental meridian is that of Greenwich, England, the meridian from which terrestrial longitudes are measured. The time zones are centered on every integral hour ($15°$) meridian west or east of Greenwich. These zones are numbered $+1$, $+2$, $+3$, et cetera for the 1^h, 2^h, 3^h, et cetera ($+15°$, $+30°$, $+45°$) if the longitude is west of Greenwich, and -1^h, -2^h, et cetera, if the longitude is east. The zone boundaries are halfway between the zone meridians. Accordingly the $+1$ time zone is entered when a traveler crosses the terrestrial meridian 30^m (or $7°.5$) west of Greenwich when he is moving toward the west, or the meridian 1^h 30^m ($22°.5$) west if moving east. The 12^h zone is centered on the $180°$ meridian from Greenwich and is divided into two half zones $+12$ from longitude $172°.5$ west to longitude 180 and -12 from $172°.5$ east to the 180th meridian. Whenever time is expressed on the zone-time system the zone designation should be given; e.g. ($+7$) 14 20 33 indicates that the civil time of the 7th hourly meridian west of Greenwich is 14 20 33 or 02 20 33 in the afternoon.

Zone time is in general use by navigators both on the sea and in the air. Approximations to zone times are used by most of the nations of the world. In the United States we use standard time and there are four zones. These are known as Eastern, Central, Mountain, and Pacific standard times and are centered on the $+5$, $+6$, $+7$, and $+8$ zone meridians. The boundaries of the zones are determined by commercial considerations rather than by the strict zonal rule. Standard time systems have been set up by the various nations. In the small nations the standard meridian adopted is frequently that of the national capital or that zone meridian which is closest to the capital.

During the present century the practice of establishing so-called Daylight Saving Time has become quite general. This is accomplished by shifting the clock readings so that they carry the zone time of the meridian one hour closer to Greenwich than is used on the standard time. For example, Eastern Standard Time becomes $+4$ zone time, Central Standard Time becomes $+5$ zone time, et cetera.

DATE AND THE INTERNATIONAL DATE LINE

Calendar dates and days of the week are always begun at midnight (zero hours) of the civil time that is used by the particular locality. This may be either local civil, standard, or zone time. Whenever a date is mentioned in connection with solar, apparent, or sidereal time that date is the civil date—there is no such thing as a solar, apparent, or sidereal date or day of the week. The data given in the American Ephemeris, the American Nautical Almanac, and the American Air Almanac, in common with similar publications of most of the nations of the world, are given for zero hours Greenwich Civil Time (00^h GCT).

In these days of rapid communication and of rapid travel over very long distances over the earth the question of calendar date has become a most confusing one. This confusion was first experienced by the officers of Magellan's first voyage around the globe. They traveled from Spain westward across the Atlantic, passed around Cape Horn, and continued back to Spain. Very accurate count was made of the elapsed days throughout the long voyage and when they returned to port they found that one day less had elapsed for them than for those who had remained at home. In other words, if they had returned on Tuesday by their own reckoning they would have found that it was Wednesday at the shore station. The explanation of this can readily be understood by assuming that a plane flies due west at such a speed that it will return to base in exactly twenty-four hours. This would be possible for planes operating from a base in high north or south latitudes. If the plane left base at eleven o'clock in the morning on Monday, 20 June the mean sun would remain one hour east of the meridian of the plane throughout the twenty-four hours. In other words, when the plane returned to base the pilot's time would still be 1100 Monday 20 June since the sun had not moved relative to his meridian throughout the flight. However the commander of the base would report that the plane returned at 1100 Tuesday, 21 June. In order that the pilot's date should be in synchronism with that of the base at the time of return, the pilot would have to alter his date at some time during the twenty-four hours of flight. Had the pilot flown in the opposite direction, i.e. toward the east, the sun would have crossed his meridian thirty minutes after departure, would have crossed his meridian at lower culmination six hours and thirty minutes after take off, would have crossed again at lower culmination eighteen hours and thirty minutes later, and would have been one hour east of his meridian at upper culmination when he landed. Since the sun had passed through lower culmination twice during the eastward flight the pilot's date would have been 1100 Wednesday 22 June on arrival but the time at base would be 1100 Tuesday, 21 June.

By international agreement a meridian of longitude has been established where moving ships alter their dates on crossing. This so-called international date line is theoretically the 12^h (180°) meridian of longitude from Greenwich. In actual practice the date line varies in places from the 180° meridian to bring some of the Pacific possessions of the various nations on the same side of the date line, and hence on the same date, as the national capitals. An interesting problem relative to the international date line arose when Alaska was purchased by the United States from Russia. Originally the international date line bent eastward to bring Alaska on the Russian side of the line, but after the purchase the line was shifted to pass through Bering Strait and thus put Alaska on the American side of the line.

Ships crossing the Pacific Ocean alter their calendars when crossing the date line. If a ship is proceeding from the United States to Japan and arrives at the international date line at three o'clock in the afternoon (1500) ship's time on Monday, 4 July the date is immediately shifted to 1500 Tuesday, 5 July. If the ship had been on passage from Japan to the United States and arrived at the international date line at 1500 Monday, 4 July, the date would have become 1500 Sunday, 3 July.

PROBLEMS

The following problems are based upon the material discussed in the various sections of this appendix, with frequent use of subjects that have been discussed earlier in the text. The symbolism used is that given on p. 310. Whenever a symbol is used that is not given in that table its significance will be indicated the first time that it is used. The problems should be solved in order, since methods of solution frequently depend upon principles illustrated in previous solutions.

In the transformation from one type of spherical co-ordinates to another, the diagrams should be carefully drawn to moderately large scale. The printed answers were obtained by trigonometric solution of the astronomic triangle. With care in the construction of the diagrams, and with sufficient practice in the estimation of angles on the projected circles, results may be obtained that will be accurate to within 10°.

Problems in conversion of time may be solved by a graphical method using a circle to represent the celestial equator and showing on it the points of intersection of the various hour circles and meridians used in the conversion. More accurate results can be obtained by use of the various definitions, expressing them in analytic form, and then making the conversions by simple arithmetic. In problems that involve two or more terrestrial longitudes many computors prefer to transfer the given time directly to Greenwich by adding the stated longitude (either local or zone)—making the necessary conversions in terms of Greenwich time—and then returning to the final longitude by subtracting the proper value from the final Greenwich time. Whenever dates are given they are civil dates (either local or zone).

In the solution of problems that require both conversion of time and transformation of spherical co-ordinates it is a waste of effort to carry through the time conversions with an accuracy of more than one minute of time. The errors in the estimation of angle on the diagram of the celestial sphere, and also the errors introduced in finding the right ascension of the mean sun (αMS) by the short cut method, are greater than one minute of time.

Suggested methods of solution are illustrated below by the printed solutions of a few of the problems.

1. An observer in latitude 42° North ($\varphi = +42°$) finds an object on the celestial sphere to have an altitude of 40° and a bearing of 105°. Find the hour angle (HA) and declination (δ) of the object.

$$HA = 20^{h}38^{m} \qquad \delta = +16°26' \qquad \textit{See diagram}$$

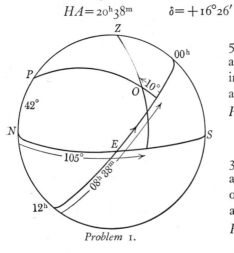

Problem 1.

2. An observer in latitude 54° North finds a star to have an altitude of 30° and a bearing of 290°. Find the HA and δ of the star.

$$HA = 05^{h}45^{m} \qquad \delta = +35° 21'$$
See diagram

3. An observer in latitude 30° South finds a star of an altitude of 20° and a bearing of 330°. Find the hour angle and declination of the star.

$$HA = 02^{h}15^{m} \qquad \delta = +32° 16'$$
See diagram.

4. In latitude $+26°$ a planet is found to have an altitude of $65°$ and to be bearing $124°$. Find the hour angle and declination of the planet.

$$HA=22^h36^m \qquad \delta=+10° \; 39'$$

5. A star is found to be bearing $52°$ South of East and at altitude $34°$ by an observer in latitude $20°$ North. Find the hour angle and declination of the star.

$$HA=21^h43^m \qquad \delta=-25° \; 00'$$

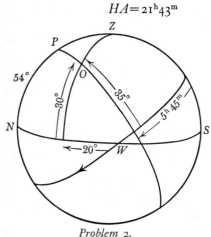

6. A certain object on the celestial sphere has an hour angle of 19^h40^m and a declination of $+36°$. Find the altitude and bearing of this object for an observer in latitude $42°$ N.

$$h=40° \; 21' \qquad B=074° \; 10'$$

7. A star with hour angle 02^h30^m and declination $+15°$ is observed from latitude $32°$ North. Find the altitude and bearing of the star.

Problem 2.

$$h=51° \; 54' \qquad B=252° \; 24'$$

8. The same star as that used in (7) is observed at the same hour angle by an observer in latitude $32°$ South. Find the altitude and bearing of the star.

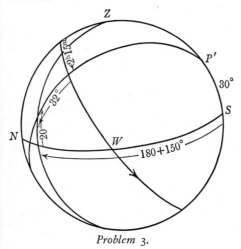

$$h=30° \; 51' \qquad B=316° \; 47'$$

9. A star of declination $+68°$ is observed from latitude $66°$ North at an hour angle of 14^h50^m Find the altitude and bearing of the star.

$$h=47° \; 17' \qquad B=021° \; 54'$$

10. A star of declination $-11°$ is at hour angle 03^h40^m for an observer in latitude $+32°$. Find the altitude and bearing of the star.

Problem 3.

$$h=22° \; 06' \qquad B=240° \; 13'$$

11. The local civil time (LCT) is 15h. 24m. 34s. on a date when the equation of time (equ.T) is +14m. 15s. Fnd the local apparent time (LAT).

$$LAT = 15h.\ 38m.\ 49s.$$

12. On a date when the equation of time is −10m. 24s. the true sun in found to be at hour angle $03^h\ 16^m\ 41^s$. Find the local civil time.

$$LCT = 15h.\ 27m.\ 05s.$$

13. Find the local sidereal time (Lθ) corresponding to LCT 20h. 30m. (i.e. 08h. 30. p.m.) on 15 August.

$$L\theta = 18h.\ 06m. \quad See\ solution$$

Solution: On 21 March   (3m. 21d.) the αMS $= 00^h\ 00^m$
                          +5m. $5\times2h.\ = 10$
           21 August   8   21 αMS$= 10\ \ 00$
                          —   6 $-6\times4m.\ = -\ \ 24$
           15 August   8   15 αMS$= 09\ \ 36$
           HAMS$=$LCT -12 $= 08\ \ 30$
           $\theta =$HAMS $+\ \alpha$MS $= 18\ \ 06$

14. Find the local sidereal time corresponding to 03h. 42m. LCT on 27 May.

$$L\theta = 20h.\ 06m.$$

15. Find the local civil time corresponding to 06h. 24m. local sidereal time on 25 December.

$$LCT = 00h.\ 08m.\ (i.e.\ 8\ min.\ after\ midnight)$$

16. Find the Eastern Standard Time corresponding to local civil time 13h. 24m. 18s. for a locality in longitude $04^h\ 50^m\ 06^s$ W.

$$EST = 13h.\ 14m.\ 24s.$$

Solution: LCT $=$ 13h. 24m. 18s.
            $+\lambda = +4$ 50   06
            GCT $=$ 18   14   24
−zone description $-+5\ \ -5$
            EST $=$ 13   14   24

17. Find the Central Standard Time corresponding to local sidereal time 21h. 15m. 24s. on 30 June for a station in longitude 05^h 20^m 13^s W.

$$CST = 01h. \; 59.6m.$$

Solution:

	Lθ	=	21h.	15m.	24s.
	$+\lambda$		$+5$	20	13
	Gθ	=	02	35	37
	$-\alpha MS$		-06	36	
	GMT=		19	59.6	
	GCT =		07	59.6	
	$-ZD$		$-+6$		
	CST =		01	59.6	

18. Find the Eastern Standard Time corresponding to zone time 07h. 34m. 56s. 16 July for an observer in λ 09^h 18^m 10^s E.

$$EST = 17h. \; 34m. \; 56s. \; 15 \; July$$

Solution:

	ZT $=(-9)$	07h. 34m. 56s. 16 July
	GCT=	22 34 56 15 July
	$-ZD$	$-+5$
	EST =	17 34 56 15 July

19. An Independence Day speech is to be broadcast from Manila, P.I., at noon zone time. The longitude of Manila is 08^h 03^m E. At what date and time will the speech be heard in a region using Eastern Standard Time?

$$EST = 23h. \; 00m. \; 3 \; July$$

20. A radiogram is sent from Washington, D.C., at 02h. 00m. EST on 5 May to the Hawaiian Islands which are on zone time ($+10$). At what date and time will the message be received?

$$ZT \; (+10) \; 21h. \; 00m. \; 4 \; May$$

21. A ship is on passage from the Philippine Islands to the United States and is approaching the international date line at ZT (-12) 16h. 00m. on Tuesday, 10 March. Find the date, day of the week, and zone time two hours later, the ship having crossed the date line in the meantime.

$$Monday, \; 9 \; March, \; ZT \; (+12) \; 18h. \; 00m.$$

22. At the time of the total eclipse of the sun in October 1939 many

newspapers carried the headline 'Eclipse Ends the Day Before It Began.' Explain the circumstances of an eclipse that would make this possible.

23. The length of the forenoon is usually reckoned as the time elapsed between sunrise and noon as indicated by a clock carrying standard time, while the afternoon is the clock interval from 1200 to sunset. A city in longitude 05^h 35^m W is on Central Standard Time. Which is the longer, and by how much, the forenoon or the afternoon at this city on a date when the equation of time is +10m.?

The forenoon is longer by 1h. 10m. than the afternoon.

24. The navigating officer of a ship on passage from England to the United States observes the altitude of a certain star at GCT 23h. 17m. 56s. on 16 November (Greenwich date). He solves the astronomic triangle by trigonometric methods and computes the hour angle of the star to be 20^h 12^m 34^s. From the Nautical Almanac he finds that the right ascension of the star is 03^h 37^m 17^s and the right ascension of the mean sun is 15^h 38^m 19^s. Find the longitude of the ship.

$$\lambda = 03^h\ 06^m\ 24^s\ W.\ or\ +46°\ 36'.0$$

25. The navigating officer of a ship on passage from the Philippines to Japan measures the altitude of the sun at ZT (-10) 17h. 00m. 41s. and by trigonometric solution of the astronomical triangle finds that the hour angle of the sun is 04^h 52^m 36^s. From the Nautical Almanac he find the equation of time to be −10m. 17s. Find the longitude of the ships

$$\lambda = 10^h\ 02^m\ 12^s\ E.\ or\ -150°\ 33'.0$$

26. Find the right ascension and declination of a star that has an altitude of 18° and a bearing of 145° at Eastern Standard Time 21h. 46m. on 4 July at a station in latitude 38° N. and longitude 05^h 20^m W.

$$\alpha = 18^h\ 44^m\qquad \delta = -25°\ 04'$$

27. Find the altitude and bearing of the star Vega ($\alpha = 18^h$ 35^m $\delta = +38°$ $44'$) at EST 02h. 37m. on 19 June for an observer in latitude 42° N. and longitude 04^h 50^m W.

$$h = 66°\ 17'\qquad B = 272°\ 30'$$

28. Find the altitude and bearing of the star Betelgeux ($\alpha = 05^h$ 52^m $\delta = +07°$ $24'$) for an observer at Bloemfontein, South Africa, in latitude

29° 06′ S. and longitude 01ʰ 45ᵐ E. at ZT (−2) 23h. 46m. on 23 January.

$$h = 45° 20' \qquad B = 320° 36'$$

29. At the same instant (not the same clock time) as in problem (28) the same star (Betelgeux) was to be observed at Washington, D.C., in latitude 38° 55′ N. and longitude 05ʰ 08ᵐ W. Find the Eastern Standard Time for the Washington observation and the altitude and bearing of the star at that time.

$$\text{EST} = 16h.\ 46m. \qquad h = 15° 08' \qquad B = 092° 41'$$

30. Find the Eastern Standard Time of sunrise and the number of hours that the sun will be above the horizon for an observer in latitude 42° N. and longitude 05ʰ 20ᵐ W. on the following dates:

Date	δ of sun	Equ. of time	Sunrise	Duration.
21 March	00°	−7m.	06h. 27m.	12.000hr.
21 June	+23.5	−1	04 49	15.073
21 Sept.	00	+7	06 13	12.000
21 Dec.	−23.5	+2	07 ·50	8.927

31. The most southerly star of the Southern Cross is α Crucis (α = 12ʰ 24ᵐ, δ = −62° 49′). Find the greatest northern latitude in which this star can be observed and find the approximate date that this star will be on the meridian and above the horizon at midnight.

$$\varphi = 27° 11' \text{ N. 27 March}$$

32. The most southerly star of the Big Dipper is in α = 10ʰ 19ᵐ and δ = +41° 44′. Find the smallest north latitude in which this star is circumpolar and the approximate date that it will be on the meridian above the horizon and below the pole at 8 p.m.

$$\varphi = 48° 16' \text{ N. 26 October}$$

33. An item in the daily press of 16 November states that a comet has just been discovered that is visible to the eye without telescopic aid. The position given is right ascension 12ʰ 40ᵐ and declination 15° S. If you are living in latitude about 40° N, at what time during darkness would you expect to see the comet and in what direction would you look?

At about 5 a.m. the comet will be above the horizon about 12° and be in the southeast by east.

34. At a seashore resort on the Atlantic coast a flashing buoy is noticed off shore. At 21h. 30m. Eastern Daylight Saving Time on 25 July you notice that the star Markab ($\alpha = 23^h\ 02^m$, $\delta = +14°\ 56'$) is directly over the buoy at an altitude of about 12°. Find the bearing of the buoy if your latitude is 41°N.

$$B = 080°.5$$

INDEX